THE PA28 (
A PILOTS GUIDE

JEREMY M. PRATT

i

First Edition 1992

Copyright © 1992 Airplan Flight Equipment

THE PA28 CHEROKEE A PILOTS GUIDE
JEREMY M. PRATT

ISBN: 1-874783-10-1

Airplan Flight Equipment, Southside, Manchester International Airport, Wilmslow, Cheshire SK9 4LL, U.K.   Tel: 0161-499 0023   Fax: 0161-499 0298

Acknowledgments

I would like to thank all those whose knowledge, help and advice went into this book, in particular :

Airspeed Aviation

Air Nova

Simon Booth

CAA Safety Promotion Section

CSE Aviation

Colourmatch

Adrian Dickinson

Steve Dickinson

David Hockings

Andy Holland

Phil Huntington

Wendy Mellor

Manchester School of Flying

Margaret Parkes

Paul Price

Ravenair

Neil Rigby

John Ross

Ian Sixsmith

John Thorpe

Visual Eyes

Sarah, Kate and Miles

Jeremy M Pratt
August 1992

Contents

Section 1 – General Description

Section 2 – Limitations

Section 3 – Handling the Piper PA28 Cherokee

Section 4 – Mixture and Carb Icing Supplement

Section 5 – Expanded PA-28 Pre-Flight Check List

© Airplan Flight Equipment 1992

Section 6 – Cherokee Loading and Performance

Section 7 – Conversions

THIS AFE PILOT GUIDE IS NOT AN AUTHORITATIVE DOCUMENT AND SHOULD NOT BE TAKEN AS SUCH

Nationality and Registration Marks: **G-BCJM**

Constructors Serial Number: **28·7425321.**

Designed and Constructed By:

Piper Aircraft Corporation
Vero Beach, Florida
U.S.A.

F.A.A. Certificate of Airworthiness
for Export:

APPROVED AEROPLANE FLIGHT MANUAL

FOR THE PIPER MODEL

PA-28-140

PREPARED IN ACCORDANCE WITH BRITISH CIVIL AIRWORTHINESS REQUIREMENTS

(APPLICABLE TO AIRCRAFT SERIAL NO. 28-20261 TO 28-7625999

OR

AIRCRAFT FITTED WITH PITOT STATIC HEAD P/N 99057-4

TO SERIAL NO. 28-7625999

27 APRIL 1973

"This is the flight manual which forms part of
Certificate of Airworthiness Number **6237**."

The approved Pilot Operating Handbook/Flight Manual (illustrated above), as amended, is the only source of authoritative information. Each individual aircraft has its own individual POH/FM, in the interests of safety & good airmanship the pilot should be familiar with this document.

The PA-28 Cherokee

CHEROKEE - a tribe of Indians that dwelled in the North Carolina and Tennessee area.

The PA-28 Cherokee first produced in 1961 continued the Piper penchant for using Indian tribal names for their aircraft. The Cherokee was introduced to replace the high wing, fabric covered PA-22 Tri-Pacer, and also to compete with the hugely successful Cessna singles that had been introduced a few years previously.

Even the early Cherokees were available in many forms and different options. These versions and derivatives continued to spawn down the years giving a whole array of Cherokees in existence, from the fixed gear, two place 140HP through 150HP, 160HP, 180HP and 235HP models to the PA-32 Cherokee Six and retractable Arrows. If you continue to follow the linage through the Warrior models with their re-designed wing and the Lance and Saratoga (derivatives of the original PA-32 Cherokee Six) you end up with far too many types to cover in the scope of this book. Production of the fixed gear Cherokees amounts to around 25000 aircraft, if you include all the various derivatives you come to a figure nearer 43000.

In this publication the Cherokee will be covered in its fixed gear models powered by the 150 HP and 180 Hp engines,(although much of the information in this book will be relevant to the 140 HP, 160 HP and 235 HP models), from 1963 through to the introduction of the new style wing beginning in 1974. The later models - still with the PA-28 designation but renamed the Warrior - are the subject of a separate publication in this series. It is good airmanship generally, but of particular reference to the prolific PA-28 variants, to remember that the individual aircraft flight manual (as amended and up dated) is the only authorative document for the particular aircraft you intend to fly.

Model Numbers and Production Years

MODEL YEAR	MODEL	PRODUCTION NAME
1964 - 1968	PA-28-140	Cherokee 140
1969	PA-28-140	Cherokee 140 'B'
1970	PA-28-140	Cherokee 140 'C'
1971	PA-28-140	Cherokee 140 'D' #
1972	PA-28-140	Cherokee 140 'E' * #
1973 - 1977	PA-28-140	Cherokee 140 * #

Key to Symbols
* also known as the Cruiser
# two seat variant known as the Flite Liner

Model Numbers and Production Years

MODEL YEAR	MODEL	PRODUCTION NAME
1963 - 1964	PA-28-180	Cherokee 180 B
1965 - 1967	PA-28-180	Cherokee 180 C
1968 - 1969	PA-28-180	Cherokee 180 D

MODEL YEAR	MODEL	PRODUCTION NAME
1973 - 1974	PA-28-180	Challenger
1974 - 1975	PA-28-180	Archer

The PA-28 Cherokee

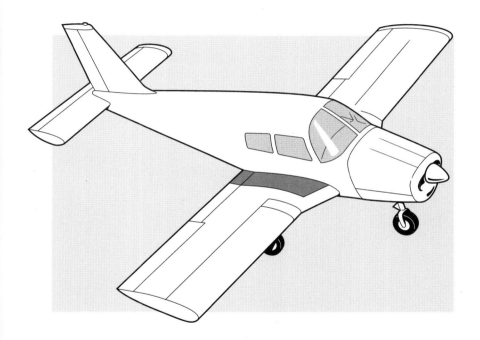

GENERAL DESCRIPTION

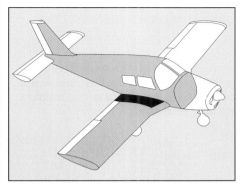

The Airframe.

The PA-28 airframe is generally described as being of all metal construction. The primary structure is constructed of aluminium alloy, with the engine mount being made from tubular steel. Some non-structural components such as the wing tips and undercarriage fairings are made from GRP.

The fuselage has a semi-monocoque structure, that is the vertical bulkheads and frames are joined by horizontal longerons and stringers which run the length of the fuselage. The metal skin is rivetted to the longerons and stringers, this arrangement is conventional for modern light aircraft and allows loads to be spread over the whole construction. At the rear of the fuselage the tail unit incorporates an 'all moving' tailplane, or stabilator. Underneath the rear fuselage a triangular combined tie down point and tail guard is fitted.

The wings are of cantilever design (unsupported by external struts or bracing) and have a positive dihedral. On the upper surface of the right wing a black walkway is marked, this is the only area of the wing to be walked on or stood on. Underneath each wing a metal ring is fitted to be used as a tie down point.

The wings have a positive dihedral.

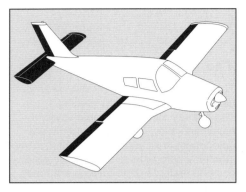

The Flying Controls.

Dual flight controls are fitted as standard and link the cockpit controls to the control surfaces via cable linkages.

The AILERONS are of the differential type, moving upward through 30° and downward through 15°. A balance weight is fitted on a short rod at the outer end of each aileron, this weight is visible inside the wing tip cavity.

The FLAPS are of the simple slotted type, and are manually operated from a lever between the cockpit seats and through a torque tube and push rods to the flap surfaces. Four positions can be selected, fully up (0°), 10°, 25° and 40°. The flaps lock in the fully up position, and only in this position can the walkway on the right hand flap be stood upon. In any other position the flaps will move rapidly down to 40° if any weight is placed on the flap walkway, dumping the unwary onto the ground!

Flap "No Step" warning.

The RUDDER is operated from the rudder pedals (which are also linked to the steerable nose wheel) and can move through 27° either side of the neutral position. A rudder trimmer is fitted in the cockpit below the instrument panel. This wheel can be used to trim out excessive rudder forces in flight. As the rudder is connected (via rods from the rudder pedals) to the nose wheel the control surface cannot be moved whilst the aircraft is stationary without exerting considerable force - this is not recommended.

The Cherokee tail section.

The Cherokee has an all moving STABILATOR, which functions as a combined tailplane and elevator, it moves up 14° from neutral and down 2° from neutral. The control functions in the natural sense, and by design provides a very powerful pitching force.

As part of its design the stabilator incorporates an ANTI-BALANCE TAB at its trailing edge, sometimes referred to as an anti-servo tab. This tab combines two functions. It moves in the same direction as the stabilator to provide a 'damping' force, increasing the feel of the control, very important with such a powerful control surface. In addition the anti-balance tab acts as a trimmer to trim out pitching forces on the control wheel, the control surface moves 3° up from neutral and 12° down from neutral. Depending on the year of construction, the cockpit control for the trimmer maybe either a roof mounted handle that rotates clockwise and anticlockwise, or a conventional trim wheel located on the cockpit floor between the seats. The floor mounted trim wheel acts in the normal sense, rotating the wheel forwards to trim nose down and backwards to trim nose up.

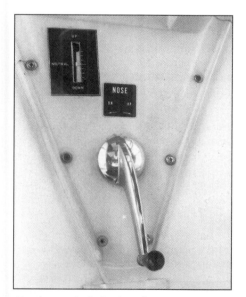

Roof mounted trim handle.

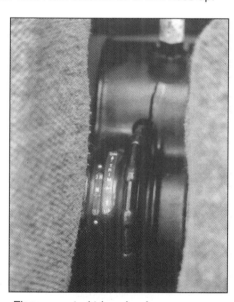

Floor mounted trim wheel.

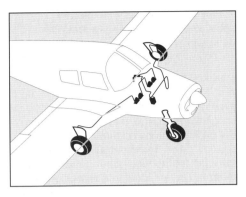

The Undercarriage.

The Cherokee UNDERCARRIAGE is fixed and of the tricycle type with a nose wheel.

The main undercarriage legs incorporate an air-oil oleo strut to absorb operating loads, normally the main gear struts should have about 4.5 inches of the piston tube exposed. The main undercarriage is fitted with 6.00 X 6 wheels, and may have optional wheel fairings. The nose gear attaches to the engine mount and also has an air/oil oleo strut to damp and absorb the normal operating loads, normally about 3.25 inches of the piston tube should be exposed. On the rear of the nose leg a torque link is fitted to maintain the correct alignment of the nose wheel, its lower arm is fitted to the nose wheel fork and the upper arm to the oleo cylinder casing. The nose gear is steerable through direct linkage to the rudder pedals, a spring device aids nose wheel and rudder centering, and is also adjustable to act as the rudder trim (see rudder before). From 1974 models on bungee springs are incorporated on the push rods to aid lighter and smoother nose wheel steering, without these bungees the nose wheel steering can be rather heavy. The nose wheel tyre is a 6.00 X 6 unit.

In common with just about all light aircraft the nose leg is not as strong as the main gear, a point that will be covered in more detail later in this book.

Main undercarriage with optional spats.

Nose wheel assembly with optional spats.

Hand brake lever.   *The brake fluid reservoir.*

The BRAKE system consists of single disc brake assemblies fitted to the main undercarriage and operated by a hydraulic system. The brake lever in the cockpit operates a master cylinder located below and behind the control panel. When the control is pulled back braking is evenly applied to both main wheels. A small button on the right of the brake lever allows it to be locked in the On position to act as a parking brake. To release the parking brake the control is pulled back (which unlatches the button), and then pushed fully forward. When optional toe brakes are fitted in addition, they are operated by depressing the upper half of the rudder pedal. With this system each toe brake has a separate brake cylinder above the pedal, and it is possible to operate the brakes differentially - to the left or right wheel. This system allows the aircraft to turn in a very tight circle, and it is possible to lock one main wheel with the use of some pedal force. Turning around a wheel in this fashion tends to 'scrub' the tyre and is generally discouraged. A brake fluid reservoir is fitted to the upper left forward face of the firewall (accessed via the left engine cowling). Here it can be inspected for fluid level and replenished if necessary.

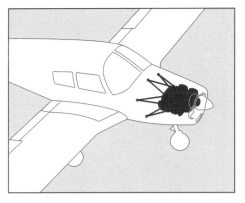

The Engine.

The Cherokee 140 is fitted with a Lycoming 0-320-E engine of 150 HP at 2700 RPM (some very early models were fitted with a 140 HP unit). The Cherokee 180 has a Lycoming 0-360-A engine of 180 HP at 2700 RPM. The 320 and 360 designators refer to the cubic capacity of the engine in inches. Apart from this difference the engines are similar and are treated as one in the following section.

The engine is a four cylinder unit, with cylinders horizontally opposed across the crankshaft. The cylinders are staggered so that each connecting rod has its own crankshaft throw, the cylinders and crankcase assembly are fashioned from aluminium alloy castings.

The engine is air cooled. Airflow enters the engine compartment at the front of the cowling, and is directed by baffles to flow over the whole engine. The cylinders feature deep cooling fins to aid cooling, the airflow leaves the engine compartment at the rear lower cowling underneath the engine compartment. The engine is mounted on a steel tubular mounting which attaches to the firewall.

Port side view Lycoming 0-360-A engine (with cowling removed).

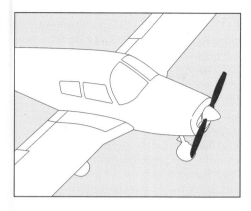

The Propeller.

The PROPELLER is an all metal, two bladed, fixed pitch design, turned by direct drive from the engine crankshaft, the propeller rotates clockwise as seen from the cockpit. For the Cherokee 140 the diameter is 74", with a minimum allowable diameter of 72.5". The Cherokee 180 propeller has a diameter of 76".

PA-28-180 propeller, painted black and white to be more visible.

The Ignition System.

The engine features a dual ignition system, fitted with two magnetos. The magnetos are small AC generators which are driven by the crankshaft rotation to provide a very high voltage to a distributor, which directs it via high voltage leads (or high tension leads) to the spark plugs. At the spark plug the current must cross a gap, in doing so a spark is produced which ignites the fuel/air mixture in the cylinder.

The magnetos are fitted at the rear of the engine, one each side of the engine centre line (hence Left and Right magnetos). The usual arrangement is for each magneto to fire the bottom spark plugs of the two cylinders on one side of the engine and the top spark plugs on the other side. Each cylinder has two spark plugs (top and bottom) for safety and efficiency. The leads that run from the magnetos to the spark plugs should be secure and there should be no splits or cracks in the plastic insulation covering the leads.

It is worth emphasising that the ignition system is totally independent of the aircraft electrical system, and once the engine is running it will operate regardless of the serviceability of the battery or alternator.

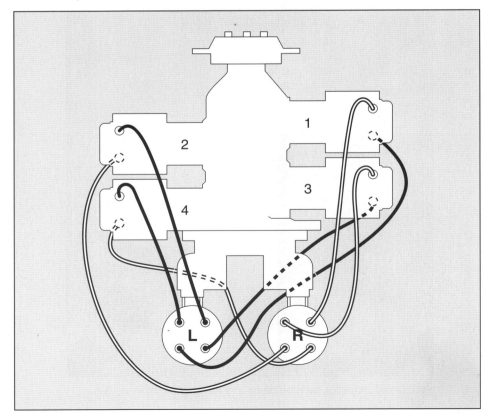

The Oil System

The oil system of the engine provides for lubrication, cooling, sealing, cleansing and protection against corrosion. The system is a wet - sump, pressure feed system. The oil sump is located under the engine, and oil is drawn from here by the engine driven oil pump and through a cooler

PA-28-180 oil filler hatch in the top of the engine cowling.

and filter and into the oil gallery of the right half of the crankcase. When the oil has flowed around the engine it drains down to the sump by gravity. An oil pressure relief valve is fitted in the upper right side of the crankcase. The function of this valve is to maintain the correct operating pressure over a wide range of temperatures and RPM settings. Above a certain pressure the valve will open and allow oil to return to the sump rather than continuing into the lubricating system.

Oil contents can be checked on a dipstick on the right side of the engine. The dipstick is graduated in US quarts and measures the contents of the oil sump. When the engine has been running the oil will take up to 10 minutes to return to the sump, only then can a true reading be taken. When replacing the dipstick care should be taken not to overtighten the cap. To do so may make it exceptionally difficult to open the cap again, and it is quite possible to strip the thread on the cap or filler pipe.

Oil filler pipe.

The oil temperature gauge and oil pressure gauge in the cockpit enable the pilot to monitor the health of the oil system.

Later model Cherokees (1975 on) are fitted with an annunciator panel at the top centre of the instrument panel below the compass. This panel has three warning lights for VAC (vacuum), OIL (oil pressure) and ALT (electrical system). A test button is fitted to check the operation of the lights when the engine is running. The OIL warning light illuminates if oil pressure falls below 35 psi.

The Starter System.

The starter motor is housed at the lower front left side of the engine. It incorporates a geared cog that engages on to the teeth of the starter ring when the starter is operated. As the engine is turned an impulse coupling in the left magneto operates, this retards the spark and aids starting. When the engine fires and begins to rotate under its own power this impulse coupling ceases to operate and normal spark timing is resumed. When the key is released, allowing it to return to the 'BOTH' position, the cog on the starter motor withdraws to be clear of the starter ring.

A STARTER WARNING LIGHT is fitted in the cockpit.
This illuminates when the starter is operated to show that the starter motor is engaging the starter ring. When the key is released the light should go out.

Starter ring, located behind the propeller.

If the light remains on this means that the starter motor is still engaged with the starter ring. In this instance the starter motor will be turned by the engine, and serious damage may be caused to the aircraft electrical system. In this case the engine should be shut down without delay.

The Fuel System.

The Cherokee has two aluminium fuel tanks, located in the inboard leading edge of each wing. From these tanks a fuel line runs through the wing and fuselage to the fuel selector valve located on the left lower cockpit wall in the pilot footwell. From this valve the fuel line runs through the firewall to a fuel strainer bowl mounted on the forward left face of the firewall. From the strainer bowl a fuel line runs through the electric fuel pump and engine driven fuel pump to the carburettor. A separate line runs from the strainer bowl to the cockpit primer and from there to the inlet manifold.

Each tank has a TANK VENT, which is a forward facing pipe on the lower surface of the wing, it ensures that ambient pressure is maintained above the fuel in the fuel tank. Should this vent become blocked a vacuum may form in the tank as the fuel level lowers, and fuel flow to the engine may be interrupted.

Underwing fuel tank vent.

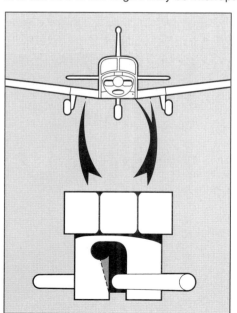

There are three FUEL STRAINERS, one at the lower rear inboard edge of each tank, accessible from the inboard lower wing surface, and one from the fuel bowl, accessed at the lower left cowling. Fuel can only be drawn from the bowl if the cockpit fuel selector is in the Left or Right position. The shape of the fuel strainers has been the cause of problems. To take a fuel sample the bar of the strainer is pushed up against a spring, and fuel will flow into the fuel tester. When the bar is released it should return to its original position, and the fuel flow ceases. The original strainer has a 'lip', which makes it possible for the valve to lock in the open position, and fuel to continue to drain through the valve even after the bar has been released. If this occurs to the tank strainers the result will be the loss of fuel from the tanks, and possible fuel exhaustion.

Engine fuel strainer with warning sign.

If the engine fuel strainer is open, the likely result is engine failure just after take-off due to fuel starvation. In documented incidents the fuel was NOT turned on for the fuel drain check, and so the fact that the engine fuel strainer was locked open was missed. The start, taxy, power checks and take-off were normal, however the engine failed just after take-off.

A recommended modification is to file off an area of the strainer valve so that the bar cannot lock in the open position. Where this modification has not been carried out care should be exercised when operating the fuel drains.

The cockpit FUEL SELECTOR of the Cherokee can also be problematical. The selector is located on the lower left cockpit wall of the pilot's footwell, and so is not easily accessible to a pilot (say an instructor) in the right seat. Being somewhat out of sight to the pilot particular care should be exercised when moving the selector lever. The selector can be used to feed the engine from either the Left or Right tank. To turn the fuel Off a spring loaded latch on the selector must first be depressed and then the lever rotated to the Off position. This operation can be a two handed operation, which should help prevent the accidental selection of the Off position, although it is apparently still possible to accidentally turn the fuel Off whilst airborne.

In normal operation the fuel is drawn through the system by an engine driven FUEL PUMP. However should this pump fail the fuel supply to the carburettor will cease and the engine will stop. Therefore a second, electrical fuel pump is fitted, this pump is selected On or Off from a cockpit switch. Normally the electric fuel pump is used during take-off and landing, and when changing tanks. A fuel pressure gauge is fitted, reading from a sender between the engine driven fuel pump and the carburettor.

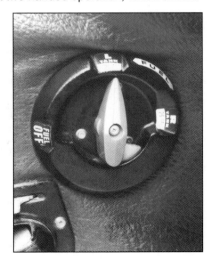

Cockpit fuel selector (left tank selected).

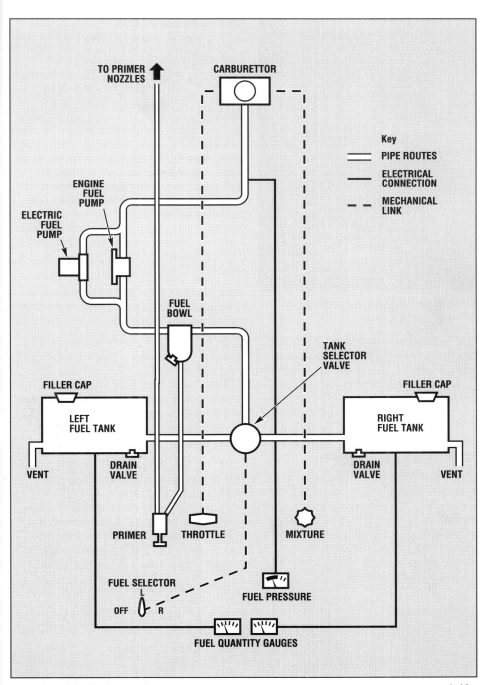

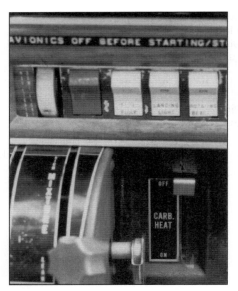

Cockpit carburettor heat controls.

The Carburettor.

The CARBURETTOR mixes air with the fuel from the fuel system and supplies the fuel/air mix to the cylinders. The carburettor is located under the engine, and takes induction air from a scoop intake in the lower front cowling. This air is filtered and then fed into the carburettor air box. In this box a butterfly valve is used to allow either the filtered air, or heated air, to be fed to the carburettor. Heated air comes from an unfiltered inlet tube which then passes into a shroud around the exhaust which heats it before it reaches the carburettor. Hot or cold air is selected via the carburettor heat control in the cockpit, the use of this control and the subject of carburettor icing are fully discussed later in this book.

From the carburettor the fuel/air mix is carried to the induction manifold and to the inlet port of each cylinder.

The carburettor is fitted with an ACCELERATOR PUMP. With a standard carburettor, rapidly opening the throttle can lead to an excessively lean mixture, causing the engine to falter, often at an inconvenient moment, this is known as a "lean mixture cut". The accelerator pump overcomes this problem by introducing a charge of fuel – if the throttle is opened quickly – to maintain the mixture. Unfortunately the system is a little too effective on the Cherokees, and opening the throttle too rapidly can actually lead to a 'rich mixture cut', caused by an overly rich mixture as the throttle is opened rapidly. Many Cherokees are fitted with a placard warning the pilot not to go from idle to full throttle in less than 2 seconds.

The PRIMER control situated next to the throttle quadrant is an aid to starting. The control is unlocked by rotating the primer until a pin on the shaft aligns with the cut out in the collar. The control can then be pulled out, filling the pump with fuel from the fuel. The primer is then pushed in, delivering fuel to the primer nozzles. When priming is complete the control should be pushed fully in with the pin aligned with the collar cut out, and then rotated about half a turn. As a check, attempt to pull the primer out, it should remain locked. It is important that the primer is fully locked, otherwise engine rough running may result.

The MIXTURE is controlled from the mixture lever located in the cockpit which adjusts the fuel/air ratio in the carburettor. The use of this control is fully covered later in the book, however in the fully forward position it gives a RICH mixture, and if moved to the rearward ICO (Idle Cut Off) position the fuel supply is cut off and the engine stops.

The power quadrant has a lever on its right side. Movement of this 'friction' control adjusts the friction of the throttle and mixture levers, and allows for them to be kept in the desired position. Generally this lever is adjusted to leave the throttle and mixture with relatively loose and easy movement on the ground, but is tightened to hold the levers in position for take-off.

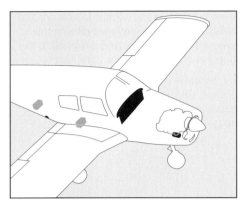

The Electrical System.

The Cherokee has a 14 volt, direct current electrical system. The alternator is mounted to the front lower right of the engine and is engine driven from a belt drive off a pulley directly behind the starter ring. The alternator is rated at 60 amps, (PA-28 140 models before 1969 and PA-28 180 models before 1966 have a 35 amp alternator). A 12 volt battery is located inside a vented box under the baggage compartment floor (PA-28 140) or aft of the baggage compartment (PA-28 180).

The ALTERNATOR is the primary source of power to the electrical system in normal operations with the engine running. The alternator produces alternating current (AC) which is converted into direct current (DC) by diodes incorporated in the alternator housing which act as rectifiers. By their design, alternators require a small voltage (about 3 volts) to produce the electromagnetic field required inside the alternator. The significance of this is that if the battery is completely discharged (flat), the alternator will not be able to supply any power to the electrical system, even after the engine has been started by some other means (ie external power or hand swinging). Output from the alternator is controlled by a VOLTAGE REGULATOR which is mounted behind the right hand side of the instrument panel.

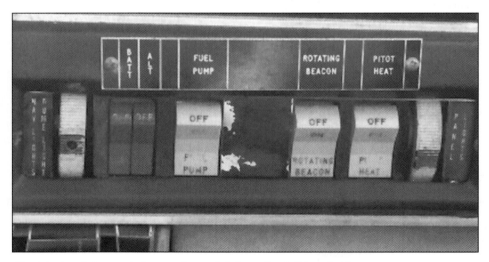

Electrical switch panel, the master switch is on the left hand side.

The primary purpose of the BATTERY is to provide power for engine starting, the initial excitation of the alternator and as a backup in the event of alternator failure. In normal operations with the engine running the alternator provides the power to the electrical system and charges the battery. A fully charged battery has a charging rate of about 2 amperes, in a partially discharged condition (ie just after engine start) the charging rate can be much higher than this. In the event of an alternator failure the battery provides ALL power to the electrical system. In theory a fully charged 35 ampere hour battery is capable of providing 35 amps for 1 hour, or 1 amp for 35 hours, or 17.5 amps for 2 hours etc. In practice the power available is governed by factors such as battery age and condition, load placed on it etc. The best advice is to reduce electrical load to the minimum consistent with safety, and plan to make a landing at the earliest opportunity.

The AMMETER, indicates in amperes the electrical load on the alternator. With the engine running and all electrical services turned off, the ammeter will indicate the charging rate of the battery. As services are switched on the ammeter will indicate the additional load of each item. For night flight the maximum continuous load will be in the region of 30 amps. In the event of alternator failure the ammeter will indicate zero, and where fitted a red 'Low Voltage' warning light will illuminate. On later models (1975 and on) an annunciator panel is fitted in the upper instrument panel (previously described in the oil system section). The ALT warning light of the annunciator panel will illuminate if the alternator fails.

The pilot controls the electrical system via the 'MASTER SWITCH' located on the left side of the instrument panel. This switch is a split rocker switch having two halves, labelled 'BAT' and 'ALT', and normally the switch is operated as one, both halves being used together. The 'BAT' half of the switch can be operated independently, so that all electrical power is being drawn from the battery only; however the 'ALT' side can only be turned on in conjunction with the 'BAT' half. Should an electrical problem occur the MASTER Switch can be used to reset the electrical system by turning it OFF for 2 seconds and then turning it ON again.

The aircraft may be fitted with an EXTERNAL POWER RECEPTACLE behind the wing root, this can be used to connect external power for starting or operation of the aircraft electrical system. Before using external power it is imperative to check that the external power unit is of the correct voltage - otherwise SERIOUS DAMAGE COULD BE INFLICTED ON THE ELECTRICAL SYSTEM. Additionally it should be remembered that if the battery is totally flat (completely discharged), it will need to be removed and recharged or replaced before flight.

To use external power the following procedure should be adopted:

1. Check that MASTER SWITCH and all ELECTRICAL EQUIPMENT is OFF

2. Ensure that the RED lead of the jumper cable goes to POSITIVE terminal of the external power source and the BLACK lead to the NEGATIVE.

3. Insert the cable plug into the aircraft EXTERNAL POWER RECEPTACLE socket.

4. Turn the MASTER SWITCH ON, and proceed with normal starting procedure.

5. After engine start turn MASTER SWITCH and all ELECTRICAL EQUIPMENT OFF and remove the cable plug.

6. Turn the MASTER SWITCH ON, and check the ammeter. If no output is shown flight should not be attempted.

The various electrically operated systems are protected by individual CIRCUIT BREAKERS, which are located to the right side of the lower instrument panel. Should a problem (eg a short circuit) occur the relevant circuit breaker may 'pop', and will be seen to be raised in relation to the other circuit breakers (CBs). The correct procedure is to allow the CB to cool for say 2 minutes, then reset it and check the result. If the CB pops again it should not be reset.

Apart from engine starting and the alternator field the electrical system supplies power to the following:

ALL internal and external lights.
ALL radios and intercom.
Turn Coordinator, Fuel Gauges.
Stall Warner, Pitot Heater, Electric Fuel Pump.

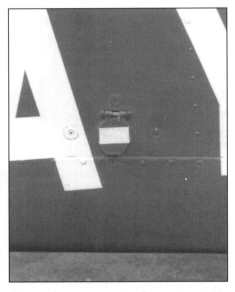

External power receptacle.

The Stall Warner System.

A light located at the extreme left side of the
instrument panel is electrically activated
from a stall warning vane on the leading
edge of the left wing. This vane moves up at
angles of attack approaching the stall, and
gives a warning at approx 5 to 10 knots
above the stall speed. The stall warner is
inoperative with the Master Switch off, and
may be inoperative with a faulty electrical
system.

Cockpit stall warning light.

Wing mounted stall warner vane.

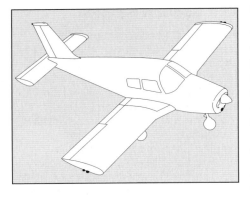

The Lighting System

The Cherokee may be equipped with a variety of optional internal and external lighting. Where wingtip 'Strobe' lights are fitted care should be used in their operation. As a general rule the strobes are not used during taxying as they can dazzle and distract those nearby, they are however very effective in the air. If flying in cloud conditions or heavy precipitation it is recommended that they be turned off as the pilot may become spatially disoriented. The landing light is fitted in the lower front nose cowling, again it should be used with some discretion, not least because of the very short life of the lamp bulbs. Navigation lights are controlled from a thumb wheel in the electrical switch cluster which also controls instrument panel lighting. When the switch is first turned on the navigation lights are illuminated at their set brilliance, the wheel can be rotated to control the level of instrument panel lighting, but the navigation lights remain at their set brightness until the switch is turned fully off.

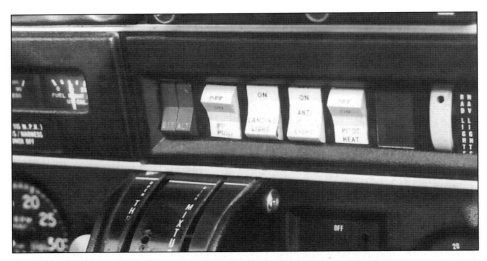

Light switches selected on, navigation lights thumb wheel far right.

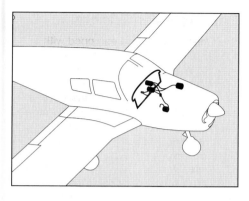

The Suction System.

An engine driven vacuum pump is mounted to the upper rear face of the engine. This pump is fitted with a plastic shear drive, so that should the pump seize, the shear drive will fail and the engine will not be damaged. The air enters the suction system through a filter, passes through the air driven gyro instruments (and is measured by the suction gauge), flows through a vacuum regulator and into the vacuum pump, from which it is expelled through a short pipe.

On some older models there may be no central filter, instead paper filters are fitted at the connection to each instrument.

Suction is used to drive the gyros in the Attitude Indicator (or Artificial Horizon) and Heading Indicator (or Direction Indicator). A suction gauge mounted on the instrument panel measures suction. For cruising RPMs and altitudes the reading should be 5.0, within 0.1 inches of mercury. At 1200 RPM suction should be over 4.0, at higher or lower settings the gyros may become unreliable. A lower suction reading over an extended period may indicate a faulty vacuum regulator, dirty screens or a system leak. If the vacuum pump fails or a line collapses the suction gauge reading will fall to zero, and the Attitude Indicator and Heading Indicator will become unreliable over a period of some minutes as the gyros run down losing RPM. The real danger here is that the effect is gradual and may not be noticed by the pilot for some time.

Suction gauge.

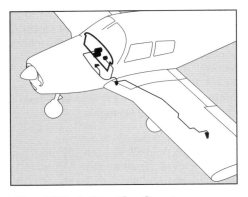

The Pitot-Static System.

The Airspeed Indicator (ASI), Vertical Speed Indicator (VSI) and Altimeter are all connected to the pitot-static system, although the VSI and altimeter use only static pressure and do not have a pitot pressure pick up.

Pressure head under left wing.

Pitot and static pressure comes from a PRESSURE HEAD which is located under the left wing. No checking system is incorporated in the system, and instrument indications

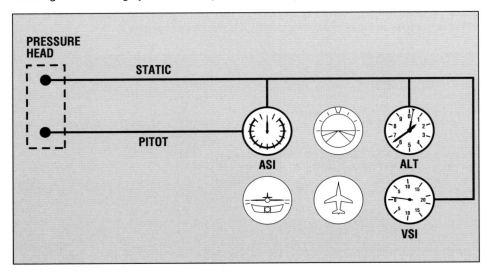

© Airplan Flight Equipment 1992

in the event of a leak or blockage are outside of the scope of this book. As an option the pitot head has a heating element which is activated by a switch in the electrical rocker switch group on the instrument panel, labelled 'PITOT HEAT'. Pitot heat can prevent blockage of the pitot head in heavy rain or icing, this not withstanding it must be remembered that the PA-28 IS NOT CLEARED FOR FLIGHT INTO KNOWN ICING CONDITIONS. Should the static lines become blocked, it is possible to get static pressure into the system by smashing the face of the VSI, thus allowing pressure from the cabin to enter the system. This action is rather drastic, probably requiring the use of the fire extinguisher, and should be considered a last resort.

The pressure head should be checked before flight to ensure that the pitot and static ports are unobstructed, the pressure head may be protected on the ground with a removable pitot cover. It is important not to blow into either pitot or static vents, doing so can result in damage to the pressure instruments.

The Heating and Ventilation System.

Cabin heating is supplied via a shroud around the engine exhaust system. This allows air which has entered from an inlet in the rear engine baffles inside the cowling to be warmed by the exhaust pipes, it can then be directed to outlets in the lower cabin (cabin heat) or at the lower windscreen (defrost) by two levers mounted at the far right instrument panel. The system is very effective once the engine is warm, although its use is governed by a couple of safety factors.

Firstly the heating system effectively opens a path through the firewall between the engine compartment and the cockpit. For this reason the cabin heat and defrost are selected OFF before engine start, or if fire is suspected in the engine compartment.

Secondly with a system of this type there is always a danger of Carbon Monoxide (CO) being introduced into the cabin. Carbon Monoxide is a gas produced as a by product of the combustion process. It is colourless, odourless and tasteless, but its effects are potentially fatal, the dangers are widely publicised. A generally accepted practice is to shut off the heating system if engine fumes (which may contain CO) are thought to be entering the cockpit. This danger arises if a crack or split is present in the exhaust system inside the heating shroud allowing carbon monoxide to enter the heating system.

The ventilation system consists of cockpit vents, individually controllable, directing fresh air to each seat. Models from between 1970 and 1973 have an additional overhead ventilation system taking fresh air from an inlet in the leading edge of the fin. When the heating system is in use it is recommended that the fresh air vents be operated to give a comfortable temperature mix. Doing so will help to combat the possible danger of carbon monoxide poisoning, and on a more mundane level will stop the cabin becoming 'stuffy' and possibly inducing drowsiness in the pilot.

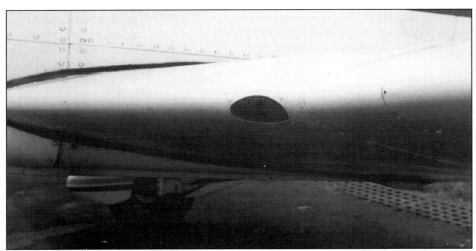

Fresh air inlet in wing leading edge.

Seats and Harnesses

The front seats are adjustable fore and aft.
The bar which unlocks the seat position is
located below the forward edge of the seat
cushion. This bar is raised and then the
seat can be moved fore and aft. When the
desired position is reached the bar is
released and the pilot should check that the
seat is positively locked in position.
Generally entry to and exit from the seats is
easiest with the seats in the rearmost
position. To reach the Left seat the flap lever
is best placed fully down (ie flaps fully up).
To reach the rear seats (where fitted) the
front seats are best moved to the fully
forward position. When the front seats are
unoccupied the seat backs can be tilted
forward to allow access to the rear seats.

Front seats and harnesses.

Harness design may vary between different
aircraft. In addition to the lap strap, shoulder
straps of some description should be fitted
and their use should be considered mandatory, as upper torso restraint has been shown
to be a major factor in accident survivability. Final adjustment of the harness should be
done when the seat is in the desired location.

The baggage area behind the rear seats may be fitted with restraint straps for the
securing of items placed in this area. For the Cherokee 140 maximum baggage to be
carried in this area is 200 lbs (90Kg), evenly distributed. On the Cherokee 180
maximum baggage is 125 lbs (57 Kg) up to 1964 models (180 B) and 200 lbs (90 Kg)
on models after that date. Attention should be paid to the weight and balance
implications of weight in this area, it also must be remembered that for some
manoeuvres the carriage of baggage is prohibited.

Doors And Windows

The Cherokee has a single door on the right hand side of the cabin to allow for access to the cabin via the right wing walkway.

The door is latched by pulling it closed, and then using the locking latch at the top of the door. This lever is turned rearwards to latch the door. This latch is almost invariably quite difficult to move, particularly for a pilot sitting in the left hand seat.

To open the door the top latch is released, by moving the lever forwards, and the small handle at the door front edge is pulled back to open the door.

Although it is important for the door to be properly latched for flight, the consequences of partial door opening in flight are usually not serious. Where accidents do occur after a door opening in-flight, they are often caused by pilot distraction rather than as a direct result of the open door.

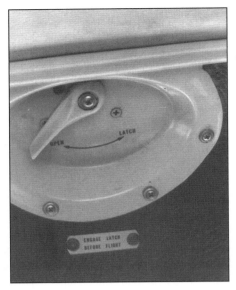

Upper door catch.

When entering and leaving the cabin, the top of the door should not be used as a hand grip to support body weight, as damage to the door and door hinges may result.

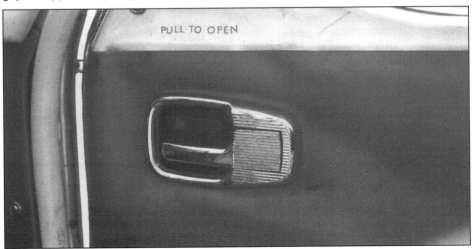

Internal door handle.

The 180 models have a rear baggage door fitted to the right side of the fuselage just behind the wing walkway.
This door allows for easy loading and unloading of the baggage compartment, and should be checked as closed and locked during the pre-flight checks.

An inward opening 'DV WINDOW' is fitted to the left hand window. This window can be opened in flight where visibility through the windscreen has been impaired, or to aid ventilation.

The aircraft design and window area gives reasonable visibility, except directly behind. However the visibility can be degraded by oil smears, insects and other matter accumulating on the windows. For window cleaning a soft cloth and warm soapy water is recommended, to remove oil and grease a cloth soaked in kerosene can be used. The use of petrol, alcohol, thinners and window cleaner sprays is not recommended.

PA-28-180 rear baggage door.

The PA-28 Cherokee

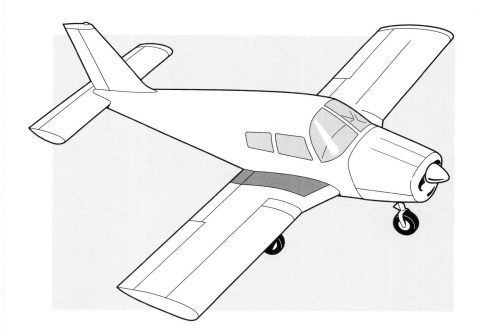

Limitations

PA-28 Cherokee 180 1974 Model

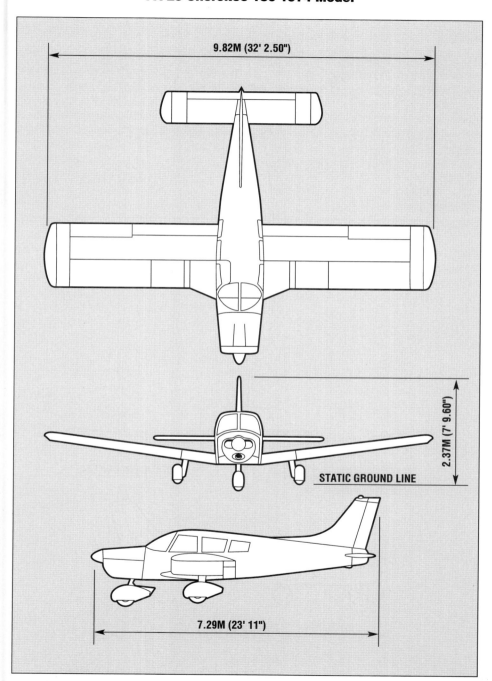

9.82M (32' 2.50")

2.37M (7' 9.60")

STATIC GROUND LINE

7.29M (23' 11")

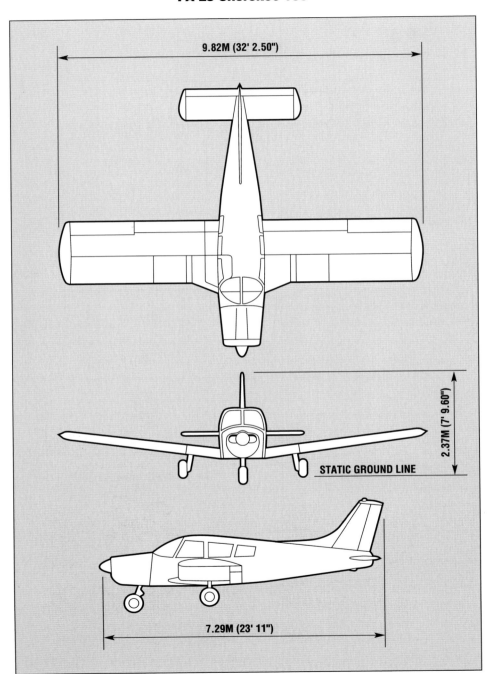

9.82M (32' 2.50")

2.37M (7' 9.60")

STATIC GROUND LINE

7.29M (23' 11")

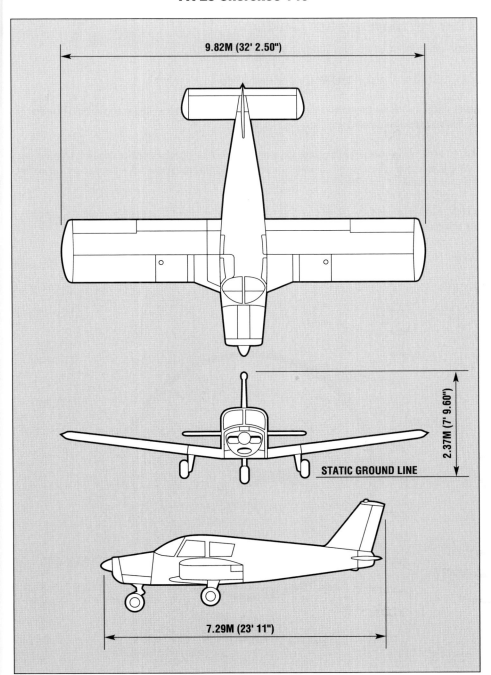

9.82M (32' 2.50")

2.37M (7' 9.60")

STATIC GROUND LINE

7.29M (23' 11")

The 'V' Airspeed Code

VS0 - (Bottom of white arc) Stalling speed with full flap.

VS1 - (Bottom of green arc) Stalling speed 0 flap.

VFE - Maximum airspeed with flaps extended. Do not extend flaps above this speed, or fly faster than this speed with any flap extended.

VA - Design manoeuvring speed. Do not make full or abrupt control movements when flying faster than this speed. Design manoeuvring speed should not be exceeded when flying in turbulent conditions.

VNO - Maximum structural cruising speed. Do not exceed this speed except in smooth air conditions.

VNE - Never exceed speed. Do not exceed this airspeed under any circumstances

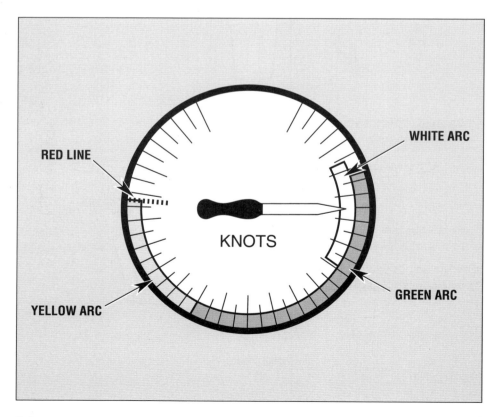

© Airplan Flight Equipment 1992

Cherokee Limitations

Airspeed Limitations - PA 28 140

(quoted speeds are CALIBRATED airspeed - CAS)

	KNOTS	MPH	KPH
VNE	148	171	275
VNO	121	140	225
VFE	100	115	185
Stalling Speed clean	55	64	103
Stalling Speed Full Flap	47	54	87

Indicated Airspeeds (IAS)

	KNOTS	MPH	KPH
VNE	155	178	286
VNO	124	143	230
VA	114	131	210
VFE	101	116	187

Airspeed Indicator Markings (CAS)

	KNOTS	MPH	KPH
RED LINE (Never Exceed)	148	171	275
YELLOW ARC (Caution range)	121 - 148	140 - 171	225 - 275
GREEN ARC (Normal operating range)	55 - 121	64 - 140	103 - 225
WHITE ARC (Flap extended range)	47 - 100	54 - 115	87 - 185

Maximum Demonstrated Crosswind Component   17 Knots

Airspeed Limitations - PA 28 180C,D,E,F,G

(speeds are CALIBRATED airspeed - CAS)

	Knots	MPH	KPH
VNE	148	171	275
VNO	121	140	225
VFE	100	115	185
Stalling Speed clean	58	67	108
Stalling Speed Full Flap	49	57	92

Indicated Airspeeds (IAS)

	Knots	MPH	KPH
VNE	153	176	283
VNO	124	143	230
VA	114	131	210
VFE	101	116	187

Airspeed Indicator Markings (CAS)

	Knots	MPH	KPH
RED LINE (Never Exceed)	148	171	275
YELLOW ARC (Caution range)	121 - 148	140 - 171	225 - 275
GREEN ARC (Normal operating range)	58 - 121	67 - 140	108 - 225
WHITE ARC	49 - 100	57 - 115	92 - 185

Maximum Demonstrated Crosswind Component

17 Knots

Airframe Limitations PA-28 140

	WEIGHTS NORMAL		UTILITY	
	lbs	Kg	lbs	Kg
Maximum Take-off Weight	2150	975	1950	885
Maximum Landing Weight	2150	975	1950	885
Maximum Baggage Weight	200	90	0	0

Flight Load Factors

	Normal	Utility
Max Positive load factor:		
FLAPS UP	3.8G	4.4G
FLAPS DOWN	2.0G	2.0G
Max Negative load factor:		
FLAPS UP	-1.76G	

Airframe Limitations PA-28 180C,D,E,F,G

WEIGHTS	NORMAL		UTILITY	
	lbs	Kg	lbs	Kg
Maximum Take-off Weight	2400	1089	1950	885
Maximum Landing Weight	2400	1089	1950	885
Maximum Baggage Weight	200	90	0	0

Flight Load Factors

	Normal	Utility
Max Positive load factor:		
FLAPS UP	3.8G	4.4G
FLAPS DOWN	2.0G	2.0G
Max Negative load factor:		
FLAPS UP	-1.76G	

Engine Limitations

	Tachometer	Instrument Marking
Maximum RPM	2700	Red Line
Normal Operating Range	500 - 2700	Green Arc

Some 180 models may have a specific 'RPM to avoid' range. Check aircraft flight manual.

Oil Limitations

	Oil Temperature	Instrument Marking
Normal operating range	75° - 245°F	Green Arc
Maximum	245°F	Red Line

*60°F on PA-28 180 models

	Oil Pressure	Instrument Marking
Normal operating range	60 - 90 psi	Green Arc
Minimum	25 psi	Red Line
Maximum	90 psi	Red Line
Caution range - idle	25 - 60 psi	Yellow Arc

	Oil Quantity	US quart	Litre
Note: dipstick is marked in US quarts			
Capacity		8	7.57
Minimum safe quantity		2	1.9
		(+ 1 per hour planned flight)	

Fuel System

	US Gal	Imp Gal	Litre
Fuel Quantity			
Note: cockpit fuel gauges are marked in US gallons			
Total Capacity	50	41.6	189
Unuseable Fuel	0.25*	0.21	0.94
Useable Fuel	49.75	41.4	188

*180 models 1973 and after unuseable fuel 2.00 US gal

	Fuel Pressure	Gauge Indication
Maximum	6.0 psi	Red Line
Minimum	0.5 psi	Red Line
Normal operating range	6.0 - 0.5 psi	Green Arc

Miscellaneous Limitations

Nose Wheel Tyre Pressure	24 PSI	1.67 Bar
Main Wheel Tyre Pressure	24 PSI	1.67 Bar

Oil Grades

Lycoming approve lubricating oil for the engine that conforms to specification MIL-L-6082 (straight mineral type) and specification MIL-L-22851 (ashless dispersant type).

Straight mineral type - known mostly as straight oil - is usually only used when the engine is new, or after maintenance work on the engine. Straight oil grades are known by their number - ie 80, 100.

Ashless dispersant oils are more commonly used in service. These oil grades carry the prefix 'W', ie W80, W100. Ashless dispersant type - 'W' oil - must not be used where the engine is operating on straight oil, nor can 'W' oil be added to straight mineral oil. It is therefore very important to check which type of oil is currently being used in the engine, and be sure only to add the same type.

Both types of oil are available in different grades, used according to the average ground air temperature. The recommended grades are set out as SAE numbers, but available in commercial grade numbers - which are different! Thankfully the situation is more simple than it appears, to get the commercial grade, double the SAE number, ie SAE 50 = commercial grade 100 (or W100). The table below shows the recommended grades for various temperature bands.

AVERAGE AIR TEMPERATURE	MIL-L-6082 Straight mineral	COMMERCIAL GRADE
Above 60°F/16°C	SAE 50	100
30°F/-1°C - 90°F/32°C	SAE 40	80
0°F/-18°C - 70°F/21°C	SAE 30	65
Below 10°F/-12°C	SAE 20	55
AVERAGE AIR TEMPERATURE	MIL-L-22851 Ashless Dispersant	COMMERCIAL GRADE
Above 60°F/16°C	SAE 50 or SAE 40	W100 or W80
30°F/-1°C - 90°F/32°C	SAE 40	W80
0°F/-18°C - 70°F/21°C	SAE 30 or SAE 40	W65 or W80
Below 10°F/-12°C	SAE 30	W65

Fuel Grades

The PA-28 Cherokee is certified for use with 100LL fuels.

The table below shows the recommended fuel grades. It is wise to pay attention when your aircraft is being refuelled, especially if at an airfield new to you. More than one pilot has found out to their cost that piston engines designed for AVGAS do not run very well on AVTUR (Jet A-1). To help guard against this eventuality AVGAS fuelling points carry a RED sticker, and AVTUR fuelling points a BLACK sticker.

APPROVED FUEL GRADES

100LL

100L

100

The PA-28 Cherokee

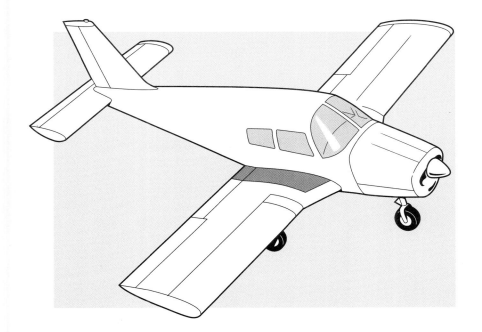

Handling

Handling The Piper PA-28 Cherokee

Engine Starting

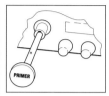

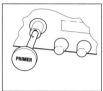

Starting of the Cherokee presents no problems, but the ambient conditions and engine temperature are the prime factors to be considered. A cold engine will require between 2 and 4 primes, a hot engine should not require any priming at all. The throttle is set to 1/4" open (that is 1/4" in), with the mixture rich and fuel set to the tank with the lowest contents (unless of course that tank is empty). 'Pumping' the throttle during starting should be avoided, as the accelerator pump will cause fuel to pool in the intake, causing a fire risk.

Cranking of the starter should be limited to 30 seconds at a time due to the danger of the starter motor overheating. After a prolonged period of engine cranking without a successful start the starter should be allowed a few minutes to cool before a further attempt is made. The starter should not be operated after engine start as damage to the starter may result. The starter warning light should go out after engine start, if it remains lit the engine should be shut down without delay.
After start the oil pressure should register within 30 seconds. Should the oil pressure not register the engine should be shut down without delay. Readings on the suction gauge and ammeter are also usually checked after engine start.

Starting With a Suspected Flooded Engine.

An over primed (flooded) engine will be indicated by weak intermittent firing, and puffs of black smoke from the exhaust. If it is suspected that the engine is flooded (over primed) the throttle should be opened fully and the mixture moved to idle cut off. If the engine starts the mixture should be moved to fully rich and the throttle retarded to the normal position.

Starting In Cold Ambient Conditions (below 0°C).

Failure to start due to an underprimed engine is most likely to occur in cold conditions with a cold engine. An under-primed engine will not fire at all, and additional priming is necessary. Starting in cold temperatures will be more difficult due to several factors. The oil will be more viscous, the battery may lose up to half of its capacity and the fuel will not vapourise readily. A greater number of primes will be required, external power may be needed to supplement the aircraft battery, and pre-heat may be necessary in very low temperatures.

Taxying

In the first few feet of taxying a brake check is normally carried out, followed by steering and differential brake checks in due course. It is common practice to check the hand operated brake lever in addition to the toe brakes (where these are fitted). The direct link, via steering rods, from the rudder pedals to the nose wheel makes the Cherokee easy to steer accurately, although on earlier models the steering is quite heavy to operate. Use of differential brake can give a very small turning circle, increased power is often required when using prolonged differential braking. Where toe brakes are not fitted the brake lever can be used in conjunction with full rudder to reduce turn radius. When taxying with a crosswind 'opposite rudder' will be required, up to full deflection. I.E. with a crosswind from the left, up to full right rudder may be required as the aircraft tries to 'weathercock' into wind. In this situation differential braking will also aid directional control

The chart below shows recommended control wheel positions when taxying with the prevailing wind from the directions shown.

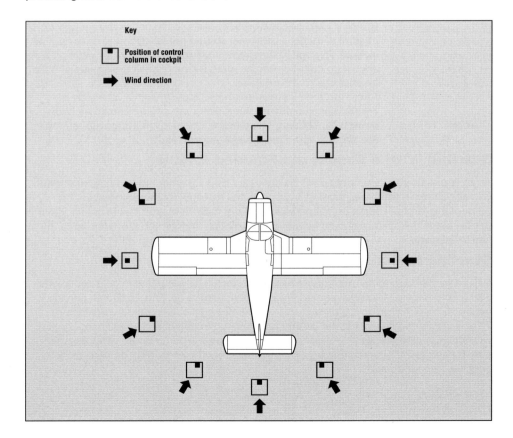

Power and Pre-Take-off Checks

The aircraft is usually positioned into wind to aid engine cooling, and before the power checks start the oil temperature should be in the green arc.

The engine is generally run up to 2000 RPM, with the fuel tank with greatest contents selected (the same tank should be used for take-off). At this RPM the carburettor heat is checked, and a small drop in RPM should be noted. The subject of carb icing is covered more fully later, however an important point to note is that the inlet for the 'hot' air is unfiltered, and so dust, grass etc may well enter the engine when 'hot' air is selected, leading to increased engine wear. For this reason the use of carb heat should be kept to the minimum necessary whilst on the ground.

The magnetos are checked individually, with no more than 3 seconds on each magneto being recommended to avoid plug fouling. A small drop in RPM is the norm and shows that the ignition system is functioning properly. No RPM drop at all when operating on one magneto may well indicate a malfunction in the ignition system, and the possibility that one or both magnetoes are staying 'live'. An excessive drop in RPM when operating on one magneto, especially when accompanied by rough running, may indicate fouled spark plugs or a faulty magneto. If fouled plugs are suspected it may be possible to clear the problem. The engine is set to about 2000 RPM with magnetos on 'BOTH', and the mixture leaned to give the 'peak' RPM. This should be held for about 10 seconds, then the mixture is returned to fully rich and the magnetos can be rechecked.

WARNING: Excessive power setting and over lean mixture settings should be avoided during this procedure. If the problem does not clear the aircraft should be considered unserviceable.

The engine gauges are checked at 2000 RPM for normal indications, together with the suction gauge and ammeter.

The throttle is then closed, the engine should idle smoothly at about 500 - 750 rpm

Take-off

Normally take-off is made with the mixture in the fully RICH position. At high elevation airfields (above say 3000' AMSL) it may be necessary to lean the mixture before take-off to give max. power.

For all take-offs care must be taken to ensure that the feet remain clear of the toe brakes (where these are fitted). It should also be positively confirmed that the brake lever is fully OFF.

At the start of the take-off run (as at all other times), the throttle should be opened smoothly and progressively. Rapid opening of the throttle should be specifically avoided because of the danger of a 'rich mixture cut'. The normal rotate speed is 73 mph, with a climb speed of 85 mph dependent on conditions and operator procedures. In crosswind conditions the rotate speed should be increased to ensure full control immediately after take-off. For 'short field' take-offs the use of 2 stages of flap (25°) is common practice.

On rough surfaces particularly, it is important to protect the nose wheel by keeping weight off it during the take-off run, although 'over-rotating' should be avoided as this will lengthen the take-off run (and ruin the view ahead!).

Climbing

An airspeed in the region of 85 mph will give the best rate of climb after take-off. The best angle of climb (the best increase in height for the shortest distance travelled over the ground), can be obtained at 78 mph with 25° of flap lowered. During climbing it is important to monitor the engine gauges, as the engine is operating at a high power setting but with a reduced cooling airflow compared to cruising flight. Lookout ahead is impaired by the high nose attitude, and it is common practice to 'weave' the nose periodically during the climb to visually check the area ahead.

Engine Handling:

Engine rough running can be caused by a number of factors. It should be remembered that the majority of engine failures in light aircraft are caused by pilot error. After carburettor icing, fuel exhaustion (running out of fuel) or fuel starvation (ie fuel on-board but not reaching the engine) are common causes of engine failure. Having sufficient fuel on board to complete the flight is a point of basic airmanship, and is accomplished through proper flight planning and thorough pre-flight checks. Keeping the fuel tanks in balance and monitoring the fuel system is a part of the cruise checks. In the Cherokee fuel starvation may occur if the engine driven fuel pump fails, in this instance the use of the electric fuel pump should restore the fuel supply to the engine and allow for a diversion to be made.

Regular monitoring of the engine instruments may forewarn of an impending problem. HIGH OIL TEMPERATURE may indicate a faulty gauge, if not accompanied by a corresponding drop in oil pressure. As with most instances the action to be taken will depend on the pilot's judgment of the situation at the time. As general guidance a diversion to a suitable airfield, whilst remaining alert to the possibility of a sudden engine failure would make a reasonable course of action. *Where high oil temperature is accompanied by a low oil pressure, engine failure may very well be imminent, and the pilot should act accordingly.* That said such a situation might occur during a prolonged slow climb in hot conditions. In this instance increasing the airspeed to provide more cooling, and reducing power if possible, may restore oil temperature to normal. In the event of a LOW OIL PRESSURE reading, accompanied by a normal oil temperature reading, gauge failure may be the culprit, and the pilot can consider actions similar to those for an oil temperature gauge failure.

Stalling

*A **Reminder:** The information in this section is no substitute for flying instruction under the guidance of a flying instructor familiar with the aircraft and its characteristics.*

The Cherokee is straightforward in its stalling behaviour. The stall warning light activates 5 to 10 mph above the stall airspeed, it is electrically operated, and so it is inoperative with the master switch off, or with a faulty electrical system. The actual stall speed can be affected by many factors including the aircraft weight and centre of gravity position. The use of power will lower the stalling speed, whilst turning flight raises the stall speed. The use of flaps, power or turning flight considerably increases the chances of a wing drop at the stall. When practicing stalls the possibility of a wing drop can be reduced by keeping the aircraft in balance during the approach to the stall. Typical height loss for a full stall with a conventional recovery (using power) is about 200'. A very gentle stall and absence of wing drop characterise the Cherokee stall.

Stalling in the Cherokee is usually achieved with the control wheel held fully aft. In this position the control wheel moves upwards, and it is possible to have this movement blocked by one or both of the front seat occupants, particularly if they have the seat in the forward position. The pre-takeoff 'full and free control movement' check will help avoid this possibility.

Spins

Always check aircraft flight manual before intentional spinning.

A Reminder: *The information in this section is no substitute for flying instruction under the guidance of a flying instructor familiar with the aircraft and its characteristics.*

The Cherokee is approved for intentional spinning when operating in the utility category.

It is very important to appreciate that spins (and some other manoeuvres) are only approved with the aircraft in the utility category. Although this is discussed further in the weight and balance section the principal limitations are max. weight 1950 lbs and an aft c.g. limit of 86.5 inches. The Cherokee c.g. position is not too sensitive to the front seat occupants, as the seats are located close to the centre of gravity. The c.g. position is however VERY sensitive to the fuel weight, which is further aft of the normal c.g. position. Without going into exact figures a reduced fuel load WILL be necessary to ensure the aircraft is in the utility category. This is a very important quirk of the Cherokee to know. For operations in the utility category a proper weight and balance check should be made, with particular reference to the fuel load. Fatal accidents - involving experienced instructors - have occurred when Cherokees have been spun with a fuel load that caused the c.g. to exceed the aft limit even by only a small amount.

As with stalling several factors can effect the behaviour of the aircraft in the spin. It is quite possible to devote a whole book just to this subject, and it is not the intention here to write a text book on spinning, however some points are worthy of mention. The weight of the aircraft (and particularly the c.g. position as discussed) has a noticeable effect on the spin.High weights tend to extend the spin recovery due to the increase in inertia. The position of the ailerons is important in spinning. The ailerons should be held NEUTRAL through out the spin and recovery.

The spin is normal, and standard recovery action is effective. In fact when properly loaded (ie in the utility category)the main problem is in persuading the aircraft to enter a proper spin in the first place.

The recommended spin recovery is as follows: (operator techniques may vary)

- Check ailerons neutral and throttle closed

- Apply and maintain full opposite rudder (opposite to the direction of spin)

- Move the control wheel forward until the stall is broken and the spin stops.

- When rotation stops centralise the rudder and recover from the ensuing dive.

Descent

The descent may be powered or glide, for the glide a speed of about 85 mph is standard. Where flaps are used the rate of descent increases, the initial lowering of flap leads to a definite nose down pitching and reduced airspeed. The low power settings usually used during the descent, and a possible prolonged descent into warmer air, provide ideal conditions for carburettor icing, full carburettor heat should be used where necessary. In a glide descent power should be added for short periods throughout the descent to help prevent spark plug fouling, rapid cylinder cooling and of course carb. icing.

Landing

For the approach to landing the mixture should be fully RICH (unless landing at a very high elevation airfield), the electric fuel pump should be on and the fuel tank with the most contents selected. The Cherokee is not a difficult aircraft to land, although the stabilator does tend to be heavy in feel during the flare, particularly with the Cherokee 180s. Despite the relative ease of landing, the Cherokees (as with many other light aircraft) appear year after year in landing accident reports. It is rare that anybody is hurt in these accidents, but the reports seem surprisingly similar:

"Piper PA28-140 Cherokee —-. Nose gear collapsed following a heavy landing at —-."

"Piper PA28-180 Cherokee —-. Nose gear collapsed on landing at —-."

"Piper PA28-140 Cherokee —-. Following a bounce on landing at —- aerodrome, the aircraft then porpoised, striking the nose wheel on the runway....."

As already covered the nosewheel is nowhere near as strong as the main undercarriage, but there is no need for its strength to be tested if a proper approach and landing technique is used. Approach speed for a normal approach with flap is about 85 mph, usually a little higher for a flapless approach. Incorrect approach speed is a primary cause of 'ballooning', which often leads to bouncing. Bouncing also arises where the aircraft is allowed to touch down at too high a speed, usually in a level attitude rather than a nose up attitude. The correct action in either a 'balloon' or a bounce is to GO AROUND without delay. The correct landing technique is to approach at the proper speed, 'flare' or 'hold off', close the throttle, and gradually raise the nose to ensure a slow touch down speed on the MAINWHEELS FIRST, with the nose wheel still off the ground. As the aircraft slows down correct use of the stabilator means the nose wheel is allowed to gently contact the surface some time after the initial mainwheel contact. Again there is no substitute for flying instruction in the proper technique with a flying instructor.

The go-around in the Cherokee does not provide any problems, even with full flap extended. The trim change when applying full power is manageable, and although the aircraft will climb with full flap extended it is common practice to raise flaps to the 2nd stage (25°) as part of the immediate go-around actions.

Parking and Tie Down

The aircraft is generally parked into wind, it is good practice to stop with the nosewheel straight so that the rudder is not deflected. All switches should be off, and the doors closed. In extremely cold weather it may advisable NOT to set the parking brake as moisture may freeze the brakes, in addition the parking brake should not be set if there is reason to believe that the brakes are overheated. If for any reason the parking brake is not set the wheels should be 'chocked'.

A well protected and tied down Cherokee.

When tying down the aircraft the following technique is recommended:

- Park aircraft into wind with the flaps retracted.
- Secure the flying control by looping the seat belt through the control wheel.
- Tie ropes, cables or chains to the wing tie down points and secure to ground anchor points.
- If desired a rope (not cable or chain) can be secured to the nose leg   and secured to a ground anchor point.
- A rope can be passed through the tail tie down point and each end secured at 45° angle each side of the tail.
- External control locks may be advisable in strong or gusty wind conditions.

It is also prudent to use a pitot cover, particularly if the aircraft will be left unattended for some time.

The PA-28 Cherokee

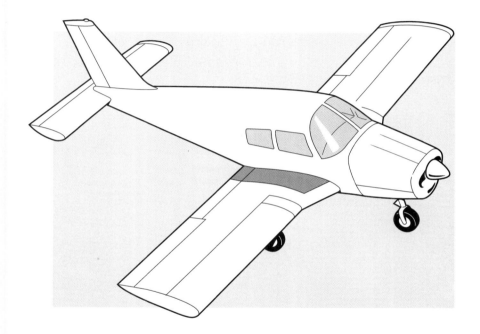

Mixture And Carb Icing Supplement

MIXTURE AND CARB. ICING SUPPLEMENT.

Carburettor Icing

Almost certainly the most common cause of engine rough running, and complete engine failures, is carburettor icing. Despite this carburettor icing remains a widely misunderstood subject, with many pilots knowledge of the subject being limited to a feeling that the carb heat should be used regularly in flight, without really knowing the symptoms of carb. icing or the conditions most likely to cause its formation.

How Carburettor Icing Forms

IMPACT ICING occurs when ice forms over the external air inlet (air filter) and inside the induction system leading to the carburettor. This type of icing occurs with the temperature below 0°C whilst flying in cloud, or in precipitation (ie rain, sleet or snow). These conditions are also conducive to airframe icing, and the aircraft is NOT CLEARED FOR FLIGHT INTO KNOWN ICING CONDITIONS, which clearly these are. So, assuming the aircraft is operated legally within its limitations, this form of icing should not occur, and is not considered further.

Carburettor icing is caused by a temperature drop inside the carburettor, which can happen even in conditions where other forms of icing will not occur. The causes of this temperature drop are twofold:

1. Fuel Icing - the evaporation of fuel inside the carburettor. Liquid fuel changes to fuel vapour and mixes with the induction air causing a large temperature drop. If the temperature inside the carburettor falls below 0°C, water vapour in the atmosphere condenses into ice, usually on the walls of the carburettor passage adjacent to the fuel jet, and on the throttle valve. Generally fuel icing is responsible for around 70% of the temperature drop in the carburettor.

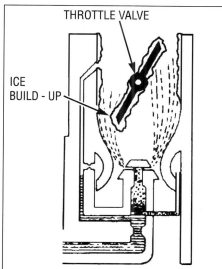

THROTTLE VALVE

ICE
BUILD - UP

2. Throttle icing - the temperature loss caused by the acceleration of air and consequent pressure drop around the throttle valve. This effect may again take the temperature below 0°C, and water vapour in the inlet air will condense into ice on the throttle valve. This practical effect is a demonstration of Bernoulli's Principle.

As fuel and throttle icing generally occur together, they are considered just as carburettor icing.

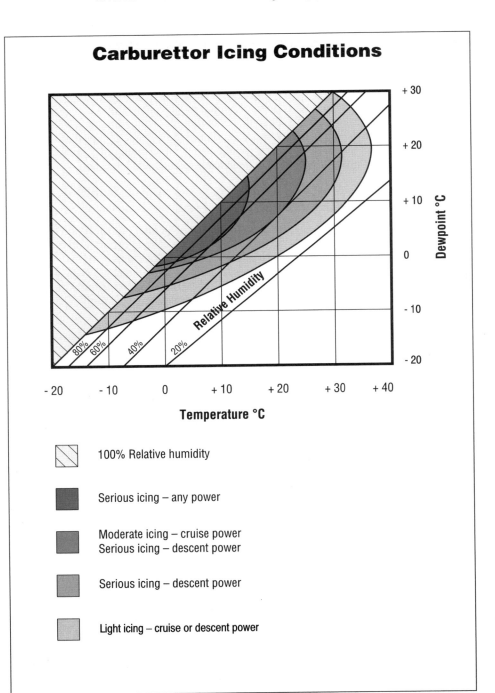

Carburettor Icing Conditions

100% Relative humidity

Serious icing – any power

Moderate icing – cruise power
Serious icing – descent power

Serious icing – descent power

Light icing – cruise or descent power

Conditions Likely To Lead To Carburettor Icing

Two criteria govern the likelihood of carburettor icing conditions, the AIR TEMPERATURE and the RELATIVE HUMIDITY.

The ambient air temperature is important, BUT NOT BECAUSE THE TEMPERATURE NEEDS TO BE BELOW 0°C, OR EVEN CLOSE TO FREEZING. The temperature drop in the carburettor can be up to 30°C, so carburettor icing can (and does) occur in hot ambient conditions. No wonder carburettor icing is sometimes referred to as refrigeration icing. Carburettor icing is considered a possibility within the temperature range of -10°C to +30°C.

The relative humidity (a measure of the water content of the atmosphere) is the major factor. The greater the water content in the atmosphere (the higher the relative humidity), the greater the risk of carburettor icing. That said the relative humidity (RH) does not to have to be 100% (ie visible water droplets - cloud, rain), for carburettor icing to occur. Carburettor icing is considered a possibility at relative humidity values as low as 30%, it is rare that the RH gets this low in Europe. Here in lies perhaps the real danger of carburettor icing, that it can occur in such a wide range of conditions. Obviously the pilot must be alert to the possibility of carburettor icing at just about all times. Flight in or near cloud, or in other visible moisture (ie rain) might be an obvious cause of carburettor icing, but - VISIBLE MOISTURE DOES NOT NEED TO BE PRESENT FOR CARBURETTOR ICING TO OCCUR.

Symptoms Of Carburettor Icing

In this aircraft, fitted with a fixed pitch propeller, the symptoms of carburettor icing are straightforward. A loss of RPM will be the first symptom, although this is often first noticed as a loss of altitude. As the icing becomes more serious, engine rough running may occur.

Carburettor icing is often detected during the use of the carburettor heat. Normally when the carburettor heat is used, a small drop in rpm occurs, when the control is returned to cold (off) the rpm restores to the same as before the use of carburettor heat. If the rpm restores to a higher figure than before the carburettor heat was used, it can be reasonably supposed that some form of carburettor icing was present.

Use Of Carburettor Heat

Apart from the normal check of carburettor heat during the power checks, it may be necessary to use the carburettor heat on the ground if carburettor icing is suspected. Safety considerations apart, the use of carburettor heat on the ground should be kept to a minimum, as the hot air inlet is unfiltered, and so sand or dust can enter the engine, increasing engine wear.

Carburettor icing is generally considered to be very unlikely with the engine operating at above 75% power, ie during the take-off and climb. Carburettor heat should not be used with the engine operating at above 75% power (ie full throttle) as detonation may occur. Detonation is the uncontrolled burning of fuel in the cylinders, literally an explosion, and will cause serious damage to the engine very quickly. Apart from the danger of detonation, the use of carburettor heat reduces the power the engine produces. In any situation where full power is required (ie take-off, climb, go-around) the carburettor heat must be off (cold).

Very few operators recommend the use of anything other than FULL carburettor heat. A normal carburettor icing check will involve leaving the carburettor heat on (hot) for 5-10 seconds, although the pilot may wish to vary this dependent on the conditions. The use of carburettor heat does increase the fuel consumption, and this may be a factor to consider if the aircraft is being flown towards the limit of its range/endurance in possible carburettor icing conditions.

With carburettor icing present, the use of carburettor heat may lead to a large drop in rpm, with rough running. The instinctive reaction is to put the carburettor heat back to cold (off), and quickly, - this is however the wrong action. Chances are this rough running is a good thing, and the carburettor heat should be left on (hot) until the rough running clears, and the rpm rises. In this instance the use of carburettor heat has melted a large amount of accumulated icing, and the melted ice is passing through the engine causing temporary rough running.

Care should be taken when flying in very cold ambient conditions (below -10°C). In these conditions the use of carburettor heat may actually raise the temperature in the carburettor to that most conducive to carburettor icing. Generally when the temperature

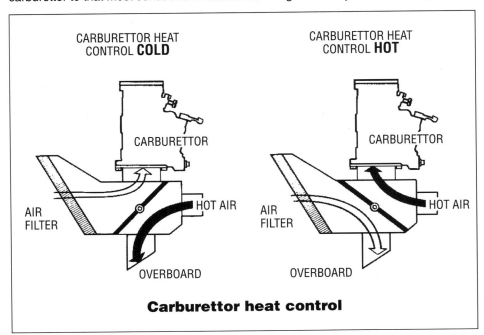

Carburettor heat control

© Airplan Flight Equipment 1992

in the carburettor is below -8°C moisture forms directly into ice crystals which pass through the engine.

The rpm loss normally associated with the use of carburettor heat is caused by the reduced density of the hot air entering the carburettor, leading to an over rich mixture entering the engine. If the carburettor heat has to be left constantly on (hot) - ie flight in heavy rain and cloud - it may be advisable to lean the mixture in order to maintain rpm and smooth engine running.

It is during the descent (and particularly the glide descent) that carburettor icing is most likely to occur. The position of the throttle valve (ie almost closed) is a contributory factor, and even though the carburettor heat is normally applied throughout a glide descent, the low engine power will reduce the temperature of the hot air selected with the carburettor heat control. In addition a loss of power may not be readily noticed as the propeller is likely to windmill even after a complete loss of power, and so a full loss of power may only be apparent when the throttle is opened at the bottom of the descent. This is one good reason for opening the throttle to 'warm the engine' at intervals during a glide descent.

The Mixture Control.

The aircraft is provided with a mixture control, so that the pilot can adjust the fuel/air mixture entering the engine when necessary. The cockpit mixture control operates a needle valve between the float bowl and the main metering jet. This valve controls the fuel flow to the main metering jet to adjust the mixture, with the mixture control in the ICO position (fully lean) the valve is fully closed.

Reasons For Adjusting The Mixture

Correct leaning of the engine will enable the engine to be operated at its most efficient in terms of fuel consumption. With the increased use of 100LL fuel, leaning is also important to reduce spark plug fouling

The most efficient engine operation is obtained with a fuel/air ratio of about 1:15, that is 1 part fuel to 15 parts air. In fact with the mixture set to fully rich, the system is designed to give a slightly richer mixture than ideal, about 1:12 typically. This slightly over rich mixture reduces the possibility of pre-ignition or detonation, and aids cylinder cooling.

As altitude increases the air density decreases. Above about 3000' the reduced air density can lead to an over rich mixture. If the mixture becomes excessively rich, power will be lost, rough running may be evident and ultimately engine failure will occur due to a 'rich cut'. It is for this reason that the mixture control is provided to ensure the correct fuel/air ratio, typically it is used when cruising above 3000'.

The flight manuals for some older aircraft recommend leaning only above 5000'. However with the increasing use of AVGAS 100LL, and the plug fouling problems sometimes associated with 100LL, most operators recommend leaning once above 3000'.

Effect of mixture adjustment

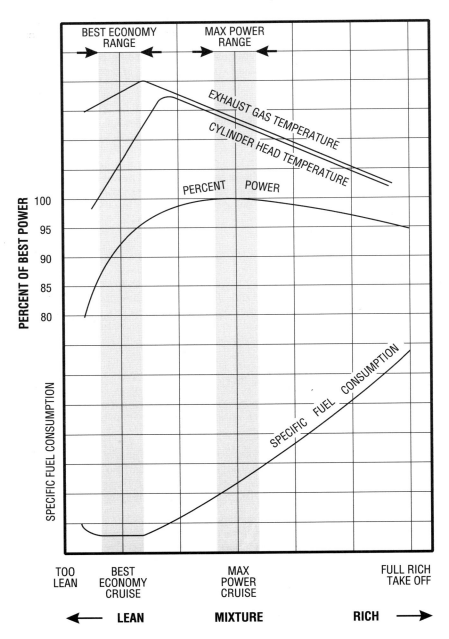

Use Of The Mixture Control

For take-off and climb the mixture should be fully rich, the only exception being operation from a high density altitude airport when leaning may be necessary to ensure the availability of max. power. On reaching a cruising altitude above about 3000' the cruise power should be set, and then leaning can be carried out (note: generally leaning with over 75% power set is not recommended). If climbing above about 5000', full throttle will be less than 75% power on a normally aspirated engine, and so leaning may be permissible to maintain smooth running.

Assuming that there is no Exhaust Gas Temperature (EGT) gauge and no cylinder head temperature gauge, the primary instrument to watch when leaning is the RPM gauge (tachometer).

To lean the engine, the recommended power setting (RPM) is set with the throttle. Next, with a constant throttle setting, the mixture control is slowly moved back (leaned). If leaning is required the RPM will increase slowly, peak, and then decrease as the mixture is leaned, if leaning is continued the engine will ultimately run rough and lose power.

If the mixture is set to achieve peak RPM, the maximum power mixture has been achieved.

If the mixture is set to give a tachometer reading 25 - 50 rpm less than peak rpm on the 'lean' side, the best economy mixture has been achieved. This setting is the one that many aircraft manufacturers recommend (25-50 RPM on the 'lean side' of peak RPM), and their performance claims are based on such a procedure.

Using a mixture that is too lean is a false economy, and will lead to serious engine damage sooner or later. Detonation (an uncontrolled explosive combustion of the mixture in the cylinder) is particularly dangerous, and can lead to an engine failure in a very short time. The use of a fully rich mixture during full power operations is specifically to ensure engine cooling and guard against detonation.

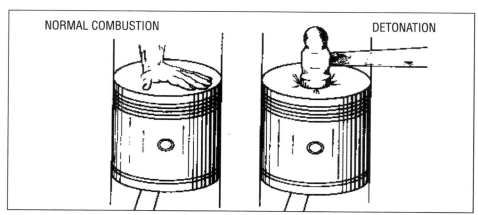

NORMAL COMBUSTION   DETONATION

For any change in operating conditions (altitude, power setting) the mixture will need to be reset. It is particularly important that the mixture is set to fully rich before increasing the power setting.

During a descent from a high altitude, the mixture will gradually become too lean if not reset, leading to excessive cylinder temperatures, power loss and ultimately engine failure. Normally the mixture is set to fully rich prior to landing, unless operating at a high elevation airfield.

Moving the mixture to the fully lean position - ICO (Idle Cut Off) - closes the needle valve, and so stops fuel supply to the main metering jet. This is the normal method for closing down the engine and ensures that no unburnt mixture is left in the engine.

The PA-28 Cherokee

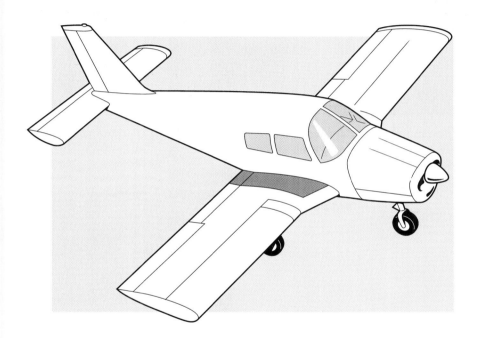

A proper pre-flight check will avoid missing the obvious (plenty of pilots have tried to get airborne with tow-bars or tie-downs still attached)...

...Or the more subtle (under-wing mud and stone damage).

Expanded PA-28 Pre-flight Checklist
Approaching Aircraft

Check for and remove any tie downs, external control locks, pitot cover and wheel chocks.

Look for any oil & fuel spillages from aircraft.

Remove any ice & frost from ALL surfaces.

Check for access to taxiways, obstructions, loose gravel etc.

Look to see if aircraft is on a level surface. This may effect the visual check of fuel contents.

In Cabin

1. **Internal Control locks & Covers**...............................Remove & Stow Securely

2. **Parking Brake**..Check On with locking plate in

3. **Magneto Switches** ....Check OFF and Key Out - OTHERWISE THE PROPELLER IS LIVE AND LETHAL

4. **Master Switch** ....On

   Turn on Pitot heater,anti-collision beacon, landing light and navigation lights. Leave cockpit and check in turn :

5. **Stall Warner Vane** ....Move gently forward to check

6. **Pitot Heat**...Check with fingers that pressure head is warm (it may take a minute or so to warm up)

7. **Anti-Collision Beacon**.........................Check operation.(rotating red light on fin)

8. **Landing/Nav lights** ....Check.
   For Navigation lights colours are :
   PORT(Left) - RED; STARBOARD(Right) - GREEN; REAR(Tail) - WHITE

   Return to cockpit and turn off electrical services as in above

9. **Fuel** ....Turn On - Check contents gauges

10. **Master Switch** ....Off

11. **Flaps**..Lower to 2nd Stage (25°)

12. **Trimmer** ....Check position neutral using indicator

13. **First Aid Kit** ....In Position,secure

14. **Fire Extinguisher**.............................In Position,secure & serviceable (gauge at top should be in green arc)

15. **On leaving cockpit do NOT tread on flap surface.**

External

Begin at rear of wing. This should also be where you complete your checks.

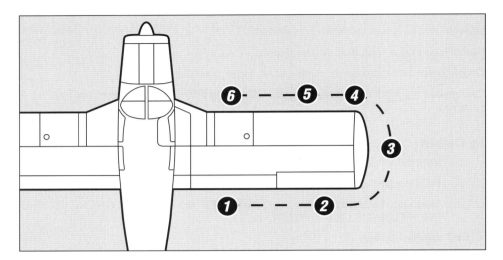

Starboard Wing

1. **Flap** ....
   Upper and lower surface condition.
   Particularly check inner lower surface for caked mud or stone
   damage from wheels. Check linkages secure and greased

2. **Aileron** ....
   Upper and lower surface condition, linkages & hinges secure, balance weight
   (inside wing tip) secure (with fingers inside hinge line hold the aileron with other
   hand - sudden down movement of aileron makes efficient cutting action!)
   Check full and free movement - DO NOT USE FORCE

3. **Wing Tip** ....Condition,Security. Navigation light
   unbroken.(This area is particularly vulnerable to hanger damage)

4. **Wing Surface** ....Upper & Lower surface condition.

5. **Wing Leading Edge** ....Check for dents along entire length

6. **Fuel Tank** ....Check contents visually, resecure cap.
   Check fuel vent unblocked. Take fuel drain sample from under tank if
   necessary - check for correct colour, water bubbles or sediment. Check drain
   not leaking.

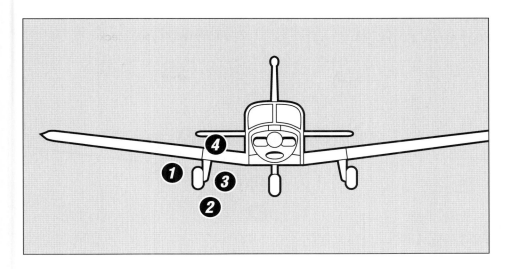

Starboard Undercarriage

1. **Tyre** ....Check for tread & general condition.Check for correct inflation. Check alignment of creep marks.

2. **Hydraulic Lines** ....Check for leaks (Red fluid)

3. **Disc Brake**..Should be shiny, not rusty or pitted.

4. **Oleo**..Check for correct extension

Look for mud or stone damage on wing & flap surface near undercarriage & flap surface near undercarriage

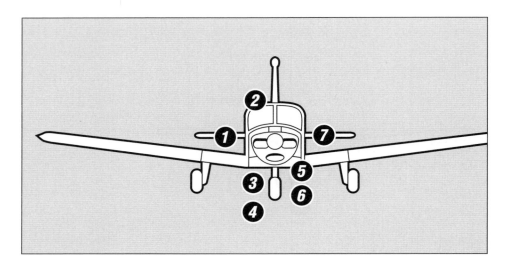

Front Fuselage & Engine

1. **Starboard Cowling** ....
   Open engine compartment, check oil level, do NOT overtighten dipstick on
   resecuring. Check cowling.

2. **Windscreen** ....
   Should be clean and insect free, OAT probe secure.

3. **Nose Leg** ....
   Oleo extension, linkages, nuts & split pins secure.

4. **Nose Wheel** ....
   Check for tread & general condition.Check for correct inflation. Check
   alignment of creep marks.

5. **Landing light** ....unbroken.

6. **Propeller** ....
   Look for cracks or chips especially leading edge. Check spinner secure and
   condition good. DO NOT MOVE OR SWING PROPELLER

7. **Port Cowling** ....
   Open cowling and check brake fluid level. Check engine compartment (ie HT
   leads secure etc). Resecure cowling. Take fuel sample if necc. Check fuel drain
   not leaking.

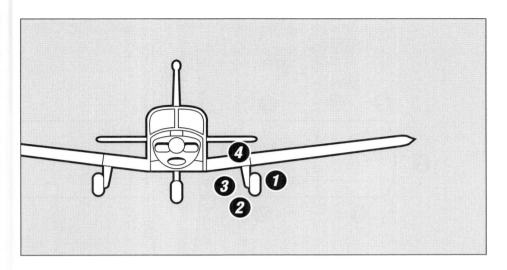

Port Undercarriage

1. **Tyre** ....Check for tread & general condition.Check for correct inflation. Look for alignment of creep marks.

2. **Hydraulic Lines** ....Check for leaks (Red fluid)

3. **Disc Brake**...Should be shiny, not rusty or pitted.

4. **Oleo**..Check extension

Look for mud or stone damage on wing & flap surface near undercarriage

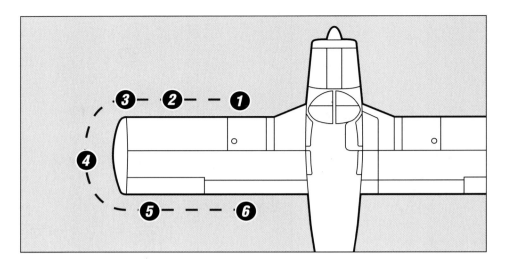

Port Wing

1. **Fuel Tank**..Check contents visually, resecure cap.

   Take fuel drain sample if necessary. Check drain not leaking.

2. **Wing Surface**..Upper & Lower surface condition

3. **Wing Leading Edge**....................................Check for dents along entire length.
   Check pressure head perforations unblocked - DO NOT
   BLOW INTO PRESSURE HEAD

4. **Wing Tip** ....Condition,Security. Navigation light
   unbroken

5. **Aileron** .... Upper and lower surface condition,
   linkages & hinges secure, balance weight (inside wing tip) secure.
   Remember to watch for aileron movement whilst checking inside hinge line.
   Check full and free movement gently - DO NOT USE FORCE.

6. **Flap** ....Upper and lower surface condition esp. near
   undercarriage. Check linkages secure and greased.

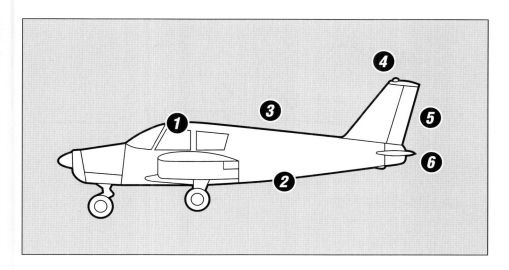

Port Fuselage

1. **Windows** ....Clean & uncracked

2. **Skin**...
General surface condition upper and lower, look for wrinkles, dents or punctures.

3. **Radio Aerials** ....Check secure

4. **Tail Fin** ....
Check skin condition,especially fairings; Check aerials and rotating beacon
secure.

5. **Rudder**..
Check condition, linkages secure & greased, nuts & split pins secure, Nav light
unbroken. DO NOT ATTEMPT TO FORCE RUDDER MOVEMENT.

6. **Stabilator**...
Check Upper and lower surface condition. Check linkages and split pins.
Check full and free movement DO NOT USE FORCE. Ensure anti-balance tab
moves in correct sense Check other side of tail fin

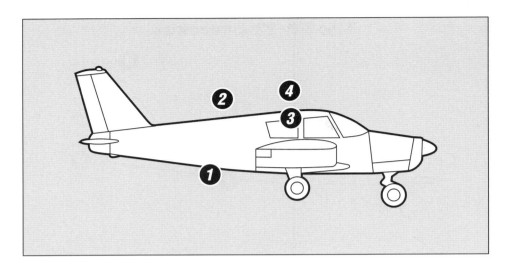

Starboard Fuselage

1. **Skin**..
   General surface condition, upper and lower, look for any wrinkles, dents or
   punctures.

2. **Radio Aerials** ....Check secure Do not tread on flap surface

3. **Cockpit door**...Check latches & hinges secure

4. **Windows**...Check clean & uncracked

IMPORTANT

**REMEMBER.FULL REFERENCE MUST BE MADE TO AIRCRAFT FLIGHT
MANUAL, PILOTS OPERATING HANDBOOK,AIP's,FLYING SCHOOL
SYLLABUS/PILOTS ORDER BOOK,ETC**

IF IN DOUBT - ASK

The PA-28 Cherokee

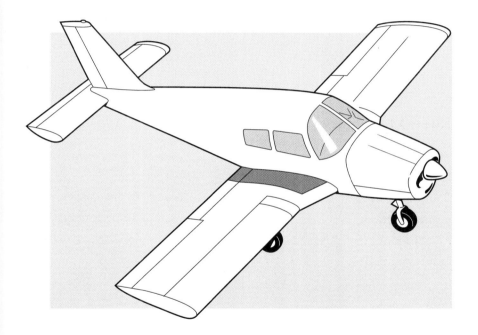

Cherokee LOADING and PERFORMANCE.

Loading

Aircraft loading can divided into two areas, the aircraft weight and the centre of gravity (c.g) position.

The aircraft must be loaded so that its weight is below the certified maximum take-off weight (2150 lbs for the PA-28 140) or (2400 lbs for the PA-28 180). The weight limit is set primarily as a function of the lifting capability of the aircraft, which is largely determined by the wing design and engine power of the aircraft. Operating the aircraft when it is over weight will adversely effect the aircraft handling and performance, such as:

      Increased take-off speed and slower acceleration

      Increased runway length required for take-off

      Reduced rate of climb

      Reduced maximum altitude capability

      Reduced range and endurance

      Reduction in manoeuvrability and controllability

      Increased stall speed

      Increased approach and landing speed

      Increased runway length required for landing

The aircraft must also be loaded to ensure that its centre of gravity (c.g.) is within set limits, normally defined as a forward and aft limit in inches aft of the datum. The forward limit is determined by the amount of elevator control available at landing speed, the aft limit is determined by the stability and controllability of the aircraft whilst manoeuvring. Attempted flight with the c.g. position outside of the set limits (either forward or aft) will lead to control difficulties, and quite possibly loss of control of the aircraft.

When loading the aircraft it is standard practice to calculate the weight and c.g. position of the aircraft at the same time, commonly known as the weight and balance calculation. Before going further it must be emphasised that the following examples are provided for illustrative purposes only. Each INDIVIDUAL aircraft has an INDIVIDUAL weight schedule that is valid only for that aircraft, and is dependent amongst other things on the equipment fitted to the aircraft. If the aircraft has any major modification, repair or new equipment fitted a new weight schedule will be produced. Therefore for any loading or performance calculations you must use the documents for the specific aircraft you will be using. As well as setting out limits the aircraft documents will also give lever arms for each item of loading. The lever arm is a distance from the aircraft datum. The weight multiplied by its lever arm gives its moment. Thus a set weight will have a greater moment the further away it is from the datum.

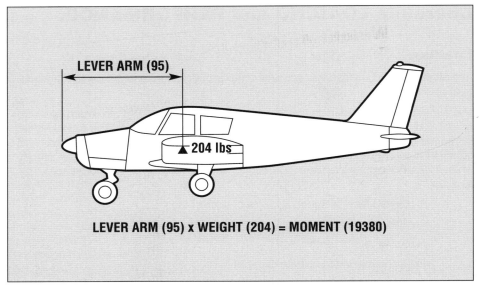

LEVER ARM (95) x WEIGHT (204) = MOMENT (19380)

The operating weight of the aircraft can be split into three categories:

BASIC (EMPTY) WEIGHT - the weight of the aircraft, including unuseable fuel (and normally full oil). The weight and c.g. position of the aircraft in this condition will be noted in the weight schedule.

VARIABLE LOAD - weight of the crew (ie pilot). The certified minimum crew for the Cherokee is one pilot! The weight schedule will give the lever arm for this load.

DISPOSABLE LOAD - weight of passengers, fuel and baggage. Again the weight schedule will give a lever arm for each of these loads.

Firstly the pilot will need to calculate a weight for the variable and disposable load. It is obviously important to work in one set of units (either lbs or Kgs). This becomes more complicated for the fuel load where volume (litres, imperial gallons or U S gallons) will need to be converted into weight. This may be done in the weight schedule, but conversion tables are set out in section 7.

Weight And Centre Of Gravity Schedule

PRODUCED BY :

GROSVENOR AVIATION SERVICES (ENGINEERING) LIMITED

AIRCRAFT TYPE: **PIPER PA38-112**

NATIONALITY AND REGISTRATION MARKS: **G-BGRR**

CONSTRUCTOR'S SERIAL No: **78A0336**

MAXIMUM PERMISSIBLE WEIGHT: **1670 lbs**

MAXIMUM LANDING WEIGHT: **1670 lbs**

CENTRE OF GRAVITY LIMITS: **REFER TO FLIGHT MANUAL REP No. FAA 2126**

ALL LEVER ARMS ARE DISTANCES IN INCHES EITHER FORE OR AFT OF DATUM.

PART 'A' BASIC WEIGHT

The basic weight of this aircraft as calculated from Planeweighs Limited Report No.1034 weighed on 08.07.88. at Manchester Airport is: **1182 lbs**

The centre of gravity of aircraft in the same condition (aft of the datum) is: **74.66 ins.**

The total Moment about the datum in this condition in lb ins. is: **88254.45**

The DATUM referred to is defined in the Flight Manual, which is **66.25 ins**. forward of Wing leading edge.

The basic weight includes the weight of 12 lbs unuseable fuel and 45 lbs of oil and the weight of items indicated in Appendix 1 which comprises the list of basic equipment carried.

Each individual aircraft has an individual weight schedule, valid only for that aircraft. The weight schedule will state lever arms for each item of loading.

Mathematical Weight and Balance Calculation

With this method of calculation the weights of each item are listed together with their lever arm. Addition of all the weights is the first step, to ensure that the resulting figure is within the maximum permitted. Assuming this is the case the balance can then be calculated. For each item (except for the basic weight where the calculation is done already on the weight schedule) the weight is multiplied by the lever arm, to give a moment. Normally the lever arm is aft of the datum, to give a positive figure. If the lever arm quoted is forward of the datum the moment will be negative (although obviously the weight is NOT deducted from the weight calculation.All the moments are then added together, to give the total moment, and this figure is then divided by the total weight. The resulting figure will be the position of the c.g. , which can be checked to ensure it is within the set limits. The weight and c.g. position can be plotted on a graph in the flight manual. If the plotted position is within the 'envelope', the weight and c.g. position are within limits.

It is obviously important for the pilot to be sure of whether the aircraft needs to operated in the NORMAL or UTILITY categories. The aircraft flight manual will advise which manoeuvres can only be carried out when the aircraft is in the utility category (eg spinning). Operation in the utility category is defined as a reduced weight (1950 lbs) and different c.g. limits. In addition baggage in the rear baggage area is not permitted. The critical importance of the fuel load in the calculation of c.g. position for utility category operations should be remembered. As an illustration here is a practical example for a well equipped Cherokee 140.

Example:

BASIC(EMPTY) WEIGHT:	Aircraft G-BCJM(PA-28 140)
	From the weight schedule for this aircraft,
	weight is 1449.16 lbs
VARIABLE LOAD:	Pilot 140 lbs
DISPOSABLE LOAD:	Co-Pilot 140 lbs
	Fuel 15 US gal @ 6.0 lbs per
	US gal = 90 lbs

Although at this stage you can simply add together the weights to check the all up weight, it is more common to make up a table to check weight AND balance. Using the information above, and the lever arms from the weight schedule, we can make up a table to calculate the moment for each item (remembering that weight X lever arm gives the moment).

Most Cherokee flight manuals do not contain a weight and centre of gravity graph. Therefore we have drawn graphs using data from the flight manuals, for a PA-28 140 and PA-28 180. These graphs are purely illustrative and not to be used for Centre of Gravity calculations.

ITEM	WEIGHT (lbs)	LEVER ARM	MOMENT
BASIC (EMPTY) WEIGHT - the weight, lever arm and moment are listed in the weight schedule			
for G-BCJM	1449.16	86.13	124818.35
VARIABLE LOAD			
Pilot	140.0	85.5	11970
DISPOSABLE LOAD			
Passenger	140	85.5	11970
Fuel	90	95.0	8550
TOTAL WEIGHT	1819.16	TOTAL MOMENT	157308.35

The total weight is below the maximum utility limit, and so is acceptable.

Dividing the total moment by the total weight gives the Centre of Gravity position:

$$\frac{157308.35}{1819.16} = 86.47 \text{ inches aft of datum}$$

When this weight and CG position is plotted on the relevant graph, it can be seen that the aircraft is loaded to be within the UTILITY category. However you can see from the weight of the pilots and the small quantity of fuel how difficult it is to properly load the aircraft to the utility category

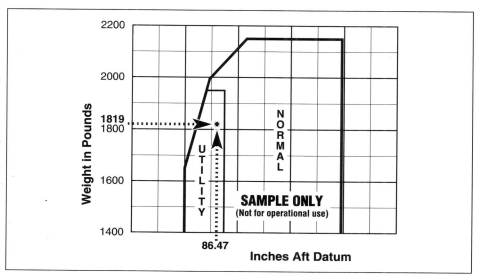

Now an example of normal category operations in a Cherokee 180:

ITEM	WEIGHT (lbs)	LEVER ARM	MOMENT
BASIC (EMPTY) WEIGHT - the weight, lever arm and moment are listed in the weight schedule (for AYAA only unuseable oil is included here)			
(for G-AYAA)	1405	86.0	120954
VARIABLE LOAD			
Pilot	160.0	85.5	13680
DISPOSABLE LOAD			
Passenger	160	85.5	13680
Fuel (Full)	302	95.0	28690
Useable Oil	15	32.5	487.5
2x Rear seat Pax	300	118.1	35430.0
Rear baggage	40	142.8	5712
TOTAL WEIGHT 2382		TOTAL MOMENT 218633.5	

The total weight is below the maximum permitted (2400lbs).

Dividing the total moment by the total weight gives the Centre of Gravity position:

$$\frac{218633.5}{2382} = 91.78 \text{ inches aft of datum}$$

When the weight and CG position is plotted on the graph (see opposite), it can be seen that the aircraft is loaded to be within the NORMAL category. However you can see that we are only allowing for some fairly light people and little baggage. You are unlikely to be able to fill a Cherokee with four adults, full fuel and full baggage and still be within limits. It is down to the pilot in command to decide what to leave on the ground!

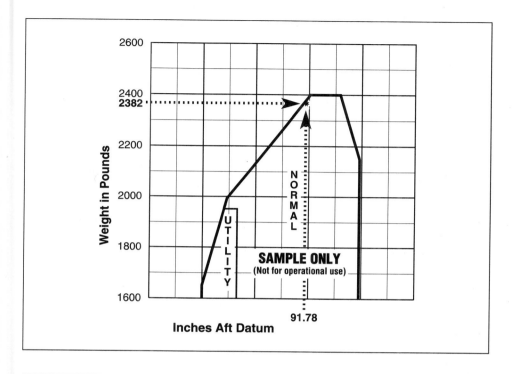

A WORD OF WARNING. As well as the safety aspect, operating the aircraft outside its weight and balance envelope has far reaching legal and financial implications. Almost the first thing an accident investigator will check after an accident is the loading of the aircraft. If the loading is outside limits the pilot is contravening the Air Navigation Order. In addition both the aircraft insurance company and your personal insurance company will be unsympathetic when they know that the conditions of the Certificate of Airworthiness (ie the flight manual limitations) were not complied with. As the pilot in command the responsibility is yours alone. The fact that the aircraft has four seats does not necessarily mean that the aircraft can be flown with all four seats occupied, baggage and full fuel load.

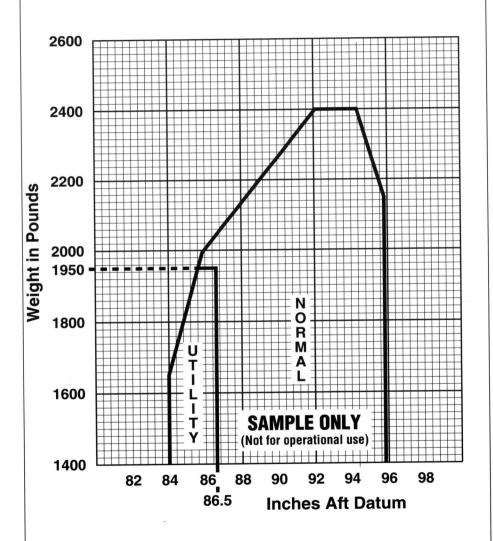

PA-28 180 Cherokee Weight Vs Centre of Gravity

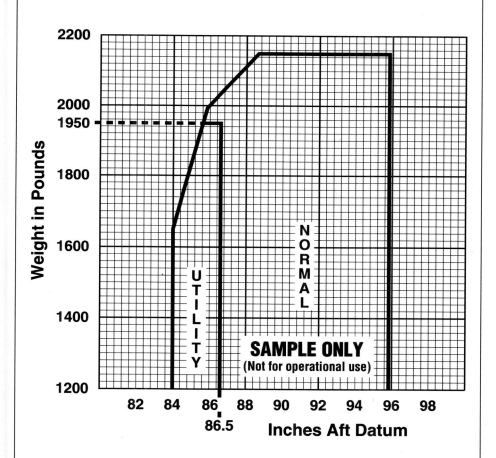

PA-28 140 Cherokee Weight Vs Centre of Gravity

SAMPLE ONLY
(Not for operational use)

Performance

The Cherokee flight manual contains a section of graphs to allow the pilot to calculate the expected performance of the aircraft for different flight phases. The most commonly used graphs are those for take off and landing performance, and those are the ones we will concentrate on here. However the same principles can be used on the other graphs. Two things to remember: Firstly the chart performance is obtained by using the recommended techniques - to get graph results follow graph procedures. Secondly you can safely assume that the graph results have been obtained by placing a brand new aircraft in the hands of an experienced test pilot under favourable conditions. To make allowances for a less than new aircraft, being flown by an average mortal in real conditions it is wise to 'factor' any results you get. Public transport operations are subject to overall factoring of 1.33 for take offs and 1.43 for landings, this figure being incorporated in the relevant graphs. It is highly recommended that the pilot apply the same factor to any graph figures ie a calculated take off distance of 500 meters becomes 500 X 1.33 = 665 meters. As with loading calculations the pilot must use the graphs and data from the documents for the individual aircraft being used. The graphs and diagrams used in this section are for illustrative purposes only, and not for operational use.

In section 7 conversion factors between feet and metres are listed, together with recommended factors for variations not necessarily covered by the flight manual graphs.

PA-28 Cherokee Take-off and Landing Performance Graphs

The take-off distance and landing distance graphs in the flight manual make several assumptions; (paved, dry, runway; use of flight manual technique).

The graphs use the term "Pressure Altitude". This is the altitude of the runway assuming a standard pressure setting (ie 1013 mb - or 1013 hectopascal if you prefer). On a day with a QNH other than 1013 you will need to adjust the actual altitude to get the pressure altitude. For instance on a day with a QNH above 1013 the pressure altitude will be less than the actual, and vica versa. To do this conversion, simply adjust the actual altitude by 30ft for each millibar/hectopascal above or below 1013.

The headwind or tailwind component is calculated from the windspeed and the angle to the runway (ie a 10 knot wind directly down the runway gives a headwind component of 10 knots. A 10 knot wind at 90° to the runway gives a headwind component of 0). There is a graph in section 7 for calculating head/tail wind component and crosswind component.

The take off distance & landing distance graphs will state the technique used to obtain the figures. Remember, to get graph results you have to use the graph techniques.

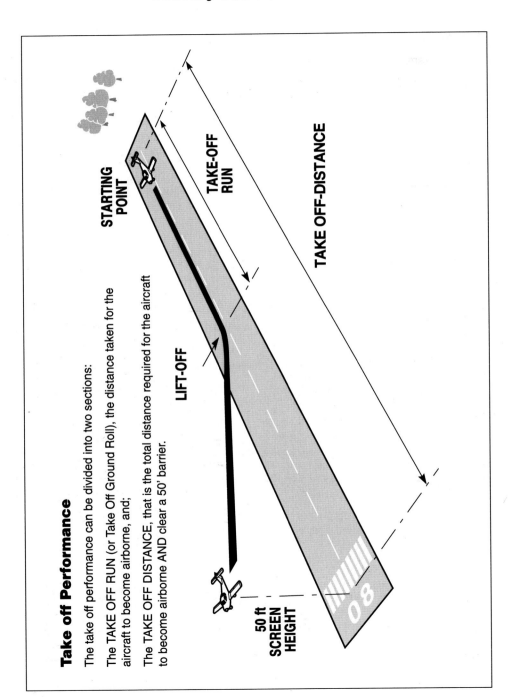

Take off Performance

The take off performance can be divided into two sections:

The TAKE OFF RUN (or Take Off Ground Roll), the distance taken for the aircraft to become airborne, and;

The TAKE OFF DISTANCE, that is the total distance required for the aircraft to become airborne AND clear a 50' barrier.

STARTING POINT

TAKE-OFF RUN

TAKE OFF-DISTANCE

LIFT-OFF

50 ft SCREEN HEIGHT

08

Take-off Distance Calculation Example

For this example we will take the conditions as:

Outside Air Temperature +25°

Pressure Altitude 1500ft

Take off weight 1700lbs

Headwind Component 10 Knots

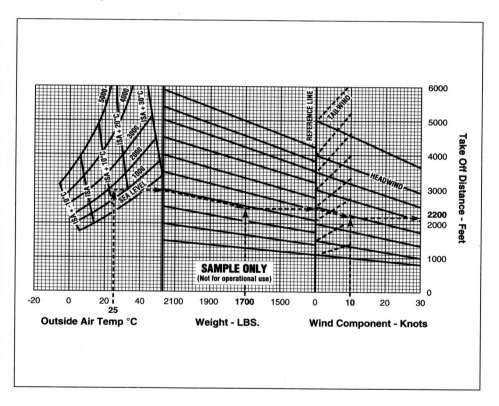

Start at the temperature +25°c, go vertically to the pressure altitude of 1500 feet, and then go horizontally to the REFERENCE LINE. From this point parallel the guideline until above the 1700lbs point. From this point take a line horizontally to the next reference line and then follow the guide line until above the 10kts point. From this point take a line horizontally to the far side of the graph and read of the take of distance of 2200 feet. This figure is then multiplied by the safety factor of 1.33 to give 2926 feet.

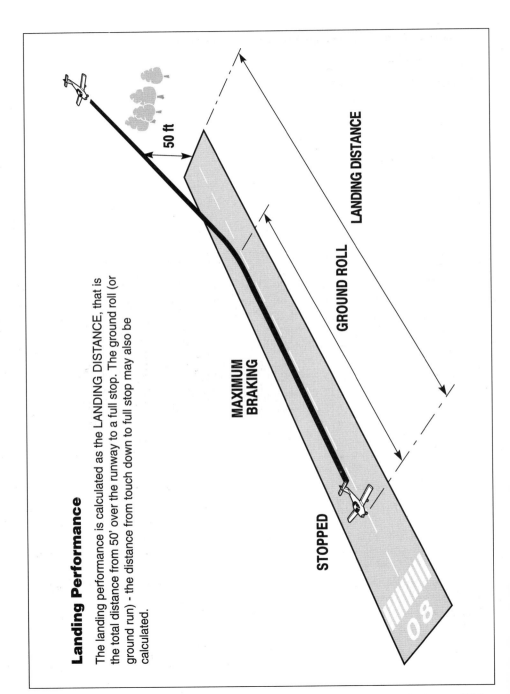

Landing Performance

The landing performance is calculated as the LANDING DISTANCE, that is the total distance from 50' over the runway to a full stop. The ground roll (or ground run) - the distance from touch down to full stop may also be calculated.

50 ft

LANDING DISTANCE

GROUND ROLL

MAXIMUM BRAKING

STOPPED

08

Landing Distance Calculation Example

For this example we will take the conditions as:

Outside Air Temperature +20°c

Pressure Altitude Sea Level

Landing weight 1700lbs

Headwind Component 10 knots

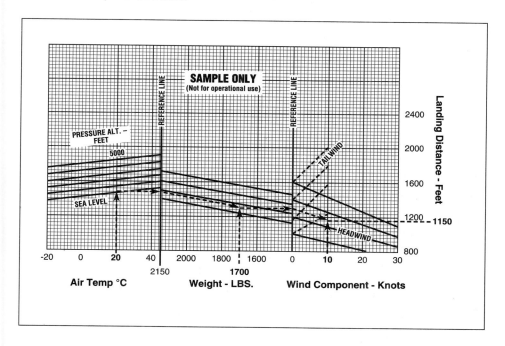

On the landing distance graph start at the temperature (+20°c) and go vertically to the Sea Level line. From this point go horizontally to the REFERENCE LINE, and then along the guideline until above the 1700lbs point. Then go horizontally to the wind reference line. From the reference line parallel the headwind guidelines until above the 10 knots point. From here take the line horizontally to the far side of the graph and read off the landing distance in feet - 1150ft. If this figure is factored by 1.43 you get the result of 1645ft.

Enroute Performance

Data may also be provided in the flight manual for calculating the enroute performance, such as climb performance. These graphs are tackled using the same technique as for the take off and landing graphs. Remember to get the graph figures use the graph techniques.

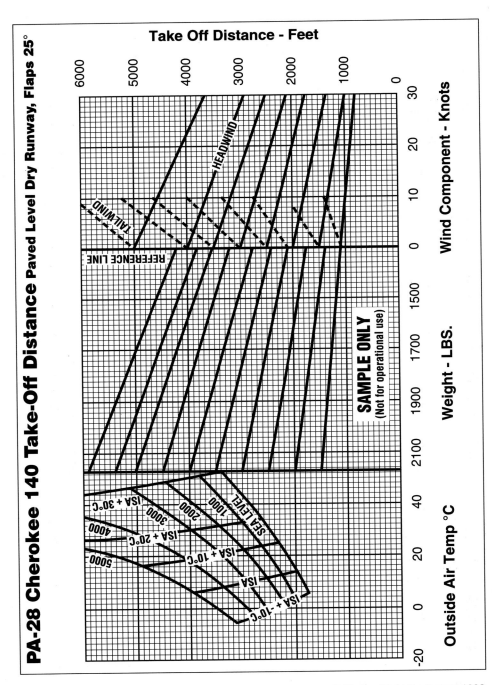

PA-28 Cherokee 140 Take-Off Distance Paved Level Dry Runway, Flaps 25°

SAMPLE ONLY
(Not for operational use)

© Airplan Flight Equipment 1992

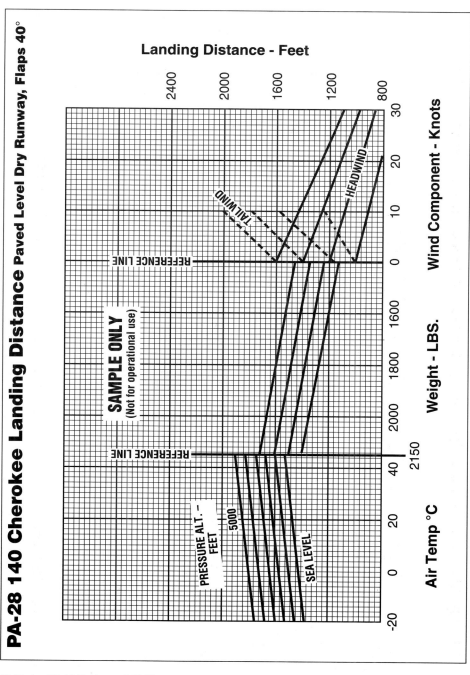

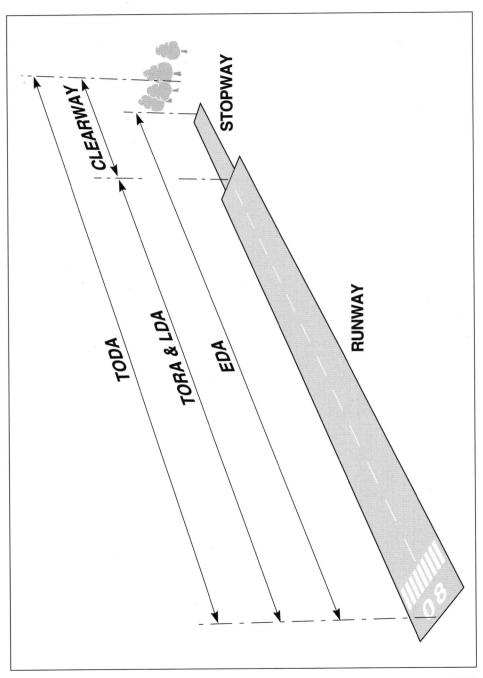

© Airplan Flight Equipment 1992

Runway Dimensions

Having calculated the distances the aircraft requires for take off or landing, the runway dimensions must be checked to ensure that the aircraft can be safely operated on the runway in question. The figures given in the AIP or airfield guide can be defined in a number of ways.

The Take Off Run Available (TORA)

The TORA is the length of the runway available for the take off ground run of the aircraft. This is usually the physical length of the runway.

The Emergency Distance (ED)

The ED is the length of the TORA plus the length of any stopway. A stopway is area at the end of the TORA prepared for an aircraft to stop on in the event of an abandoned take off. The ED is also known as the

ACCELERATE - STOP DISTANCE AVAILABLE.

The Take Off Distance Available (TODA)

The TODA is the TORA plus the length of any clearway. A clearway is an area over which an aircraft may make its initial climb (to 50' in this instance). The TODA will not be more than 1.5 X TORA.

The Landing Distance Available (LDA)

The LDA is the length of the runway available for the ground run of an aircraft landing. In all cases the landing distance required should never be greater than the landing distance available.

The PA-28 Cherokee

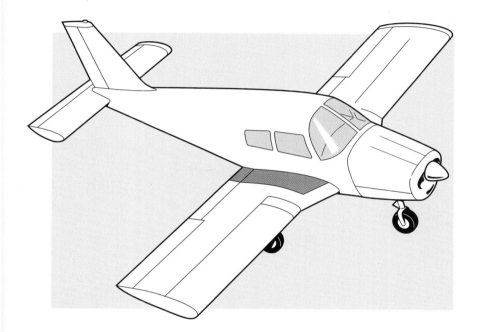

Take-off Distance Factors

The following factors will allow the pilot to make allowance for variations that may effect take-off performance. Although some of these factors are covered in the Cherokee performance graphs, the table is produced in its entirety for completeness:

VARIATION	INCREASE IN TAKE-OFF DISTANCE (to 50')	FACTOR
10% increase in aircraft weight	20%	1.2
Increase of 1000' in runway altitude	10%	1.1
Increase in temperature of 10°C	10%	1.1
Dry Grass		
- Short (under 5 inches)	20%	1.2
- Long (5 - 10 inches)	25%	1.25
Wet Grass		
- Short	25%	1.25
- Long	30%	1.3
2% uphill slope	10%	1.1
Tailwind component of 10% of lift off speed	20%	1.2
Soft ground or snow *	at least 25%	at least 1.25

* snow and other runway contamination is covered on page 7.3.

Landing Distance Factors

The following factors will allow the pilot to make allowance for variations that may effect landing performance. Although some of these factors are covered in the Cherokee performance graphs, the table is produced in its entirety for completeness:

VARIATION	INCREASE IN LANDING DISTANCE (from 50')	FACTOR
10% increase in aircraft weight	10%	1.1
Increase of 1000' in runway altitude	5%	1.05
Increase in temperature of 10°C	5%	1.05
Dry Grass		
- Short (under 5 inches)	20%	1.2
- Long (5 - 10 inches)	30%	1.3
Wet Grass		
- Short	30%	1.30
- Long	40%	1.40
2% downhill slope	10%	1.1
Tailwind component of 10% of landing speed	20%	1.2
snow *	at least 25%	at least 1.25

* snow and other runway contamination is covered on page 7.3.

Runway Contamination

A runway can be contaminated by water, snow or slush. If operation on such a runway cannot be avoided additional allowance must be made for the problems such contamination may cause - ie additional drag, reduced braking performance (possible aquaplaning), and directional control problems.

It is generally recommended that take-off should not be attempted if dry snow covers the runway to a depth of more than 60mm, or if water, slush or wet snow covers the runway to more than 15mm. In addition a tailwind, or crosswind component exceeding 10 knots should not be accepted when operating on a slippery runway.

For take-off distance required calculations the other known conditions should be factored, and the emergency distance available on the runway should be at least 2.0 X the take-off distance required (for a paved runway) or at least 2.66 X the take-off distance required (for a grass runway).

For landing any water or slush can have a very adverse effect on landing performance, and the danger of aquaplaning (with negligible wheel braking and loss of directional control) is very real.

Use of the Wind Component Graph

This graph can be used to find the head/tail wind component and the crosswind component, given a particular wind velocity and runway direction.

EXAMPLE:

> Runway 27
>
> Surface wind 240°/15 knots

The angle between the runway direction (270°) and wind direction(240°) is 30°. Now on the graph locate a point on the 30° line, where it crosses the 15 knot arc. From this point take a horizontal line to give the headwind component (13 knots) and a vertical line to give the crosswind component (8 knots).

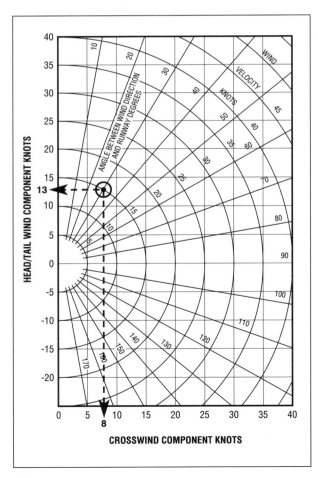

On the main graph overleaf the shaded area represents the crosswind limit for this aircraft. If the wind point is within this shaded area, the crosswind limit for this aircraft has been exceeded.

Note: Runway direction will be degrees magnetic. Check the wind direction given is also in degrees magnetic.

Wind Component Graph

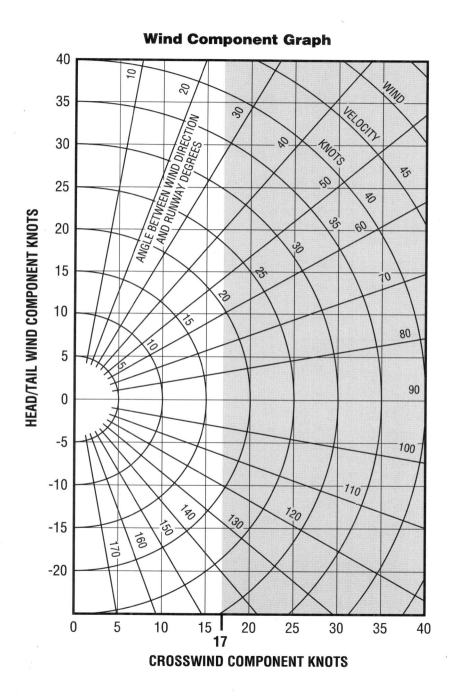

TEMPERATURE

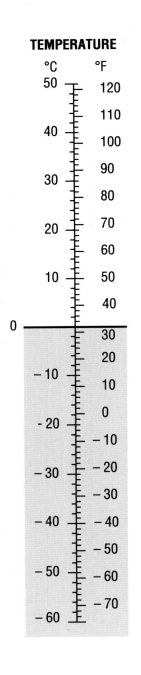

PRESSURE

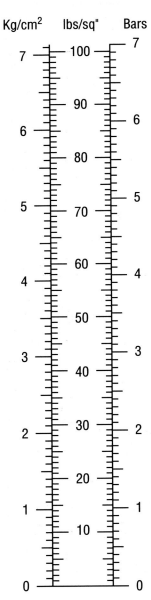

Distance-Metres/Feet

Metres	Feet
1	3.28
2	6.56
3	9.84
4	13.12
5	16.40
6	19.69
7	22.97
8	26.25
9	29.53
10	32.81
20	65.62
30	98.43
40	131.23
50	164.04
60	196.85
70	229.66
80	262.47
90	295.28
100	328.08
200	656.16
300	984.25
400	1,312.34
500	1,640.42
600	1,968.50
700	2,296.59
800	2,624.67
900	2,952.76
1000	3,280.84
2000	6,561.70
3000	9,842.50
4000	13,123.40
5000	16,404.20
6000	19,685.00
7000	22,965.90
8000	26,246.70
9000	29,527.60
10000	32,808.40

Feet	Metres
1	0.30
2	0.61
3	0.91
4	1.22
5	1.52
6	1.83
7	2.13
8	2.44
9	2.74
10	3.05
20	6.10
30	9.14
40	12.19
50	15.24
60	18.29
70	21.34
80	24.38
90	27.43
100	30.48
200	60.96
300	91.44
400	121.92
500	152.40
600	182.88
700	213.36
800	243.84
900	274.32
1000	304.80
2000	609.60
3000	914.40
4000	1,219.20
5000	1,524.00
6000	1,828.80
7000	2,133.60
8000	2,438.40
9000	2,743.20
10000	3,048.00

Conversion Factors:

Metres to Feet x 3.28084
Feet to Metres x 0.3048

© Airplan Flight Equipment 1992

Distance-KM/Nautical Miles/Statute Miles

NM	Km	St
1	1.85	1.15
2	3.70	2.30
3	5.56	3.45
4	7.41	4.60
5	9.26	5.75
6	11.11	6.90
7	12.96	8.06
8	14.82	9.21
9	16.67	10.36
10	18.52	11.51
20	37.04	23.02
30	55.56	34.52
40	74.08	46.03
50	92.60	57.54
60	111.12	69.05
70	129.64	80.55
80	148.16	92.06
90	166.68	103.57
100	185.2	115.1
200	370.4	230.2
300	555.6	345.2
400	740.8	460.3
500	926.0	575.4
600	1111.2	690.5
700	1296.4	805.6
800	1481.6	920.6
900	1666.8	1035.7

Km	NM	St
1	.54	.62
2	1.08	1.24
3	1.62	1.86
4	2.16	2.49
5	2.70	3.11
6	3.24	3.73
7	3.78	4.35
8	4.32	4.97
9	4.86	5.59
10	5.40	6.21
20	10.80	12.43
30	16.20	18.64
40	21.60	24.86
50	27.00	31.07
60	32.40	37.28
70	37.80	43.50
80	43.20	49.71
90	48.60	55.92
100	54.0	62.1
200	108.0	124.3
300	162.0	186.4
400	216.0	248.6
500	270.0	310.7
600	324.0	372.8
700	378.0	435.0
800	432.0	497.1
900	486.0	559.2

St	NM	Km
1	.87	1.61
2	1.74	3.22
3	2.61	4.83
4	3.48	6.44
5	4.34	8.05
6	5.21	9.66
7	6.08	11.27
8	6.95	12.87
9	7.82	14.48
10	8.69	16.09
20	17.38	32.19
30	26.07	48.28
40	34.76	64.37
50	43.45	80.47
60	52.14	96.56
70	60.83	112.65
80	69.52	128.75
90	78.21	144.84
100	86.9	161.0
200	173.8	321.9
300	260.7	482.8
400	347.6	643.7
500	434.5	804.7
600	521.4	965.6
700	608.3	1126.5
800	695.2	1287.5
900	782.1	1448.4

Conversion Factors:

Statute Miles to Nautical Miles x 0.868976
Statute Miles to Kilometres x 1.60934
Kilometres to Statute Miles x 0.62137
Kilometres to Nautical Miles x 0.539957
Nautical Miles to Statute Miles x 1.15078
Nautical Miles to Kilometres x 1.852

Weight

lbs	Kg	Kg	lbs
1	.45	1	2.20
2	.91	2	4.41
3	1.38	3	6.61
4	1.81	4	8.82
5	2.27	5	11.02
6	2.72	6	13.23
7	3.18	7	15.43
8	3.63	8	17.64
9	4.08	9	19.84
10	4.54	10	22.05
20	9.07	20	44.09
30	13.61	30	66.14
40	18.14	40	88.18
50	22.68	50	110.23
60	27.22	60	132.28
70	31.75	70	154.32
80	36.29	80	176.37
90	40.82	90	198.42
100	45.4	100	220.5
200	90.7	200	440.9
300	136.1	300	661.4
400	181.4	400	881.8
500	226.8	500	1102.3
600	272.2	600	1322.8
700	317.5	700	1543.2
800	362.9	800	1763.7
900	408.2	900	1984.2
1000	453.6	1000	2204.6
2000	907.2	2000	4409.2
3000	1360.8	3000	6613.9
4000	1814.4	4000	8818.5
5000	2268.0	5000	11023.1
6000	2721.5	6000	13227.7
7000	3175.1	7000	15432.3
8000	3628.7	8000	17637.0
9000	4082.3	9000	19841.6
10000	4535.9	10000	22046.2

Conversion Factors:

lbs to Kilograms x 0.45359
Kilograms to lbs x 2.20462

Volume (Fluid)

Litres	Imp. Gall	U.S. Gall	U.S. Gall	Imp. Gall	Litres	Imp. Gall	U.S. Gall	Litres
1	0.22	0.26	1	0.83	3.79	1	1.20	4.55
2	0.44	0.53	2	1.67	7.57	2	2.40	9.09
3	0.66	0.79	3	2.50	11.36	3	3.60	13.64
4	0.88	1.06	4	3.33	15.14	4	4.80	18.18
5	1.10	1.32	5	4.16	18.93	5	6.00	22.73
6	1.32	1.59	6	5.00	22.71	6	7.21	27.28
7	1.54	1.85	7	5.83	26.50	7	8.41	31.82
8	1.76	2.11	8	6.66	30.28	8	9.61	36.37
9	1.98	2.38	9	7.49	34.07	9	10.81	40.91
10	2.20	2.64	10	8.33	37.85	10	12.01	45.46
20	4.40	5.28	20	16.65	75.71	20	24.02	90.92
30	6.60	7.93	30	24.98	113.56	30	36.03	136.38
40	8.80	10.57	40	33.31	151.41	40	48.04	181.84
50	11.00	13.21	50	41.63	189.27	50	60.05	227.30
60	13.20	15.85	60	49.96	227.12	60	72.06	272.76
70	15.40	18.49	70	58.29	264.97	70	84.07	318.22
80	17.60	21.14	80	66.61	302.82	80	96.08	363.68
90	19.80	23.78	90	74.94	340.68	90	108.09	409.14
100	22.00	26.42	100	83.27	378.54	100	120.09	454.60
200	44.00	52.84						
300	66.00	79.26						
400	88.00	105.68						
500	110.00	132.10						
600	132.00	158.52						
700	154.00	184.94						
800	176.00	211.36						
900	198.00	237.78						
1000	220.00	264.20						

Conversion Factors:

Imperial Gallons to Litres x 4.54596
Litres to Imperial Gallons x 0.219975
U.S. Gallons to Litres x 3.78541
Litres to U.S. Gallons x 0.264179
Imperial Gallons to U.S. Gallons x 1.20095
U.S. Gallons to Imperial Gallons x 0.832674

PA 28 Cherokee - Index

ELEMENTS
OF AROUSAL

Also by Lars Eighner:

Lavender Blue
Bayou Boy
B.M.O.C.
Travels with Lizbeth
American Prelude

 **A RICHARD KASAK BOOK**

Second Edition of *Lavender Blue:*

Elements of Arousal

How to Write and Sell Gay Men's Erotica

LARS EIGHNER

Acknowledgments

This book first appeared as *Lavender Blue: How to Write and Sell Gay Men's Erotica* (Austin, Texas; Caliente Press, 1987). The present edition has been revised extensively by the author.

"Dale and the Glory Hole" appeared in *Torso* (September 1984).

"Smuggler's Moon" appeared in *Drummer* #81 (1985).

Part of the new material in the chapter on the erotic scene first appeared as "Nine Rules for Comeshots" in *The Guide* (October 1989).

"Why I Write Gay Erotica" first appeared in *The Masquerade Erotic Book Society Newsletter,* 1:4 (September/October 1992).

Some new material in this edition first appeared in various issues of *Austin Writer,* the newsletter of the Austin Writers' League.

First Richard Kasak Book Edition 1994

First Printing October 1994

ISBN 1-56333-230-2

Cover Art by Judy Simonian
Cover Design by Kurt Griffith

Manufactured in the United States of America
Published by Masquerade Books, Inc.
801 Second Avenue
New York, N.Y. 10017

Each word of a work of gay erotica is a spear for the eyes or groin or gut or heart of straight society. Make every word as sharp as you can.

—Chapter 4

To Clifton Bert Hexamer
and
to the memory of
Randall Bryan Jensen

Contents

Preface to the Second Edition

This book was written as a complete introduction to the writing and marketing of gay men's erotica. It will still answer that purpose. My students have discovered, however, that it is a fair guide to writing for publication in many genres, and many authors who never intended to write erotica for gay men have found it useful.

Many particulars and many examples still pertain to the gay market and to erotica written for it. But the principles of sound writing are largely independent of subject, audience, and genre. No one should be surprised that what makes good erotic writing is often indistinguishable from what makes any other writing good. I have had to add only a small amount of material to make the present edition usable as a guide to writing for publication in general.

Nothing in a style manual or guidebook will substitute for the writer's conviction that what he or she is writing is worth writing and worth reading. I still believe that gay erotica is worth writing and is worth reading. Users of this book will have better results if they choose to write about subjects that inspire a similar conviction in them.

In the first edition of this book, which appeared as *Lavender Blue,* I put much material about the writing business and technical information about the preparation of manuscripts in the early parts of the book because I wanted to emphasize these aspects of the trade that are often overlooked by aspiring writers and their instructors. I have moved this material to the back of the book the better to conform to readers' expectations. I hope that readers will not think that I now regard that material as less important.

I have added several exercises. I have somewhat revised my views on electronic word processing, and the present edition reflects this change of mind and the changes in publishing that have occurred recently.

Lars Eighner
Austin, Texas
Summer 1994

Author's Note to the First Edition

I am indebted to Steven Saylor, Aaron Travis, Scott Winnett, and John Preston. Their names might have been cited in many more places in the text for their reminders and suggestions and, in several cases, for apt expressions I was unable to improve upon. I also thank those who gave me the benefit of their insights but who preferred not to be named here. Occasionally, however, I have insisted on inserting my own opinions and emphasis. That will account for the errors and shortcomings.

My ideas on the subjects of fiction and English composition have been influenced by several great masters: William Strunk, Jr., and E. B. White, of course Gertrude Stein; George Williams of Rice University; and another.

The existence of this book owes to Tom Doyal who suggested it and published it. Without his confidence I would never have presumed to attempt such a work.

As always, I am grateful to Bunch, the past and present management, and the staff of Sally's Apartment (Austin) for their continued support and enthusiasm.

Lars Eighner
Austin, Texas
1986

Introduction to the First Edition
by John Preston

Picture this:

An associate editor of *The Journal of Gay Erotic Love* staggers into his office on a Monday morning. His boss, the editor, is stern-faced as he looks at his watch. The turncoat machine says that the associate editor is fifteen minutes late, again. The boss announces that they have to have a piece of fiction chosen for the next issue, and it must be decided upon *today*.

Trying desperately to cope with his hangover and to squelch his frustration that his lover wouldn't put out the night before, the associate editor vows that there will be no problem. He doesn't admit that the story promised by his most beloved author hasn't arrived yet (it's already weeks past the deadline). The associate editor collects his mail and goes to his desk.

The associate editor sees the return address of his most beloved author on a suspiciously slim envelope. He rips it open to read the impossible news that the story will not be forthcoming. The stars weren't in the proper position for the creation of art. The associate editor moans. He didn't want art, he wanted a decent short story to fill the white space that is making a gaping hole in his magazine's layout!

He opens more of the mail and discovers a virulent letter from a writer whose latest work he had rejected. The writer is furious that the "New York conspiracy" has once again turned against him. All those editors who lunch at the Four Seasons with mega-agents are members of a plot that is fomenting to keep him from achieving his rightful place in the literary world.

The associate editor groans. Actually, he's from West Virginia, and he *loathes* New York himself. Rather than thinking it's the center of the universe, he perceives it as a trap he fell into, one that continues to ensnare him because it's the one place he can find gainful employment at this odious vocation of his. The last time he had lunch with another editor had been with his college classmate, who works for *Plumber's Monthly*. They went to Burger King.

The associate editor is not in a good mood as he opens the larger envelopes that came in today's mail. He retrieves the manuscripts from them and piles them on his desk. Like any other periodical in the country that pays money for writing, *The Journal of Gay Erotic Love* receives many, many, more submissions than it could ever use. Today there are about a dozen. One of these has a good chance to see print.

Now, the associate editor wants one of these submissions to be good enough for publication. He has options: he can go to his back files and pick out a story he was holding; he can write something himself; he can probably cut a deal over the phone with a book publisher to allow him to reprint an excerpt from an upcoming title.

He doesn't want to do any of these things. That back file exists because he was hoping to create some themed issues in the future and he wants to hold certain pieces for those. Other stories in the back file are from tried-and-true contributors. He would prefer that the same names didn't appear very often in too many issues of the magazine. Not only does that make it look as though *The Journal of Gay Erotic Love* is dependent on a few people, but the associate editor—when he can push aside sour memories of his lover's lack of carnal interest—really is a nice guy and would like to give someone new a chance.

One of the magazine's great secrets is how much of its material is written by its staff—without extra pay—under a host of pen names. One of the last things the associate editor wants to do in his condition is to write something himself. The hangover isn't the only problem: he has never quite reconciled himself to the lousy salary he's getting. The idea that he should have to give his employer his creative work in addition to the draconian hours he has to put in at the office is too depressing. But he may have to do it, and he has to admit that it could make life a great deal easier. At least the associate editor knows precisely the space the magazine has available in this issue. There are also so many other variables of which he's cognizant and which an outsider couldn't be aware of that he is tempted to take on the assignment.

Negotiating a book excerpt has a certain appeal but there are problems as well. If he takes a chapter from X's book, he knows that Y—X's dreaded literary enemy—will scream and yell until he takes one from him as well. Aside from that, some excerpts simply cost too much money, or involve such complicated negotiations with big-time agents that they end up being a waste of the associate editor's time.

No. What he really wants is to find something just right in this stack of submissions. He takes up the pile of paper and puts it in front of him. He opens his container of coffee which he has bought at the corner deli on his way to work and swears to himself. The cheapskate publisher decided to cut corners and increase productivity by removing the coffee machine from the office to eliminate not only the cost of the coffee, but also the time employees spent talking to one another.

He starts in on the manuscripts.

He takes up a story written by someone who has decided to display his gay pride by typing his manuscript on lavender paper. The associate editor runs a hand over his brow. He cannot face it. Deep in his heart, he knows this person is trying to make a statement; and if his head were in better shape, maybe he could get into it. But not today. The associate editor doesn't even read the first paragraph. He puts the story in the file, to be returned with a printed rejection letter.

He picks up another manuscript. *The Journal of Gay Erotic Love* prides itself on its celebration of gay erotic love. It says so right in its title. This manuscript is a story based on the impossibility of finding any such thing. It's a tale of a louse who cheats on his mate, leaving him devastated and feeling unwanted and insecure, leading him into a pattern of anonymous sex with strangers who talk dirty to him.

(Now, *The Journal of Gay Erotic Love* has nothing against dirty talk, mind you, but it doesn't want its characters to mean it when they say, "You dirty scumbag cocksucker." That language can appear in the *Journal*'s pages only when it is clearly a term of endearment between men who are committed to a long-term relationship.)

The associate editor hates this story. He damns the audacity of the writer, who obviously hasn't read an issue in years or else he would know what kind of stories they used. The manuscript is rejected. But, more than that, the associate editor is incensed by the gall of this person who would dare put into print his own worst fears. (The associate editor is convinced that he'll end up as that discarded lover; last night's refusal of conjugal bliss was only the beginning; he's sure of it.) The associate editor isn't going to let this bastard get away with it! Not only will this author get a pink slip, he's going to get an acidic note telling him never to darken *The Journal of Gay Erotic Love*'s P.O. box again!

The next manuscript is typed on erasable bond. If he were to take this story—the associate editor hasn't even read the thing yet—he knows the typesetters will hate him and yell at him and call him unerotically ugly names. Every hand that touches it smudges more type, possibly even removing some of it from the page, making it increasingly difficult to read. No. Just the thought of the grief he would get for sending this manuscript on its rounds is too much. Into the rejection file it goes.

Another writer has decided that script type fits the mood of his romantic story the best. No. What was, in fact, the perfect story for the Valentine's Day issue of *The Journal of Gay Erotic Love* is rejected because the type is unreadable.

But it was sent from heaven compared to the next submission, which was printed on a cheap computer. Letters like *g* and *j* don't descend beneath the line; they are bunched up. The dot-matrix printer has left gaping holes as it tried to type many of the letters. The computer paper edges are covered with ugly little nubs. A work which the associate editor will never know was written by a true literary genius goes into the rejection pile.

Worse, the next manuscript was done on one of the fancy printers that can alter typeface at will. There's italicized print for emphasis; there's oversized gothic print for drama, there are little flowers around the margin...an associate editor with a hangover doesn't need this.

The next-to-last manuscript is covered with a formal invoice which includes the author's attorney's name and address for reference and which informs *The Journal of Gay Erotic Love* of the precise conditions it will have to meet if that periodical chooses to have the good sense to publish what the author irrefutably knows to be a work of art. Payment will be many times more than *The Journal of Gay Erotic Love* would have been willing to pay Stephen King for a story. A check will have to be sent the moment the manuscript is accepted—not on publication, the way every other contributor is paid—and on and on.

This associate editor just had his totally justifiable request for a raise rejected by the tightass of a publisher who won't even provide him with a cup of fucking coffee in the morning, and this moron thinks that the associate editor is going to go to bat for him, have corporate policy reversed, take the time and effort to deal with someone who's so defensive he *begins* with an introduction to his attorney...oh, no, not a chance.

The associate editor's at his wit's end. He's more and more convinced that he's going to have to write the damn thing himself, and wonders how he's going to come up with an erotic story line when his lover's a frigid stone in bed who hasn't given him the genital time of day in nearly a week.

And then he finds it.

The manuscript is typed nicely on white bond paper. There are adequate margins all the way around it where the associate editor and the copy editor would have to make their marks. The author has his name, address, and social security number typed right there where they can be found easily. The title— which still might have to be changed—isn't half bad. The typing was done with a sharp, clear carbon ribbon, easy to read. The pages are numbered. They are held together with a paper clip—not a staple—so even that little annoyance doesn't have to be dealt with.

The editor begins to read. To his amazement, the first sentence contains a noun and a verb in the proper order. There's a hook in the first paragraph that captures his attention. The story's hot! The sex scenes are realistic and still a turn-on. The associate editor is swept up in the small drama of the story, a little dubiously at first, since it appears that a lover's going to get the emotional shaft once more. But no! There's hope here. The narrator made a mistake, and his lover comes through with style and finesse and an ending that leaves the reader feeling like a decent human being. The associate editor is moved by the piece; he really doesn't want his lover to leave him and really does want to believe that these things can work out.

He stands up, jubilant. He yells to his boss, "This one! It's perfect! A little short, but I can arrange for some pullouts in large print to stretch it enough. We can use that photograph left over from the Atlanta shoot for an illustration."

The associate editor is very, very happy. The editor looks over the piece and agrees it'll do the trick. He may not have consciously noticed all of the factors of the presentation, though he certainly would have noticed if the associate editor had handed him a manuscript on lavender paper. The editor gives his approval. The associate editor sits back down to his own typewriter and composes a note to the author, telling him how very happy everyone is that *The Journal of Gay Erotic Love* will be graced with his publishing debut.

That, gentle reader, is how it mostly happens.

There is, of course, another side to this story. There is the tale of what happens to our author once he gets this notice of impending publication.

He is ecstatic!

Our author began the road to writing his story years ago. When he was a young boy, he used to go on camping trips. He loathed them. He remembered being someone outside the group who would listen to the stories around the campfire and never hear anything in those tales that had anything to do with him or his life.

Instead, he would daydream on his own. He would conjure up imaginary playmates much more loyal—and just as handsome—as the boys who were so content to shun him on those outings. There would be a day, he would fantasize, when he wouldn't have to be such an outsider, and when the stories he had to tell would be about things that were real to himself and to his new friends.

Our author hung on until he got to the place in his life where he could see just why he always had thought he was so far away from the center of things on those particular camping excursions. And, as soon as he did understand it, he began to go on new ones, far, far different than any his camp leaders could ever have envisioned for him.

Now he wasn't on the periphery. He was in the middle of the action, and that action excited and terrified him. It made him feel wanted and a part of the group. *Too bad,* he thought, *that there aren't any campfires on this trip. I'd love to become a storyteller now!*

He did begin to write letters, though. He wrote to some friends who had been among the first with whom he had explored his new world and he wrote to others, from further back, who had never quite understood why our author hadn't seemed always to be there in all ways. He used his letters to explain some things he had left out in the past, to describe the colors of his new life, and to start to paint the vision of what he thought the next scenes might hold for him.

Everyone loved his letters. When he thought they were especially funny, he would show them to his roommate. When he was having a hard time explaining to his new boyfriend just how wonderful their erotic adventures were, he began to write out his feelings in very private letters to him alone.

They all said, "You must become an author! You must publish this writing!" (Even the boyfriend who thought it might be awfully hot to have himself described in the pages of a magazine, especially of a certain kind. He was the one, in fact, who suggested *The Journal of Gay Erotic Love.)*

"Do you really think so?" You see, it mattered a great deal to our author. He had been harboring secret dreams about becoming a writer for a while now. Our writer wondered how many of these comments were really honest and how many were really just those things that people said. But the idea lingered, and one day he took a few of his letters and wove them together to make them into a story. He took out the elements which were distractions from the main plot, and he worked very hard at all of it. When it was finished, he decided it was worth a try. After all, he would never know if he could be an author unless he at least submitted a story.

Now, with the letter from the associate editor in his hands, he understood that he had made it. He took the letter to show all of his friends, and they were happy for him. They stood around the bar, and they all wondered just what pictures would accompany the story and just which model would be used to portray our author's boyfriend.

They waited for the piece to appear. And then they waited some more. Finally, the rest of them gave up waiting. Our author had to face one of the horrible facts of publishing life: it takes *forever* for his words to go from their beginning as his manuscript to their eventual place on the printed page. If he's lucky, the issue of *The Journal* with his story might appear in six months. It might just as easily take a year to reach the newsstand in his home city.

If our scribe is a dilettante, he might give up at this point. Or, if he is really driven to make this attempt at the start of a career, his acceptance will drive him back to compose more and more stories. He will submit more and more stories, and he may receive more and more rejections—even though *The Journal of Gay Erotic Love* has christened him an author!

Whatever his luck—or lack of it—our author will finally see his first story in a magazine. He will hold it in his hands, and then he will go through one of the most terrible and wonderful experiences than any writer can ever have: he will read his own words in print.

There is nothing like it. Our author will berate himself for the awkwardness he never saw in his typescript. He'll never believe that he could possibly have made a certain structural error—but then he will go back to his manuscript and discover he did. He will be furious that the editor didn't find that embarrassing word repetition. There'll be nothing like it all. He's seen his words on the printed page.

Once he is over those moments, he will want to go out to receive the real rewards of a writer, the ones that he's dreamed of since he received the associate editor's letter.

He goes to the bar that night and he nonchalantly drops the issue of the magazine on the counter for all his friends to see. No matter how much they respond to the physical evidence that he has achieved his success, it will be insufficient. Because our writer now has to experience another harsh truth: No one cares as much about a writer's words as he does himself.

But he is not dismayed. After all, this is erotica he has published. Even if that boyfriend of old has left him—what was his name?—this will help him find another one. There's a hot new man in town who our author has been longing to get into bed. Certainly he would be willing to indulge in a little star-fucking and take a well-known author into his arms.

Our scribe ever so subtly makes the stranger's acquaintance and manages—with a little less subtlety—to mention that he is the one who wrote the lead fiction piece in this month's *Journal*. The man doesn't fall into his arms at all. In fact, he beats a quick retreat.

Our writer is shocked. He was sure he'd at least get laid from all this. He asks his best friends about it. Our scribe is told politely that, since he has described having sex only with demigods in his story, the man obviously was terrified that he could never match up to his expectations. That, or else he was much more discreet than that old boyfriend and had no intention of having his most intimate secrets read about in a monthly magazine. It will be a sad-but-true experience that will repeat itself often now that our writer is being published: pornographers seldom get laid.

Well, at least he will be getting money. Just as promised, there's a check in the mail. Our author tears open the envelope, visions of a down payment on a new sports car are filling his head.

But when he reads the amount on the check, he suddenly realizes that he'll be lucky to pay for the old Chevy's tune-up with his new earnings. Wealth is not the reward of the erotic writer.

But he won't be defeated easily. He will at least broaden his horizons with this new experience of being a writer. He can go to the Literary Circle meeting at the nearby college. The members will certainly be glad to have him join them now that he has been published.

So our author dresses in his best and takes his rolled-up copy of *The Journal* to the meeting. He introduces himself to the people there, expecting a warm welcome. He has to leave soon to go to the men's room, though, to check the mirror to make sure he hasn't come down with the measles. That would be the only reason he could think of for the cool—no—cold welcome he's gotten.

It appears that, while the Literary Circle is just now raising money to protect the freedom of writers in various left- and right-wing dictatorships, they are hardly anxious to extend that hand of friendship to a (shudder) pornographer—and a faggot one at that!—and they do wish that such a demented young man would go away.

And so our author is left having waited many months to have any concrete evidence of his accomplishment. When he finally did receive it, he discovered that very few, if any, of the people in his group understood what it meant to him. He also had to give up fantasies that writing erotica would make him a sex star or a wealthy man. Any dreams that he could now join that rarefied coterie of literati have been smashed.

He walks the streets of his hometown and he wonders just what the hell he's done and why he's bothered. Most people would have given up by now. But he is our hero, so we'll give him the benefit of the doubt.

Our scribe realizes that he's pretty damned proud of himself. There are people all around him who are always saying that they're going to write, but never do. Maybe he hasn't written much more than one story for *The Journal of Gay Erotic Love,* but damn it, he did write it! Someone published his story. Someone wrote him a check for it, a final proof of its worth.

(Truth to tell, our author might eventually learn that most members of the Literary Circle never got one of those checks in their lives. Their publishers get off easily, never having to pay since there are so many who are so desperate to see their names on the table of contents in the literary magazines that they will give their work away for nothing, which is usually a fair price.)

Eventually—since he's our hero—our author will realize that he can always hold this piece of writing in his hands when he is plagued with self-doubt about being a writer. There will be proof that he is. He will eventually be able to read through that harshly real printed copy of his story, and he will be able to learn from it. He can study just what the editor did to make his prose flow more cleanly, and he can try to incorporate at least some of those alterations into his next work.

Our author can now dream—and he has this right, absolutely. No Literary Circle should be able to take this dream away from him. He can dream that he has joined that small circle of people who are writers. He can imagine that someone is reading his work, that someone was sitting with him at a campfire that he had built all by himself and listened to his words as he spun his tales.

In fact, in a while—perhaps a long while—our author will achieve that final, quite overwhelming pleasure of his craft. He will get an envelope in the mail containing something forwarded to him by *The Journal*. He will open it up, and inside will be a letter from someone who has especially enjoyed his story.

When our author reads this note about how much his words meant and how well they told the story, how much the correspondent understood what was being said and how long he had waited for just that tale to be told, then our scribe can be happy and—no longer needing other proof—know that he is an author.

Because getting a letter like that is an affirmation more powerful than any other he will ever receive.

And this, too, gentle reader, is sometimes how it really happens.

In my years as an editor at *The Advocate* and *Mandate*, among other periodicals, I was astonished by how far many writers would go to hinder the publication of their work. They seemed to believe that the editor owed them something, or that putting together a publication had nothing to do with a work week, schedules, or any other real issues.

That is simply not true. The story of our associate editor had much more to do with the realities of the publishing world— including book publication—than all the romantic notions authors have about their art.

There have always been books and magazines for potential scribes which could have eased many of the rough spots on the road to publication if they had been read carefully and their advice followed. Some are rip-offs; other are classics. But none have been available which would meet the needs of one certain group of people: gay writers, and in particular, gay writers who were interested in exploring erotic subjects.

Lars Eighner explains it all for you.

Lavender Blue: How to Write and Sell Gay Men's Erotica is one of those acts of love that gay men commit for one another. Another person might have been willing to write a short essay on hot writing and then tell you to go and read someone else's book on the craft. But not Eighner. He has done nothing less than create a gay *Chicago Manual of Style*.

While the obvious potential reader of this volume will be that gay man who is interested in pursuing at least a part-time career in writing, I hope it reaches more people than that. Because, while the book is a step-by-step guide to the profession of writing, it also demystifies the act of writing.

We all have stories in us. It is one of the worst things that has been done to us as gay men that we were told that our stories don't count. We were told especially that our erotic stories don't count. That is not true. That is a lie which has been a large part of making us feel unable and unwilling to reach for our self-pride in many other ways.

Our stories are our history. Our experiences are the things that draw us together as a people and then, as a people, separate us from the rest of society. There are those of us who are writing as many stories as we can and doing it as well as we can. But there is always room for more.

I hope this book encourages anyone reading it to try to put

down his story. I hope it shows him the way to do that as well as he possibly can. I hope it tells him at least some ways by which he can best share that story with the world. To commit oneself and one's life to paper is not just an act of craft—though it might be—and it is not only a matter of craft—though that has a definite role in the matter. Writing out stories is also an act of courage, it is a means of sharing parts of ourselves with one another. It is a way to leave a mark on the world.

John Preston
Portland, Maine
August 1986

1. *Some Essentials*

This book was written as a complete guide to producing gay erotica in a publishable form, marketing the finished work, and establishing a freelance writing career. While the particulars of gay erotica provide most of the examples in this book, the qualities of good writing, the methods of marketing literary work, and practices of sound business are the same, whatever the kind of work.

Those who hope to write for publication on any subject must begin with an ability to write a reasonably good sentence. This ability ought to have been acquired in high-school grammar courses, and anyone who can write a coherent business letter or a book report has it. Unfortunately, many beginners believe that simple literacy is enough, and having made good grades in English courses, they think they have all the writing skills necessary to produce a best-selling novel.

Writing for publication, however, requires more highly developed and specialized writing skills. Bridging the gap between mere literacy and the ability to write for publication is the subject of this book.

While I wrote this book with the affection I feel for the subject and I have made many examples light and pertinent, parts of this book are not especially entertaining. If there is a giggle in the part about taxes, I do not know it. Some parts are meant to be used as a handbook, to be kept at your desk and referred to as necessary. Points of editorial style and manuscript preparation, like any other technical material, should be skimmed in armchair reading. The part on taxes will be helpful when you set up your account book, but much of it will be easier to follow when you have the tax forms in front of you.

There are two kinds of material in this book. The material in the latter part (of this edition) is about setting up a freelance writing career, preparing the manuscript, and selling the finished product. Such material is factual. Occasionally you may find an editor who wishes you to handle some detail differently. Tax rules may change. A beginning writer should follow the directions in the latter part of the book until or unless he or she knows a very good reason to deviate from them.

The material in the first part of this book is of a different kind. It deals with composing the literary work in general and the work of gay erotica in particular.

Gay erotica is the principal historic form of gay literature. Literature is an art. In art, rules and principles are hardly more than good advice, the best surmises of the modern and ancient masters of our craft. If the latter part of the book is knowledge, in the first part I have put into my own words and passed on to you what seems to me to be wisdom.

Unfortunately, wisdom does not always succeed, and folly sometimes does. Hardly anything I recommend in the first part of the book is done all the time by every successful writer. At least one genius has provided a counterexample to each rule I give. What I give you is the main chance, the things most likely to make your stories good if you do them most of the time.

In the latter part of the book I say to use white paper for manuscripts. In the first part, I advise against writing in the second person. Some second-person stories do appear—but editors hardly ever buy stories submitted on lime green paper. In the first part I advise against shifting tenses. But I have shifted tenses at times with some success. In the second part, I tell you never to staple a manuscript; I never have and I never will.

In a few cases, I have not defined some peripheral terms. I hope that you will take these opportunities to establish a closer relationship with your dictionary. Of someone who is becoming a writer, this is not too much to ask. I have taken some liberties with other terms, saying, for example, "the verb of the sentence" rather than "the predicate." Many students are never exposed to the more precise terms, and I hope that those who know better will indulge my attempt to make this material broadly accessible.

I have sometimes revealed my assumption that the writer of gay men's erotica is a gay man. In principle, there is no reason this should be so. Although, especially in books, lesbian literature now does relatively well commercially, in the past lesbian authors have written successful male romances. Several good writers of gay erotica are women, both lesbian and nongay. Gay men sometimes write straight erotica. At least one author in the gay men's market is a man who is married to a woman. Nonetheless, a person with doubts about gay sexuality and gay culture had better work in another market. If you can write convincingly about things you do not believe in, there are plenty of things more lucrative to write about while you do not believe in them.

I assume that no reader of this book needs a lecture on the naturalness of gay sexuality in gay people, the value of gay culture, the justice of the gay-liberation movement, and the importance of literature that serves gay people. In places I make unflattering remarks about Political Correctness. Those remarks, of course, are not directed at the principle of serving gay people through gay literature, but at the superficial, simpleminded application of that principle. It is childish to insist that all fictional gay men be admirable fellows, that no characters be drag queens, that every story read like a safe-sex manual, that every occurrence of a very large cock is reprehensible, that readers will emulate every act described in a work of fiction, and that every evil that exists in the world can be blamed on white, nongay, male capitalists.

To entertain gay readers for a while is laudable; entertainment is sufficient reason for gay erotica to exist. We cannot expect cardboard, bloodless, unsexed characters to be very entertaining. But if we can do our duty to entertain and also tell something of the truth of our history, show some of our pride in our gayness, reveal the justness of our cause, or illuminate some neglected possibility, so much the better. Gay people deserve not a propaganda, but a literature, a literature as full and rich and complete as any people ever had. Such a literature cannot be encompassed by doctrine, bounded by dogma, or imprisoned by the lefter-than-thou.

Beginning writers often have misconceptions of what they need and do not need to succeed in writing. Certain misconceptions are so common and so predictable that anyone who raises such issues will be identified immediately as a rank beginner. Although many of the following points are covered in more detail in appropriate parts of this book, they are the concerns that beginners always raise, and in raising the points mark themselves as rank amateurs. The answers are provided here, so that you need not embarrass yourself by asking the questions at a seminar or workshop.

You do not need to worry about copyright.

Do not put copyright notices on material you submit in the ordinary manner to established magazines and book publishers, and do not even ask about copyright registration.

I do not know why beginners believe piracy is a big problem. But they do believe it. In fact, piracy is extremely rare. These remarks apply only to print; screenwriting is different.

The mundane facts of copyright are explained later in this book. Do not worry about theft until you are producing material worth stealing. Meanwhile, if you have the opportunity to question a writer in a seminar or elsewhere, do not waste the opportunity by asking about copyright.

You do not need an agent.

Fortunately. You cannot get a real agent. Some contributors of gay erotica are active in other markets; their agents may handle the gay erotica as part of a package deal. Most writers do better marketing in this specialized field than any general agency could.

Although the reasons differ, the resulting advice is not much different for beginning writers in other markets. You are unlikely to produce enough material that does well enough that an agent could make a profit representing you. From time to time agents do accept new clients who have small, but promising careers. This is speculation on the agent's part. Fifteen percent of what a beginner makes will not cover the cost of the phone calls, postage, and copying required to sell his work. More usually, an agent is engaged when a writer is negotiating his or her first book contract with a major house.

Manuscripts must stand on their own merit. A writer who sends a work to every appropriate publication in the market without receiving an offer does not need an agent, but needs to learn to write better. The beginner who moans, "If only I had an agent!" may entertain his or her friends with this routine, but knowledgeable people will understand that the complaint really is "If only I had some talent!"

Unfortunately, the belief that an agent can work miracles with unpublishable material leads some would-be writers to employ services that seem to be literary agencies, but are not. Real agents get paid only when they have sold a manuscript. Real agents accept only clients who are already producing marketable work. Real agents do not attempt to teach their clients how to write. And real agents do not charge reading or consulting fees. Agencies that advertise for clients are criticism services (or worse), not literary representatives.

When he cannot recall how many of his books are in print, or when she falls behind in her bookkeeping because the checks are arriving so often, a writer will have little difficulty in engaging a real agent. However, a lover or roommate pressed into service as a business manager may do as well, and this exact solution suits several mass-market writers.

Yes, I have an agent. And truly, I did not make a great deal of money from writing until I had one. But I had sold several dozen stories, was selling virtually every story I wrote, and had two books in print before I got an agent. My agent is not really in the business of being a literary representative, but is a successful novelist who represents, besides me and himself, only one other client. Here is something my agent did for me:

He submitted several chapters of my memoir to a prestigious magazine. The editor said the magazine might like to run the piece in its reprint section. But to be reprinted, the piece had to be printed in another publication first. The editor suggested that a little literary magazine that might be interested in the piece. My agent submitted the piece to the little literary magazine, and sure enough the editor of the little literary magazine snapped it up enthusiastically. When my agent got back to the prestigious magazine, however, interest had evaporated. My agent sold a second piece to the little literary magazine.

Up to this point, my agent had done nothing more than I would have done, had I had the audacity to approach the prestigious magazine in the first place. Then my agent did something that never would have occurred to me. He sent the second piece to the prestigious magazine. The prestigious magazine ran an excerpt of the second piece in its reprint section, and this event proved to be the turning point in my career.

Having been through the loop once with the prestigious magazine, my personal feelings of rejection would have prevented me from sending anything to the prestigious magazine again. But my agent did not have *his* personal feelings on the line. What he perceived of the first rejection was not the rejection, but that the editor of the prestigious magazine had been interested in my work, interested enough to have suggested the little literary magazine. In other words, my agent saw a positive sign, where I would have seen only a negative one.

He did not take the editor of the prestigious magazine to lunch. He did not use his literary clout, because he did not have any big-name clients to use as leverage on the editor. He simply went about marketing my work systematically and objectively, just as I might have done, had I been marketing someone else's work. This was my agent's first sale to the prestigious magazine, his first two sales to the little literary magazine and, besides his own work, his first sales outside the gay market.

A less-sensitive writer with a mailing address could have done everything for him- or herself that my agent did for me, and any writer's friend or companion with a head for business and copy of *Writer's Market* might have done the same. That does not make my agent's or any agent's services less valuable. I merely mean to point out that having an agent is not a mystical, magical key to writing success.

You do not absolutely have to have a computer or an electronic word processor, but you must learn to type.

The advantages of a computer are so great that any writer ought to get one when it is within his means. A new system more than adequate for a writer's needs costs less than $1,500. But I began writing on a typewriter, and my first computer came from a Dumpster.

Although now I write on a computer and could hardly do the work I do without one, computers do have several drawbacks. The principal drawback is that computers can make attractive manuscripts of even the most inferior material. Making revisions with a computer is very easy, but sometimes a manuscript may look so pretty that the writer will not realize a revision is necessary. Many things can be done with computers that seem to be work, but do not actually produce new material. Computer files can always be better organized, old work can be called up for review with a touch of a button, material needs to be archived and backed up, new programs which promise greater efficiency can be installed, and the computer has some very enticing games. You can spend whole days at a computer without having written anything.

The desktop publishing features of many computers may entice beginners to attempt to produce work in camera-ready form. Editors will not bother reading material prepared in this manner, but a writer may continue to produce his dreamworld books in this manner for a long time before someone enlightens him. Some beginners will spend time worrying which computer to buy and learning to do useless things with the computers they do buy when their time would be better spent in learning to write.

Time spent learning to use a keyboard, however, is *not* wasted. Modern typesetters will not work from handwritten manuscripts. Publishers will not pay for typing. Most editors will return handwritten manuscripts unread. Whether you compose early drafts in pencil or do even the first versions at a keyboard, the entire manuscript must be keyed or typed—perhaps many times over. Few writers have the resources in either love or money to get someone else to do this work. Manuscript preparation differs from general typing or word processing; an office typist, even if his or her services can be obtained, will need detailed instructions to prepare a manuscript properly.

Since each keying or typing of the manuscript is a chance to make minor revisions, the writer does not need great typing speed, but the hunt-and-peck method is too tedious. If your fingers know the locations of the keys and you achieve a speed of 20 or 30 words per minute, that is adequate for a beginner. Those who cannot type at all can borrow a touch-typing manual from a library and can learn the locations of the keys within the usual two-week loan period. Speed is achieved through practice that, it is to be hoped, the writer obtains by writing.

The QWERTY keyboard (so called by the letters over the left hand's home row) will remain the American standard. Writers who feel limited by the 60, 80, or 100 words per minute obtainable on the QWERTY keyboard may investigate faster keyboards (such as the Dvorak) with the understanding that skill in a system other than QWERTY will restrict a writer to special-order typewriters and to word processors with programmable keyboards. (But writers who do not have full use of two hands should investigate special Dvorak keyboards designed for them.)

You may benefit from writers' clubs or groups.

Writers' clubs offer several advantages: opportunities for book signings and other promotions, group insurance or credit-union membership that may be unobtainable otherwise, programs and speakers, discounts on workshops, cooperative purchasing of materials, and exposure to working writers. A writer in the gay market may blame the gay market for his problems: late payment, disadvantageous offers, and slow reporting. The horror stories of writers working in other markets will put the gay writer's experiences in perspective.

Drawbacks of writing clubs are legion: many are not ready to deal with frankly gay, frankly erotic material, or its author; some writers' groups become mutual-admiration societies that avoid the sharp criticism a writer has a right to expect from her peers; others are literary snake pits in which criticism of the writer's work is little different from criticism of his character or personality; many members of writers' clubs are the hopelessly unpublishable whose advice, criticism, and company may be worse than useless.

You will need a small library.

As will become clear, you need a good, current, college-sized, American dictionary—no matter how well you spell and no matter how much confidence you have in your electronic spelling checker. The name *Webster's* alone is now a generic name used freely by publishers of dictionaries both good and bad. Some authoritative dictionaries do not use the name *Webster's,* and many dictionaries that bear the name *Webster's* are not reliable.

Several dictionaries are authoritative. If you have a current edition of an authoritative dictionary, use it. If you are starting from scratch, or if your dictionary is ten years out of date, you cannot go wrong with the current Merriam-Webster *Collegiate,* which contains as many entries from gay patois and erotic language as any general dictionary.

An unabridged dictionary is unnecessary. Unabridged dictionaries, besides being unwieldy, are not revised often enough to be useful for ordinary composition. If you own one, use it to resolve points not resolved by your college-sized dictionary. For consistency's sake, your college-sized dictionary and your unabridged dictionary should be published by the same company. First consult the current college-sized dictionary and prefer its usage.

The *Oxford English Dictionary (OED)* is available in a tiny-type, so-called compact edition. It is the *historic* record of English. People who love words can derive many hours of pleasure from the *OED,* but it is worthless as a daily tool in modern composition.

Strunk and White's *Elements of Style* is an inexpensive paperback. It is the crowning jewel of the English language, a mentor and an exemplar, and a fountainhead of wisdom and beauty. Get a copy and study it. After you have read it through several times, retire it to the throne room where it can be reviewed in odd moments.

A thesaurus is helpful if the tip-of-the-tongue sensation of knowing a word without being able to evoke it occurs frequently. That sensation is the proper reason to consult a thesaurus. Word-shopping to gussy up your prose with words you do not command would be unwise. The better way of enriching your vocabulary, if you need to do so, is to search out new words in their natural habitat, which is fine literature.

Bruce Rodgers's *Gay Talk* (New York: Paragon, 1979; formerly *The Queen's Vernacular,* San Francisco: Straight Arrow Books, 1972) is a guide to gay dialect, present and past—and some entries are very past. It is valuable if used with restraint. Many seminal documents of the modern gay-liberation movement were issued as mass-market paperbacks and can be had secondhand for a pittance. Classics of gay erotica seldom appear at used-book shops, but many of them have been reissued by Badboy Books and other publishers.

The Chicago Manual of Style (not to be confused with *A Manual for Writers,* which is about academic papers) is an expensive book that contains many details that are not pertinent to fiction. For an understanding of issues of editorial style and the publication process, the latest edition is not necessary. If money is an issue, borrow this book from a library or obtain a previous edition secondhand.

Fowler's *Modern English Usage,* even as revised, is badly dated. Fowler's principles remain sound, although scattered in an annoying alphabetical system. Many misusages Fowler exposes are with us yet, and Fowler is good company. Several other modern usage books call attention to contemporary controversies of English usage but are sometimes wrong and are seldom more helpful than the usage notes in the *Collegiate.*

The Writer's Handbook is inspirational: short on matters of style, strong on techniques of fiction, worthless as a market guide. One edition will do for a whole career. If you have one, read it when you are feeling stuck or hopeless. *The Writer* is a related magazine. The few issues I examined years ago caused me to wonder whether *The Writer* knew the gay market existed or would care to know. The general market listings include many first-rate magazines, but not so many that seem promising to beginning writers, whatever their subject or genre.

Coverage of the gay market is slight and often misleading in *The Writer's Market* (although owing to the way it is compiled, its editors probably are not to blame). *Writer's Digest* is the related magazine. Many editors of gay magazines would just as soon not be listed in *Writer's Market* or *Writer's Digest*. When *Writer's Digest* mentions a gay magazine, that magazine is flooded with submissions from the large part of *Writer's Digest*'s vast readership that has yet to learn what "Know your market!" means. Unless your byline is recognized by the editors of the publication, your fine erotic story will wait a long time in the slush pile with stories of how God cures homosexuality, poignant heterosexual romances, book-length poems about being gay (cheerful, joyous, carefree) and other inappropriate submissions. No doubt the same thing happens to every magazine mentioned in *Writer's Digest,* but the logjam effect is especially pronounced at periodicals with small staffs, which includes virtually every gay title.

Although editors of gay magazines are especially open to submissions from new contributors, they suppose—and rightly, I think—that writers likely to come up with an appropriate submission will find the right place to send their submissions without the guideposts of listings in *Writer's Digest* or *Writer's Market*. Nonetheless, *Writer's Digest* is full of good advice for beginning writers. Anyone beginning a writing career might benefit by subscribing for a year or two.

But *Writer's Digest,* or anyone else, has only so much to say to raw recruits. *Writer's Digest*'s advice is repeated, year after year, with only slight variations. Some beginners do benefit from much repetition of good advice, and *Writer's Digest* repeats good advice often. Until you can put magazines containing your stories or your book on your coffee table, you can put

Writer's Digest there so that callers will know you are a writer. Beware, however, of ads in *Writer's Digest* suggesting that money can buy a shortcut to publishing success.

Some professional writers use *Literary Market Place* and subscribe to *Publishers Weekly,* both of which are expensive and unavailable in general-interest bookstores.

Market information, however, dates too quickly to be accurate in any book (and for that reason no market list is included in this book). As will be made clear in the chapter on marketing, the theory of marketing according to someone else's published list is wrong. Consult market books at the library to be sure you have not overlooked something, but market according to your own list.

No market listing is as telling as the recent issues of a magazine you want to sell your stories to. Writers in the gay market have to get recent issues to discover where to send their stories; writers in other markets are the ones most tempted to overlook recent issues as source of market information. Read as many books of gay erotica—or whatever your subject is—as you can. The kind and number of reference works a writer needs depend upon her subject. Many economies are possible. Last year's almanac will serve a fiction writer as well as the current edition. An old stack of *National Geographic*s may still contain some maps that will be superior to the maps in a very expensive atlas, and the stories may suggest locales, both nearby and exotic, both recent and ancient. Part of the game in textbook publishing is issuing new editions that entail only trivial changes but that students must buy; the old editions can be had for a dime on the dollar.

You do not need contacts.

Contrary to a popular notion, you do not need to know somebody to break into the gay market, or into any other. Maybe sometime, somewhere, a writer got into print because he became familiar with the right person. That, perhaps, works once at one magazine. Whether you have been published once, a dozen times, or not at all, an editor will make a decision whether to buy your story according to the quality of the words that are *under* your byline.

I am sorry to be the one to tell you: readers do not notice bylines. In the gay market, only three or four writers have anything like a following. They did not get that following until they had published several books and many dozens of stories. Four or five stories will not make you famous in any market. The bright side of this distressing fact is that editors know this, too. Although they would like to put a very famous name on the cover, most editors would prefer a good story by you to a mediocre story from a regular contributor. Your name will not sell magazines. The regular contributor's name will not sell magazines. As far as the fiction sells magazines at all—which is not very far at most magazines—printing the best stories he can get is the editor's best strategy.

A working writer develops contacts as a result of working in the market. These contacts help him to get the right manuscript to the right place at the right time—perhaps. Such contacts are primarily business relationships of the sort that exist in any other kind of commerce. There is no arcane brotherhood or literary mafia.

Aaron Travis reminds me of a way a beginner can obtain some contacts, although it is hardly necessary to do so. In *Chapters from an Autobiography* (San Francisco: Grey Fox Press, 1981), Sam Steward (Phil Andros) tells how he came to know many of the principal literary figures of his youth. He wrote to them.

Write a fan letter to a writer whose work you admire. Send the letter to his or her book publisher or to a magazine in which his or her stories appear. Ask the editor to forward the letter. Only a few of the most popular mass-market writers receive an overwhelming amount of fan mail. The letter will probably reach the writer—although there may be an inordinate delay in forwarding—and the writer will probably read it.

Try to say something perceptive about the writer's work. You might hint that you are interested in writing yourself, but a fan letter should mostly concern the work of the person you are writing. Write to an author whose work you admire so that what you write might be sincere. Do not request a reply, but do not be surprised if you get one. Once you receive a reply, do not request that the writer tell you everything he knows about writing and the gay market. Your letters should have the character of a correspondence, not that of an interrogation. You may ask for a specific bit of information that you cannot easily find elsewhere: Does magazine X pay on time? Is magazine Y really staff written (the same bylines appear so often)? Do not try the writer's patience by asking him to do your legwork, or by asking a beginner's question that could be answered by reading the remainder of this book or simply by asking of a reference librarian. You must treat as confidential any inside information you obtain, such as the true names of those who use pen names. (You may not publish material from letters you receive without the permission of the person who wrote the letters.)

Never send a writer a manuscript without his permission. He may offer to look at some of your work, but you must not request that he do so. Remember that you are asking for something valuable: information he has acquired through hard work and hard experience. It is his to give, and though he may give it gladly, it is not yours to demand.

Writers who are very popular or who have recently received a great deal of publicity will not be able to give your letters the attention they deserve, no matter how much the writer wishes to do so. So far, I have read and answered all the fan mail that has reached me, but at times I had difficulty justifying the time and expense of doing so. I have not yet resorted to a form letter, but I have been stung by the accusation that I use one. If you think you received a form letter, you ought to accept it with good grace. But if your original letter was couched in very general terms, you may never know whether the reply you received was a form letter or not.

You do not need vanity presses.

A vanity press (or, more politely, a subsidy publisher) prints books for authors who pay.

At their best, subsidy publishers provide a means of publishing important, often scholarly, books expected to sell only to a few specialists and libraries. Once subsidy publishing was the only way to get research and thought on homosexuality into print.

Gay people are better off today because subsidy publishing allowed a few authors to keep a candle burning through the Great Darkness. Today, although homosexuality is not the hot mass-market topic it was in the early 1970s, important work on the subject is printed by general publishers and university presses at no expense to the author.

Vanity presses have had their success stories. Poetry, for example, is virtually impossible to publish except by vanity press. Several renowned poets have paid at one time or another to have their work printed. But so have many more poets manqués who remain unknown. Possibly a novel, thought too kinky or too narrow by publishers of gay books, but published by a vanity press, might tap a new vein in the gay market. It is hard to imagine such a novel. The most likely reason that publishers of gay books do not want a gay novel is that the gay novel is not good enough.

At worst, vanity presses are scams. Although they often promise to promote their works, their lists are not taken seriously by bookstores or critics. Distribution is a serious problem. Distribution of gay books is difficult enough for publishers who deal exclusively in gay books. A vanity press, which prints books for all comers, will not know how to promote or to distribute a work of gay erotica. The odds of an author recovering the major part of his money are slight, and much less that the book will turn a profit. A rich queen who cannot get published otherwise and who merely wants copies to give to his friends and to force onto his tricks will get his money's worth from a vanity press. Of course, the rich queen who has used money in place of talent and merit to get published can never expect to enjoy the esteem of real authors, however much his tainted volumes may impress naïve young men.

Since computers have made so-called desktop publishing possible, writers who are willing to pay can now get into print through self-publishing. Vanity presses take the author's manuscript, edit it, design the book, have it printed, attempt to distribute it, and promise to promote it, all for a fixed fee. Self-publishing, although often as much in vain, is a bit different. A self-published author may edit and design his book electronically, take bids for the printing of his book directly from printers, and promote and distribute his book himself.

Certainly no one should self-publish who cannot afford to lose the investment. Publishing from top to bottom is a risky enterprise—the next time you pass a remainder table in a bookstore, you might consider the hopes, dreams, and hard cash that each of the failed volumes represents. While investing in yourself is, in general, a good policy, investing your life's savings in your book may not be.

Some kinds of self-published authors have a chance of success. A poet who is making the coffeehouse circuit anyway, who is giving well-received readings, and whose audience begs for more than can be fit into a single reading, ought to consider having a small volume printed up. But a poet who thinks he or she can have several thousand volumes printed, drop them off at B. Dalton, and retire to his or her ivory tower to wait for the checks to roll in, would do better to put the money in a mutual fund.

A traveling minister in a small sect who has his most inspirational sermons printed up and who hawks the books to the congregations he visits may make a profit on his book. Like the coffeehouse poet, he has access to groups with a special interest in his subject. The minister will sell far more books to a hundred people in a congregation he visits than he ever could to the next hundred people walking into Barnes & Noble. He is traveling to these groups anyway, and he does not mind schlepping around his books.

Civic and church groups have had great success in raising money by selling self-published cookbooks. Of course, the success of these ventures depends upon selling many books to those who contributed recipes, to other members of the organization, and to friends and relatives of the aforesaid. Like a cakewalk, the book has not really generated much revenue from outside the interested group, but has succeeded in lightening the purses of those affiliated with the group. In a similar way, little poetry groups can sometimes break even by issuing little anthologies, whereas a chapbook by a single poet might have a less-desirable bottom line.

Evidently some would-be novelists believe that very good novels (i.e., their own) will be overlooked by big publishers. This is untrue. Oh yes, *Gone With the Wind* was rejected by very many houses. But someone did buy it at last. Publishers are looking for marketable novels; finding them is how they make their money. A manuscript may be overlooked at one house or given to a dyspeptic reader at another. But if ten people at ten houses, who rely on their literary judgment for their livelihood, think that your book is not marketable, there is a distinct possibility they are correct.

Almost everyone who makes a success of self-publishing (or of any other new small business) does so by finding a niche in the market that is not being filled. A few writers in the gay market, who already had considerable followings and conventionally published books in print, have had mixed success in issuing small books and booklets devoted to narrow fetishes or scenes—one offered stories tailored by computer to the subscriber's checklisted preferences. These writers had special access to groups likely to be interested in their subjects: one of the writers had a mailing list because he operated an adult mail-order business; another had access to free advertising in a magazine that reached readers likely to be interested in his subject. The potential of making a small profit exists here because these markets are too small to be served by larger publishers. But for that exact reason, one's market is soon saturated, and everyone who is interested in the book has either bought it or decided not to. This sort of operation is nothing for a beginner to undertake with the object of making a profit or advancing a writing career.

Possibly because I am too lazy to motivate myself otherwise, I always think that whatever I am working on at the moment is the best stuff ever written. In retrospect, however, I find that some things turned out better than others. Not many authors, and especially not many novelists, have any capacity for evaluating their own work accurately.

If you are a poor salesperson, or if you do not have special access to groups with interest in your subject, you will have a hard time with a self-published book. You will find it difficult or impossible to get bookstores to carry your book; but even if you do get your book into a bookstore, it will be only one title out of the thousands available in the store. The big houses have the clout to get their books displayed prominently—sometimes. You do not.

Do not deal with a vanity press and do not self-publish.

You may need space.

Physical space is a valuable asset. An area five feet by five feet is adequate to begin with. More is not especially useful since the idea is to arrange things within arm's reach. Such an area will hold your essentials: a table large enough for the typewriter or word processor and the copy, drawers for gadgets and supplies, a bookcase, a not-too-comfortable chair, a cardboard box to hold files.

The home-office expense cannot be claimed on your income-tax return unless your work space is closed off from the rest of your home and used for no other purpose than your work. But a beginner will have difficulty claiming any writing-related expense until the writing enterprise is showing a profit, so you might as well set up where you can and get started.

Many writers have done without a special space, have set up on the kitchen table, worked, and afterward stowed their writing gear. No doubt that promotes an orderly way of working. One of my most productive periods was spent in a boardinghouse, when I did not dare leave my writing gear in the public area where I worked.

The essential kind of space is not physical.

Writers are difficult people to live with. Perhaps the television cannot be turned on when the writer says he is working. (A publishing writer I know of made his lover throw a TV in the garbage.) When the sun is shining and the spring zephyr is sweet, the writer wants to sit in a stuffy room, typing. When it is dreary out, the writer does *not* want to have some friends over for cocktails.

Compelled to attend a party, the writer disappears for hours and is found crouched in a corner, scribbling away on paper towels. It is not as if he made a great deal of money at it—

certainly nothing compared to what other professionals make at similar stages in their careers.

Not all of a writer's requirements are owing to amateurish temperament. Many of a writer's problems are shared by others who work at home. People do not respect the workplace in the home as they would a "real" office. They do not understand that though the writer is home, he may be working. They do not identify the things on a writer's desk as tools. ("What does this button do?")

When the muse is singing, it is difficult to lure the writer away from the keyboard. "I'll be there in a minute" means in a kind of minute that may last for hours—days is not unheard of. A writer's lover wonders, "If there is a fire, will he save me or the manuscript?" Silly question.

Nothing funny happens if a man tries to come between a writer and his keyboard.

Only a special kind of person can be a writer's lover or roommate. Some who think it would be romantic do not have what it takes. The talent for loving a writer may be rarer than the talent for writing itself. It certainly is more mysterious.

Books are not dedicated for nothing.

You might need courses or workshops.

While classroom study is usually not necessary, some talented writers may learn this way when they can learn by no other. freelance writing in any market is not especially lucrative. One way writers supplement their incomes is by teaching courses and workshops. Occasionally writers to whom the honorarium is next to meaningless will teach a course out of their dedication to the craft.

The best courses spend time on the fundamentals of marketing and writing. Most students will hear the instructor repeating the maxims: "Know your market!" "Write every day!" "Write what you know!" and so forth. This cheerleading is useful to some students. Unfortunately, students demand courses like "How to Market your Screenplay" when they have never taken a course on "How to Write a Marketable Screenplay." Look for the courses of the latter kind.

One advantage to such courses is the chance of observing the process of word-by-word revision. The realization that this is something that people really do may be the most valuable part of a revision demonstration. One course I taught had only four meetings, and I asked students to revise a page of manuscript before I had the chance of treating the subject of revision in lectures. I discovered that most students could do a fairly good revision. They simply had not revised their manuscripts until someone told them to do it. Very well, I will tell you: Revise your manuscripts.

When there is time, student papers may be revised in class. But when your own work is under consideration, the outrage may be too great to bear. Perhaps more can be learned by observing what is done to others' work and then perpetrating similar acts, in private, on your own work.

Mail-order courses lack the personal interchange and the experience of the process as it unfolds—which may be the only worthwhile parts of writing courses. On the other hand, correspondence courses lack the intrusions of know-it-all students. If you feel you need and can afford a writing course, you may be more comfortable studying by mail. Ask whether the school will deal with gay erotic fiction. Correspondence courses have no trade secrets to teach you. What you need to know is in this book, is also available in other books, and is taught in workshops and community-college courses.

Blue-pencil and criticism services, the less honest of which advertise themselves as literary agents, are essentially ghostwriters who work with your outline. Marking up a manuscript is a laborious task that requires a specialized skill. A person who believes that he needs such a service should expect to pay for it. He should not think, however, that the result will be a marketable manuscript, that writers gain their professional status thus, or that criticism services are likely to teach him the skills he needs to work on his own.

You will need persistence, and you may need time.
The elements of a successful writing career are persistence, talent, and luck. You can get by on two out of three, and the

more you have of any one of the qualities, the less you need of the others.

In general, physicists are washed up if they have not done their principal work by the time they are thirty. Writers, the occasional much-celebrated boy genius aside, reach the peak of their powers much later in life. Often the boy genius is a stylist. Literature of substance requires experience in living, or so it would seem.

That does not mean that you must put off writing if you are young. Indeed, it is desirable to learn technique as early as possible. Someone has said that a writer must write a million words of shit before he can write anything worthwhile. The sooner you start, the sooner you will be through the million words.

If you are determined to make writing your career, you must prepare yourself to see your classmates progress ahead of you in life, garnering material advantage and the esteem of society while you seem to be getting nowhere. You must be prepared to be the object of taunts and, what is worse, of pity. Save an extraordinary stroke of fortune, you will see others achieve most of the milestones of life while you have hardly advanced beyond the starting line. If this seems like the fable of the hare and the tortoise, it is—except that it is your fable, and you will not be sure of the moral of the tale until you come to its conclusion. And even should you win, you may end up wondering whether the race was worth the running.

Fortunately, the gay market has plenty of room for youthful work. A writer in the position to portray the youth scene authentically is hardly handicapped. (Have you ever read a punk story by a writer who has missed the scene by at least twenty years?)

Persistence is valuable both in a career as a whole and in marketing a single story. You will hear the tales often: the story that was filed away as unsaleable, but which sold immediately when taken out again after many years; the book that is now a best-seller, but which was rejected by publisher after publisher; the writer who suddenly is in demand after many years of obscurity.

In fact, the gay market often provides more encouragement

sooner than other markets. That does not diminish the importance of persistence. Things will seem hopeless. No one else will believe.

You do not need criticism from friends, lovers, or your mother.

"Yes, dear, I liked it very much," or "Why do you waste your talent on trash like that?" or "It was very hot. I got off on it," are not criticism. What you need in a reader is the ability to spot typos that are always invisible to the author until the story appears in print (and thereafter are the only parts of the work that the author can see); misspellings, omitted prepositions or articles, wrong tense endings.

Few writers have available readers who can be of more service: tell her she is being too laconic to be understood, distinguish errors of grammar from stylistic usages, notice whether a minor character is called by different names, or discover a violation of viewpoint. Even knowledgeable readers are apt to confound their estimation of the author with their evaluation of the work, and this effect occurs quite independently of any conscious desire to flatter or to disparage. Good criticism is scarce in any case, but some writers cut themselves off from valuable help by reacting temperamentally the first (and last) time that serious, knowledgeable criticism is offered. The beginner's mistake is that of rejecting criticism. The experienced writer is more likely to err by taking ill-founded criticism to heart.

You do not need to follow all of the rules.

"Write what you know!" "Write every day!" "Keep a journal!" "Always write at the same time and place!" "To be a writer you must love to write!"

Rules are excellent advice for most people. The rule "Write every day!" exists because some people like to think of themselves as writers and to be regarded by others as writers, but never get a word on paper. Some writers who really are writers do not write every day—at least not on paper—but they work sporadically, perhaps forty-eight hours running, and then not at all for a week. Writing every day is a good habit, one that every writer should try to form. But it is not the only way to work. If you get words on paper, you need not write every day.

Keeping a journal is a good idea. A scrap of conversation is overheard. A peculiar coincidence occurs. A smell unlocks a memory. A detail of experience disrobes and lolls about in the tall grass. The journal keeps such moments from being lost. But if keeping a journal is an artificial drudgery, if it is only filling so much space on a page when the writer is tired, when the keenness of the moment is lost, then the journal does little good. You can have the good of keeping a journal by jotting little notes on scraps of paper and putting those scraps into your wallet until the wallet must be emptied into your scrap box.

It is good if a writer likes to write. Some superb authors take such pains with their writing that every moment is agony.

"Write what you know!" is good advice. This does not mean that if you work in a sewage plant, you must write watersports and scat. It means to write about the human things you know. It means write so that even if your protagonist is a robot with microchips for a soul, what you write about it will interest human beings.

The rules are expressions of underlying truths. The tendency of beginners is to think of themselves as exceptional. I do not mean to encourage that often-destructive tendency. You will be bound by the underlying truths, whether you observe them or not; but if you do observe them, you may not have to follow the letter of every rule meant to express them. I mean to encourage those who do work, but who work in their own ways. Do not give up if you work differently from the way the books say to work. What counts is that you work, however you do, and that you not kid yourself when you are not working.

You probably will need some other source of income.

To my knowledge, no one is making a living solely from writing gay erotica. This situation is unlikely to change because the gay market is relatively small. Moreover, not many people are making a living writing in any genre.

I was surprised to learn of the number of writers who appear to be successful in literary terms but could not support themselves on their writing incomes alone. I have now met many mystery and romance writers who are in situations I thought only authors in the gay market experienced. They have a new hardback book from a major publishing house every fall. The books do well enough that publishers welcome the next volumes, and the titles invariably go into paperback. But, the authors tell me, they would be unable to keep body and soul together if they did not have spouses or companions who have good incomes, or inheritances, or day jobs.

Anyone who can be discouraged by this news probably ought to be. The realities of a writing career are much more discouraging. Writing as a hobby or a sideline is one thing, but the commitment to writing as one's principal vocation should not be undertaken lightly.

Some writers, of course, do eventually make a living from writing; if not altogether from novels, then from a combination of novels, articles, and stories, and writing-related activities such as lecturing and teaching. But a beginner ought to have some alternatives in mind in case such success is delayed.

2. *Learning to Write for Publication*

Although anyone reading this book has taken English courses, learning to write for publication is akin to learning a new subject altogether. Some part of a foreign-language course is devoted to an organized presentation of the grammar of the foreign language. But the real learning of the language is done in conversational practice, in the learning of dialogues, and in the parroting of taped examples in the language laboratory. In the lecture section of an organic chemistry course, the professor may join two molecular models in an instant, but in the laboratory the corresponding synthesis may require many tedious hours or days and may never run to completion. In learning to drive a stick-shift, one may understand the operation of the clutch and the gearshift long before one can shift gears smoothly. Clearly, there are two kinds of knowledge involved here: theory of the operation of the gears, and practical skill in operating the gears. The theory is far from useless, for it can direct practice rightly—and wrong practice is worse than no practice at all. But theory without practice is empty.

So it is in learning to write for publication. The theory may or may not seem simple, but all that is in a book can be understood easily. Obtaining the practical skill requires much more effort, and in particular requires practice.

By far the best sort of writing to practice on is trivial: journals or diaries, letters, letters-to-the-editor, small essays, anecdotes.

...nlock. Practice ... ...s gained in th...
...i these little improvements will be more evi...
...us more rewarding, when the subject is less than...
Practice your powers on little things, for if you reserve p...
for some great work of literature that you plan to compose o...
day, you will find on that day you have no powers at all.

To this point I may add the following fable (which I first read, in different form, in Judith Martin's "Miss Manners" column):

Once, or so the story goes, there was a foolish young maid who received as a gift a bolt of the finest white linen. She put it away in her trousseau, to be reserved, she said, for something special. By and by, she came of the age that a young woman was presented to the eligible young men of the region. It was suggested to her that she make her coming-out dress of the fine white linen. "Oh, no," she said, "I am saving it for something special."

But she did meet a fine young man who proposed to marry her, and she accepted. "Such a wedding dress we could make of that bolt of fine white linen!" her mother said.

"Oh, no," replied the foolish young woman. "I am saving it for something special."

"Then we will make a fine sheet for your marriage bed."

"Of course not. I am saving it for something special."

And so it was her whole life long. The linen was not used to wrap her firstborn son, nor to lay on the table when the king came to dine. On every occasion she said, "Not now. I am saving it for something special."

Her daughter was married in a gown of coarser cloth. The baptismal robes of her grandchildren were made of common fabric. "Not now," she said. "I am saving that linen for something special."

But the linen was used at last. They made her shroud of it.

Moral: Do not feed your talent to the worms.

Simple literacy, as taught in high-school grammar courses, is by no means easy to achieve, but it is, in a certain sense, simple to learn. Mrs. Grundy, the archetypal English teacher, presents the rules. The student need only follow the rules. The student has no doubt what a rule is. It is something which if transgressed results in a big red mark from Mrs. Grundy's grading pen. Subject and verb must agree in number. The book says so. Mrs. Grundy says so. The student believes it and tries to make his subjects and verbs agree in number because he believes in the rule and because he wants to avoid a red mark.

Unfortunately, learning to write for publication is a less simple process. First, there is the question of what is a rule.

In giving a series of workshops, I proposed to students of creative writing the following rule:

When a comparison like "as red as a rose" is given in a negative sense, change the first "as" to "so," making the result "not so red as a rose," "never so red as a rose," "hardly so red as a rose," and so forth.

Immediately half the class rose in mutiny. "We have never heard of such a rule." Naturally, I apologized quickly for attempting to teach them something they did not already know. When I returned to my office, I looked through the grammars, style guides, and usage books I had there. One of them might have contained the controversial rule; but if so, I did not find it. I doubted my sanity. Where had I come up with such a notion?

But when I turned to my book of quotations, I quickly found several dozen examples in which writers from Chaucer to Churchill, including some Americans, observed my rule. Well, was it a rule or not? Evidently my students had got through school writing things like "not as red as a rose" without getting a red mark from Mrs. Grundy. I seriously doubt that any editor would accept or reject a manuscript on such a fine point.

For myself, I will choose to go with Chaucer and Churchill and Adams and Austen whenever I notice the point. But I still do not know whether it is a rule. It is my advice. And whether a student should follow it or not is a matter of judgment. Certainly there are writers who have not followed this rule but who have done well enough in their careers. And I can find violations of the rule in my own work.

But almost all the difference between literate writing and fine writing is made up of such fuzzy little bits of advice that cannot really be called rules. In writing for publication, there is no Mrs. Grundy, ready to snap her desk with her ruler and snap the wool-gathering student back to attention. Very few editors will ever make a mark—much less a red mark—on a rejected manuscript. Moreover, these bits of advice occur as anecdotes, for no stylebook I have found—and not even this book—has managed to catalog all the bits of good advice in the way the rules of English are cataloged in a high-school grammar text. And for these reasons not every student who can learn to write well enough to please Mrs. Grundy will learn to write for publication.

In the immediately following chapters, I present something of the theory of writing for publication. I have forced the theory into various more or less neat categories, and the categories have been more or less neatly organized. But in practice, of course, various questions of style occur willy-nilly.

The theory, as I present it, may seem very simple, or indeed obvious (or perhaps just the opposite). The difficulty in practice is in recognizing the places in which the theory applies, and often in choosing which of the sometimes-conflicting principles to apply in the particular case. Although I have organized the presentation of this material in a way that seems logical to me, I would advise you to keep a notebook organized as you see fit—although you might use index cards or an electronic file instead of a notebook. I have tried to give a number of examples at each point, but in practice you will encounter examples that seem more illustrative to you, and these belong in your notebook. The English language contains numerous pitfalls. Although I have listed many, you are bound to discover more, and to have more trouble with some than with others. These belong in your notebook. I can hardly list all the trade names in a book this size, and several volumes of hyphenation examples could be issued without resolving every possible question. When you have researched one of these matters, keep a record of your results—issues of this sort are likely to recur within a writer's particular orbit.

Do not begin climbing with Mount Fuji, but start with a local, commonplace hill... Practical skill is... in small, haphazard steps, and...dent, and th... heroic.

...ractice

...one

The student's notebook, of course, is the real text, and only the student is the student's true teacher. I cannot teach a student to write as I write, but can only show the way that the student may learn to write as best she can, which may indeed be better than I write but can never be the same.

It is not a matter of mastering the theory and then writing. Perhaps no one ever achieves complete mastery of writing. The only way to gain a degree of mastery is by writing. When you write regularly, you will discover that you do not have to look up the rule to remember which side of a quotation mark the period goes on. Although you may never remove all of the weak constructions from your writing, you will learn to remove more and more of them, and eventually you will learn to write fewer of them to begin with. Strong writing, like baseball, is very much a matter of percentages. You cannot expect to bat a 1.000 all season, but you may reasonably aspire to improve from .127 to .250, and that may be all the difference between winning and losing.

The strategy I suggest in learning style is given in the maxim: Learn the rules, and then learn to break the rules. By this I mean, try at first to strip your writing of mannerisms and weak constructions. Try to write the most vigorous and transparent language you can. Your ideal should be something like the style Hemingway is generally supposed to have used (but did not really): precise noun, action verb, precise object, period, precise noun, action verb, precise object, and so forth.

Of course, were you ever to gain that ideal, you could not write a whole novel in such stripped-down, streamlined prose; readers could not bear the tension. But few beginners are in danger of writing too tersely. Once you are writing fairly concise prose, you can relax a bit, let bits of color in. Then, however, you are in a position to relax in a controlled and conscious manner. Your narrator's mannerisms can then be his own and will not be clouded with your own unconscious mannerisms. If your writing is vague or abstract, it will be vague or abstract where you mean it to be vague or abstract, instead of being vague or abstract merely where you are incapable of being precise and concrete.

Most fine writing seems to flow smoothly and naturally, and

one word seems to follow the other with a kind of obvious inevitability. The writer seems to achieve his or her effects spontaneously, or at least effortlessly. This, of course, is an illusion. Somehow people know that what the ballet dancer or the figure skater does is not so easy as it is made to appear. But too many people think there is no work to writing well. Almost everyone has dreamt, I suppose, of sitting down to a piano and producing beautiful music without ever having bothered to learn to play the piano. But most people who try to play the piano without having practiced can quickly ascertain from the sounds they produce the difference between their dreamworld and the real one. Unfortunately, would-be writers can do the most discordant things on an innocent piece of paper without ever being aware of having hit a sour note.

Writing well is hard work, and learning to write well is even harder. While this is a sobering thought, it has its hopeful aspect. Of the many who aspire to write, only a few will write anything. Of the many who write anything, only a few will bother to try to write well. Of the few who bother to try to write well, only a few will reflect upon what they have written and revise. Competition in the literary world grows continually, but it is nothing you need worry about if you are resolved to be one of a few of a few of a few.

3. *Structure and Strength*

The paragraph is the natural structural unit of English. Although a sentence has been defined as one complete thought, it is not by sentences, but by paragraphs that arguments are advanced or plots developed.

Paragraphs of fiction sometimes differ in important ways from paragraphs of essays. Not all paragraphs of fiction, for example, have topic sentences. Stories unfold as events. Events are usually best ordered chronologically. Logically related information is distributed among paragraphs throughout the story. If this were not so, fiction would be impossible. A paragraph about a murder, if organized logically, would contain at the least the name of the victim and the name of the perpetrator. If this paragraph were written, the point of the story would be lost.

The logical order of what happened to John's lover Mike begins with Mike: he was kidnapped and raped but finally released when the kidnapers discovered that they could not get any money from John. The next subject is John: what he did when he got the ransom note, that he did not have any money, what he decided to do, and so forth. Then there is the hard-boiled private eye John appealed to for help: how the detective tracked down the kidnappers, how he convinced them that John was maintaining his affluent appearance with a credit card, how he apprehended the culprits once Mike was released. Then the kidnappers: why they wanted the money, why they thought

John had money, and so forth. We might convey the whole story in a fictional essay.

That essay might be a very helpful tool for the writer, but it would not be a short story or a novel.

Journalism and essay writing aim to provide the reader with answers. But fiction aims to provide the reader with questions: Will the kidnappers kill Mike? How will John convince the private eye to take the case without a cash retainer? Is the private eye screwing the right person to get the information he needs? What will happen to Mike when the levelheaded kidnapper goes out, leaving Mike alone with his demented crony? Is Mike only humoring the kidnappers, or is he developing a strange sympathy with them, à la the Stockholm Syndrome? Does John really want Mike back? Is Mike sure that he did not really enjoy being raped? Was he raped, really?

Most, but not necessarily all, of the questions are answered *eventually*. Important questions are answered as near the end as possible. Secondary questions are posed and answered in an overlapping manner. Questions and answers are evident in a suspense or mystery novel, but the questions and answers are necessary in all kinds of fiction, even if they are sometimes more subtle. The reader begins with the question: What is going here? That question must be replaced as soon as possible with the question: What will happen next? Necessary questions cannot occur if the writer grasps his subject by a topic sentence, tells all he knows of the subject, and moves on to the next paragraph.

The story begins:
1. There is a noise in the living room which wakes Mike up.
2. Mike calls out, "John, is that you?" Mike thinks it is not John. Mike thinks he remembers seeing John get dressed for work. John was putting on one of the expensive suits which he really cannot afford on a teller's salary.
3. Mike hears no response. He is alarmed although he is still groggy from the sleeping medication he took. Since he is fully dressed, Mike gets up from the bed. "Who is it?" Still no answer.
4. Mike stumbles into the living room.

Logically, the kidnappers have broken into the apartment, and the demented one has knocked over a lamp in the process. They are being very quiet in order to jump Mike when he comes out of the bedroom. The reader does not know it is kidnappers, but because this is a detective novel, the reader knows that something bad is in the apartment.

In making a story of this information, the writer posed the question: "What (or Who) is in the living room?" He used the time to plant the seeds of other questions and story elements.

The reader now knows that John does not really have money: he cannot afford the suits he wears. When the ransom note arrives, the reader will wonder, as John does, what will happen to Mike, since paying the ransom is out of the question. Kidnapping is now a plausible outcome of whatever is going to happen in the apartment. John wears expensive suits, and he works in a bank. The kidnappers will have noticed.

Mike takes downers and sleeps in his clothes. What kind of relationship do John and Mike have? Is Mike very happy in his present life? Is it possible that he will have a degree of ambivalence about being kidnapped and raped?

Could be.

Knocking over a lamp is a shopworn device. Maybe it will do. The place for an unlikely or trite device or for an implausible premise is at the very beginning. The reader accepts such things in the beginning to see what is made of them. To rescue the heroes at the end by a similar device is to ask too much. The question of the lamp will be reconsidered at the time of the first revision. With Chapter One rolling along well, the writer does not look back.

The writer might or might not have the whole fictional essay in mind when she begins, but the paragraphs of her story are very unlike the paragraphs of the fictional essay.

The structural hierarchy of English.

The natural structure of English builds up from the word to phrase to the clause to sentence to the paragraph; or, in descending order, the structures of English are:

Paragraph
Sentence
Clause
Phrase
Word

The principle of structural significance.

Although paragraphs of fiction are not organized on the same scheme as paragraphs of an essay, the reader of fiction shares with the reader of essays the expectation that each paragraph is about as important as any other paragraph. Each paragraph has a unit of significance.

A paragraph's significance is distributed more or less equally among its sentences, the first and last getting a bit more than their share. The share of significance that a sentence gets must be divided among its clauses, each clause's significance is shared by its phrases, and so down to the word which receives a bit of the phrase's importance. In a paragraph of many sentences, with sentences of many clauses, clauses of many phrases, and phrases of many words, the value left to a single word is paltry. When a clause makes up a whole sentence, the clause receives all of the sentence's importance; when a phrase can be promoted to a clause, it receives the whole attention a clause deserves; promoted to a sentence, the phrase becomes even more important. The word, elevated through the steps, gains confidence, looks the world in the eye, raises its voice.

Shouts.

An adept writer who is familiar with the principle of structural significance can thumb his nose at the tawdry exclamation point. He has command of the whole dynamic range of English, not just of one loud note.

The applications of the principle of structural significance can be summarized thus:

1. The significance of a substructure increases as the number of substructures decreases. Or, in other words, the fewer the sentences in a paragraph, the more attention each sentence receives, and so forth.

2. When a lesser structure takes the place of a superior one, the lesser structure will receive the attention afforded the superior structure. Or, in other words, when a word replaces a phrase, the word receives the attention a phrase deserves, and so forth.

In writing fiction, as opposed to answering essay questions, writers need not give the most space to important ideas. Important ideas may get fewer words, but the words are important words, words that have been promoted structurally. Loss of detail is avoided by choosing words carefully:

> John moved quickly on his feet.
> John ran.
>
> Jesus broke down and shed tears.
> Jesus shed tears.
> Jesus wept.
>
> to carry on the future advance of progress.
> to progress.

Various degrees of significance can be attached to ideas, using the principle of structural significance. Compare:

> "I am ready for my coffee at this point in time."
> "I am ready for my coffee now."
> "I am ready for my coffee. Now."
> "Coffee. Now."

The right word can replace a whole phrase not only without a loss of detail, but also with a more exact expression of detail. "John moved quickly on his feet," leaves the reader in the dark as to what exactly John is doing. Is he dancing? "John jogged," "John trotted," "John ran," and "John dashed" all tell what John did with more concreteness and detail, and in each case the expression is stronger for letting the single verb do the duty of the phrase "moved quickly on his feet."

Fiction may be approached by successive technical corrections. If a writer has written "moved quickly on his feet" but recognizes that this is a weak expression, then the writer may stop to envision what it is John did. The writer may start with a vague idea or not much of an idea at all. The vague idea, because it is vague, must be expressed in fuzzy words. If the writer can spot fuzzy words, he can see where his story needs more work. The better idea often arises from the process of substituting better words. While nothing is wrong with coming to the keyboard with a clear vision of the story one means to tell, for some writers the words come first and the vision afterward.

A traditional therapy for writer's block is to type the word "The," the word to come next, the word after that, and so forth. To carve an elephant out of a block of marble, chip away everything that does not look like an elephant. When enough words have been captured on paper, there is a story. The job is cutting out the parts that do not belong and replacing the "moved quickly on his feet" expressions with precise words. Inspiration is not a lightning bolt.

The parts of speech.

Beyond the importance that words derive from their position in English structure, words have value according to their functions; that is, according to their identities as parts of speech. Here, and elsewhere, I do not pretend to give an academic treatment of English grammar, but mean only to provide sound advice to a creative writer. For present purposes, the parts of speech in descending order of strength are:

Verb (strongest)
Noun
Adjective
Adverb (weakest).

The verb.

The verb is the strongest part of speech. Verbs express all the action a sentence possesses. Movies and television shows prove it hardly matters whether the things are stock cars, speedboats, helicopters, or horses. What counts is chasing, shooting, crashing, and exploding.

Verbs themselves have a natural hierarchy:

Doing (best)
Saying
Thinking and feeling
Being done to
Being (weakest).

Doing verbs express action, and this is why they are the strongest. *Saying* verbs will be discussed in greater detail when we take up the subject of dialogue. *Saying* verbs are relatively strong because sometimes the action of the story is the speaking. *Saying* verbs can be weak if what is said is not pertinent to the story or if speaking takes the place of the real action. Similarly, *thinking* and *feeling* verbs are stronger when they are the developments of the story at a particular point and are not merely reactions to events. *Thinking* and *feeling* verbs are weaker than *saying* verbs because they can only involve one of the characters.

Being-done-to verbs are those, as grammarians would put it, in the passive voice. Sex and grammar are confusing enough without confounding the two. The passive voice is wrong, wrong, wrong. The passive position is quite another thing. Be sexually passive in the active voice: *not* I was being fucked by Al, *but* Al fucked me.

Passive verbs do express some action, although in a backhanded way, but *being* verbs are so weak that they are hardly verbs at all, or as certain philosophical arguments put it: being is not predicate. In many languages, including the language of movie-screen cavemen, the *being* verb is often omitted ("Fire good") with no loss of sense.

The quality of the verb determines the quality of the sentence. From weakest to strongest are these examples:

Jack was angry at Jim. (being)
Jack was being made angry by Jim. (being done to)
Jack thought he could not stand any more of Jim. (thinking)
"You really piss me off," Jack said to Jim. (saying)
Jack hurled the Ming vase at Jim's head. (doing)

Some forms of a given verb are stronger than others. In general, verbs that require auxiliary verbs ("can," "could," "will," "would," "were," "had," "have," and so forth) are less strong than the forms that do not require the auxiliary. "Went" is stronger than "was going" or "had gone" or "did go."

Sense or grammar often requires the use of the auxiliary verb, but sometimes does not. "He did go to the store," should be "He went to the store," unless there is some question as to whether he did. "He was walking down the street until the policeman stopped him," should be "He walked down the street until the policeman stopped him." When the time is understood, the simple past tense can often be substituted for the past perfect: "He had gone to the store yesterday," might be "He went to the store yesterday." "I have come" should be "I came."

If most of your sentences are of the being type, some of them should be recast in a more powerful form. As exercise, revise several pages of your work to raise each verb that is not already a saying or doing verb at least one notch in the hierarchy. Try to compose entire passages without committing a nondoing sentence to paper, except dialogue. Although some senses cannot be conveyed smoothly in doing sentences, beginners often give up too easily.

As no sustained piece of music should be fortissimo throughout, no sustained literary work can rely entirely on *doing* sentences. Single words should only rarely be promoted to stand as paragraphs. A succession of simple sentences with active verbs and unadorned nouns becomes wearisome. As a rule, an author should reserve his strongest writing for the erotic scene (or whatever the climactic scene, according to the genre), and the next-strongest writing should be used in developing important story elements.

A new writer, however, had best attempt to repair any weak expression he perceives. He will perceive only a few of his weaknesses and will not know how to improve some of the weak parts he finds. Few writers ever need to worry about making the background parts softer. The problem always is to make the foreground more vivid.

Some verbs to watch out for.

Some verbs need revision although they seem to be *doing* verbs. A few such verbs are "make," "take," "use," "do," "have," "become," and "employ." More weak combinations including these verbs exist than can be illustrated here, but a few examples should make such combinations easier to recognize:

"to make (or take) a decision" ought to be "to decide"
"to make a mistake" ought to be "to err"
"to make progress" ought to be "to progress,"
"to lose strength" ought to be "to weaken"
"to make use of" ought to be "to use," and often can be further revised; for "to use a shovel" should be "to dig," if the shovel is used in the usual way
"to have a thirst" ought to be "to thirst"
"to make humble" ought to be "to humble"
"to employ a needle" ought to be "to sew"
"to become healthy again" ought to be "to recover" or "to heal"
"to make yourself known to" often should be "to introduce yourself to"
"to make a late entry" may better be "to enter late"
"to do wrong to" should be "to wrong"

and so forth.

Some of these phrases use abstract nouns, which are weak for being abstract: "decision," "mistake," "progress," et cetera. Incorporating their senses into the verbs strengthens the sentences.

"Make" and "take" and the other verbs are not so weak when they are being used in their literal senses: "to make a chair," "to take an extra roll." Even in such cases, a more precise verb may be found: "to make lace" might be "to tat."

Among the *doing* verbs, those which are stronger are precise and concrete. Precision is one reason that "ran" should be preferred to "moved quickly." Concreteness is the issue treated by the writer's maxim: "Show us, don't tell us."

"Susan loved Amy" suffers a bit from imprecision, for "loved" has many senses. But it suffers more from being abstract. The idea is conveyed better by a sentence in which Susan does something loving, just as Jack's anger was most strongly conveyed by his throwing something. Sometimes, of course, Susan and Amy are minor characters, and the nature of their relationship must be summarized in a few words. But if the story hangs on Susan's love for Amy, we had better have some evidence of it.

Nouns.

Like verbs, nouns derive their strength from being precise and concrete. Do not write that a bird was singing. Tell us whether it was a canary, a sparrow, a mockingbird, or a grackle. Besides strengthening the sentence, the more precise noun may give us an idea of the season or the setting. When the noun is fixed, the verb may need revision. Mockingbirds scold; grackles do not sing. Do not write of an arm muscle if you can write of a biceps.

As with verbs, abstractness is a warning bell. Love, anger, truth, justice, and pride do not do things. Do not write of being horny; show us a hard cock.

To know the name of something is to have power over it, and the more precisely you can name something, the more power over it you have. Do not write of a "board" if you can write of a "two-by-four" or "stud" or "purlin" or "decking." Certain do not call something a "big, thick piece of lumber" if what you mean is a timber. When you write of things outside of your daily experience, a major part of your research should be devoted to leaning what things are called. Many readers, of course, will never know the fine distinctions you make, but those who do know the distinctions will notice if you gloss over them.

Most imprecise nouns do not represent the writer's ignorance, but his lack of thought. "Truck," for example, stands for such various vehicles that most writers should select "pickup" or "van" or "semitrailer." Few people would need to do research to know the differences the more precise terms represent. The writer who writes "truck" probably knows which kind of truck she means, and she will probably picture the same kind of truck every time she rereads the passage she wrote. So long as she writes "truck" in a journal that will be read only by herself or in a letter to a friend who can guess reliably at her meaning, the writer is justified in considering herself perfectly literate. But when published, the word "truck" will fail to convey to many readers what the writer had in mind.

Call a cock a "cock." Yes, sometimes it should be "fuckpole." "One-eyed snake" never was erotic and no longer is funny. Depending upon your narrator, it might be "dick" or even "peter." (When it is "dick," you must write "head of his dick." "Cockhead" works. "Dickhead" doesn't.) To paraphrase Strunk and White: never call a cock a pee-pee without good reason. Fresh figures and colorful expressions are most effective when strictly limited.

Some nouns have become wordy for no good reason. "Time span" is an example of such a noun. Usually the word "span" should be deleted; other times "period," "era," or some other precise noun should be substituted for the whole of "time span."

Because precision is so important in nouns, it follows that proper nouns, being perfectly precise because they refer only to one person (or thing), are among the strongest nouns. Call your characters by name often, both because the names are stronger and because using names avoids problems of pronoun reference.

You need not vary an apt noun for fear that readers will tire of it. Some writers avoid using any noun often. A rose is once a rose, again is a red flower, then a fragrant scarlet blossom, this blushing beauty amid the thorns that was a rose but can never be called a rose again. Readers do not tire of words so quickly as writers think.

Calling characters by epithets (that is, "the Caped Crusader" for Batman or "the Bard of Avon" for Shakespeare) was required by Homer's meter, but nowadays is the way of pulp novelists. Your character may be called by slightly different versions of his name by his mother, his lover, and his boss, but for narration pick one name and stick to it.

Adjectives.

Adjectives may do either harm or good.

Some adjectives bring added precision to the nouns they modify. The image produced by "ladder-back chair" is more precise than that of "chair," and if we are supposed to picture the chair for some reason, the adjective "ladder-back" is very helpful. On the other hand, unless the writer has done something to present the possibility of other colors of roses, we will assume a rose is red, so the adjective of "red rose" may not do great harm, but certainly does little good.

As with nouns and verbs, precision and concreteness are the attributes of desirable adjectives. This is true even of the simplest adjectives, the articles. The precise article is "the." A thing of importance often should be "the" thing. A brush on your character's dresser should be "the brush," unless of course there are many. "The" is the definite article, and in most cases the author should be as definite as possible.

Almost all abstract adjectives are worthless or worse. "Good," "bad," "ugly," "beautiful," "special," and similar adjectives tell us only the author's opinion of the thing named, and nothing about the thing itself. The language is littered with the bones of adjectives that have been abused into meaninglessness, and many of these are abstract: awful, terrific, nice, cute, clever, fine, tremendous, wonderful, marvelous, fantastic. Careful writers may be able to use a few of these in their original senses. But almost all such adjectives are better omitted.

A number of other adjectives are relative in their meanings: "big," "tall," "small," "short," and so forth. We all know that an adult elephant is big. If you write "big elephant," we may wonder what you mean. You might be telling us that an elephant is big, which we already know. Or you might be trying to tell us that this elephant was even bigger than is usual for elephants. If you mean the former, you ought to leave out the "big," and if you mean the latter, you must say something else to make it clear.

Of the adjectives which are precise and could add something to a sentence, the danger is that they will proliferate. "Rose," "scarlet," "crimson," and "cardinal" are good words. But some writers will reach for "scarlet" or "crimson" whenever they mean "red." Not every noun requires an adjective to be complete. Few nouns require a string of fancy figures in adjective form. See how the sentence reads with the gold-plated adjective.

Adverbs.

Most adverbs are up to no good. Verbs are the source of strength in sentences. Because adverbs limit verbs, adverbs weaken sentences.

Adverbs not only enfeeble sentences, but they also indicate wrong verbs. We have seen that there are many verbs we should prefer to "moved quickly." We want "ran" or "raced," or "sprang" or "jumped," or perhaps "spun" or "whirled." If we realize we have written something as empty as "moved quickly," we will correct ourselves. But such weaknesses are hard to spot.

We can spot weaknesses by looking for the bad old adverb—in this case "quickly." The bad old adverb props up an impotent verb.

The "tightly" of "held tightly" is a tattletale. It indicates that "held" is the wrong verb. We want "grasped" or "clasped" or "clutched." "Smiled broadly" should be "grinned," and we will realize that when we see the bad old adverb "broadly." A way of finding imprecise verbs is to look for adverbs. A few vague verbs will transpire such a dragnet, but not many. Moreover, this method will turn up redundant adverbs; we will find that someone has "raced swiftly," which suggests that a less-motivated person might have "raced slowly."

Not all bad old adverbs are attached to verbs. In one manuscript I found I had written that my dog Lizbeth was "apparently ferocious." "Apparently" was redundant because "ferocious" means "apparently fierce." "Seemingly," "apparently," and similar adverbs express the suspicion that the appearance and the fact differ. If no suspicion exists, these adverbs serve only to weaken writing.

Moreover, many adverbs are what is called in commerce weasel words: "practically," "rather," "virtually," "mostly," "usually," "somewhat." The purpose of these words is to weaken sentences (and as such they do have some legitimate uses, as when an instructor hopes to remind students that he is speaking in generalities, or that rules have some exceptions). Overly cautious writers sprinkle their prose with these weakening words. Curiously, some adverbs that were invented to strengthen expressions now have a weakening effect too because they have been overused: "very," "much," "great," "extremely," and so forth.

Although little could be written without some adverbs, most of the adverbs a beginner puts on paper should be eliminated, either outright or by revising the verb to which they are attached.

Other parts of speech.

Some attention must be given to other parts of speech: the function words and words that make up phrases.

Function words such as "when," "while," "where," and "there" are invariably stronger if used in their literal senses. "While" is best used to mean "at the same time as"; "when" is best used to express time; "where" and "there" are stronger if used to refer to physical places.

Many writers have pet words or phrases that need to be deleted almost every time they occur. "Just" is a problem for some writers. When it does not mean "fair," it may mean nothing. Technically, the useless "just" may be an adverb, but may not be recognized as such because it is so empty. "Just" is a bad habit that some writers have. Other writers have other bad habits that they should learn to watch out for. In other cases, wordiness results from simple carelessness, from not paying attention to what is being written.

Considerable wordiness is contained in phrases. "At first light," for example, should be "at dawn." Sometimes lengthy phrases are almost empty of meaning. For example: "Many of the popular porn stars are short" says nothing more than "Many popular porn stars are short." The "of the" has almost no meaning, and "of the" occurs in many wordy expressions.

Examples:

While red roses are common, some roses are white.

("While" here does not really have anything to do with time. *Better:* Although many roses are red, some are white, *or:* Red roses are common, but some roses are white.)

While I showered, Jack undressed.

(Appropriate use of "while.")

One of the drivers behind us sounded his horn.

("One of the" means "a." *Better:* A driver behind us sounded his horn.)

"Jimmy is there among my memories..."

("There" is no real place and adds nothing to the meaning. *Better:* Jimmy is among my memories...")

"Today as I sit here in front of the window..."

(As "in front of the window" specifies where you are, "here" is meaningless. Probably "Today" adds nothing because we know the time meant is when the writer sits by the window. *Better:* As I sit in front of the window...)

Phrases containing "manner," "method," "fashion," and "way" may be better translated to adverbs. The adverbs, in turn, must be treated with the suspicion due all adverbs. "Moved in a quick manner" is simply the bad old "moved quickly" in disguise. Other phrases do not use any of the words above, but amount to the same thing. "With quickness" may be another form of "quickly."
Examples:

"in a strange manner" might be "strangely"
"in a careful way" might be "carefully"
"in a mindless fashion" might be "mindlessly"
"with passion" might be "passionately"

and so forth.

4. *Revision*

For most writers, revision is a necessary part of production. I want to emphasize, however, the importance of revision as a way of learning. New writers produce flawed work not because they are slovenly, and sometimes not even because they lack knowledge of writing, but most often because they are unable to perceive the flaws. And while they see nothing wrong with their work, they are unwilling to change a word. Some new writers think they have revised a work when they have checked it for spelling errors and typos.

I can—and will—provide several examples of revisions, but no one can learn what revision is without practicing it on his or her own work. Learning revision is the process of learning to perceive flaws in your work. At first it is difficult to find anything wrong. The writer knew what he meant, put it on paper as best he could, and since it was the best he could do, he sees no way it could be done better. In this early stage, if he is to learn revision at all, the writer must look through his work to see where he has written things that are like the bad examples in the book. Then he must mechanically make changes like those suggested in the book, whether or not he really understands the reasons for the changes, and regardless of his feeling that his work was pretty much okay to begin with.

This process alone can advance a writer only so far. The writer will not see errors unless they are very like the bad examples in the book, and no book can provide enough examples to cover all the variations of error. With practice, however, the writer will come to see errors in his work which are not precisely the same as those illustrated by bad examples in the book, but which violate the principles the examples in the book are meant to illustrate. At this point, the writer should begin to compose a book of his own bad examples. As the weaknesses of writers differ, the writer must become a specialist in overcoming the weaknesses which are most pronounced in his own writing.

After so many revisions, the writer may learn to stop himself as he is putting a flawed construction on paper; and then, perhaps after much more revision, he will not have to stop himself because the flawed construction will no longer occur to him. In truth, very few writers reach the point where they need no revision at all. But most do learn to avoid their more serious blunders altogether.

Many readers of this book are not quite so green as that hypothetical new writer. Most students can revise, if only they will do so. Of course, not every revision results in a publishable manuscript. But every revision ought to result in learning to revise better. For this reason, it is worth practicing revision even when publication of the material is not contemplated. I advised writers to practice writing with trivial pieces, and trivial pieces are ideal for practicing revision. If you have not learned the benefits of revision from practicing on pieces that you are relatively indifferent to, you may not be able to apply the knife to a work about which you have strong feelings.

I suggest that writers who use computers practice their first revisions on double- or triple-spaced printouts. I think it is useful to see the original wording along with the revision and to see whole pages of corrections at once. When you begin to make revisions without paper, I think it is instructive to save the uncorrected original files for comparison with the revisions (as well as for backup).

As a goal of revision, most beginners should aim to reduce the word count of their work by about 30 percent without altering or sacrificing sense. That is, you should be able to say everything you said in about 30 percent fewer words. Sometimes, of course, stronger expressions require more words that weaker ones, and brevity, of and for itself, is not the goal. But most weaknesses in beginners' writings are wordy, and a 30 percent reduction is a realistic and desirable goal for almost all beginners.

Some writers work by expanding outlines or sketches so that successive drafts contain more words. But these are not revisions. The revision is what is done to the story once all of its elements are in place. Something is wrong with a revision that does not reduce the word count.

In the hopes that writers will be motivated to attempt the performance of similar acts, I offer the following example of a word-by-word revision. As drafted:

A good editor can save an author considerable embarrassment. One of the editor's jobs is to correct errors in the author's manuscript without doing damage to variations in usage which could reasonably be considered to be literary style and without harming the special voices of narrator and the characters. Since some editors are not so good as others, authors must make every effort to make the manuscript as consistent and as nearly perfect as can be. If an error in print reproduces an error in the manuscript, the author has no one to blame but himself. (96 words.)

In the first sentence, we notice the adjective "good." "Good" belongs to a suspect group of adjectives. It must prove necessary or be eliminated. In this sentence it is not necessary. Any editor can save. Good ones do. We could simply strike out the "good." However, the most important thing we can do with any sentence is to improve its verb. Verbs with auxiliaries are, in general, weaker than verbs without auxiliaries. In this example, "saves" would be stronger than "can save." If we leave the "good" in, we can substitute "saves" for "can save," and this is what we choose to do. The "considerable" is also suspect, but let us move on.

The second sentence is horrid. Clearly, "correct errors" is redundant. A good editor would not correct anything except errors. We should strike "errors in." In "doing damage to," we recognize "do," which is another verb, like "make" and "take," to watch out for. "Do" is coupled with the abstract noun "damage." Clearly, this sentence would be improved if we could incorporate the sense of this abstract noun into the verb. This is done easily because "damage" is itself also a verb. We substitute "damaging" for "doing damage to." "Could reasonably be considered to be" is a weasely construction for which we substitute "are considered." "Narrator" requires an article, and we always try to use the definite article "the" when we can. Insert "the." "Special" is another suspect adjective. The voices in a work of fiction are necessarily special. We delete "special." As we have decided that we are writing about a good editor, we do not suspect him of doing harm, so "harming" is changed to "altering." The verb of this sentence is "is." We cannot make it "crashes" or "explodes," but we can make it "includes," which is a little stronger than "is." But to do so we must drop the "One of." This is just as well. "One of" is a phrase that can and should be cut every time it occurs. That makes "jobs" become "job." We cannot do without the adjective "literary" of "literary style," because we must distinguish it from "editorial style."

In the third sentence, we see immediately that "make every effort to" has to go. We have written "must" which in itself already means "make every effort to" and then some. The sentence is in two clauses of the form "since this, as a consequence that." Delete "since" and change the comma to a semicolon. This works better if it is not done too often. Now the problem is that "authors" are working on "the manuscript." "An author" is the solution. Then it should be "he can" at the end, which is stronger than "can be."

We relax a bit for the final sentence. It is the topic sentence, and it is in one of the two places (first and last) a topic sentence can occur. "Has" is too weak a verb to remain. "May blame" is not very strong because it includes the auxiliary verb "may," but it is certainly stronger than "has." So we write "may blame no one," rather than "has no one to blame."

The paragraph as revised:

A good editor saves an author considerable embarrassment. The editor's job includes correcting the author's
manuscript without damaging variations in usage which
are considered literary style and without altering the
voices of the narrator or the characters. Some editors are
not so good as others; an author must make the manuscript
as consistent and as nearly perfect as he can. If an error
in print reproduces an error in the manuscript, the author
may blame no one but himself. (79 words.)

Ninety-six words have been reduced to seventy-nine. That is
a reduction of only about 18 percent, but this author is not a
beginner.

Real writers really do revise. A practiced writer thinks hard to
remember the reasons for making changes such as have been
demonstrated. He revises more quickly than he can explain.
Seasoned writers do not commit such atrocities to paper in the first
place. They have internalized many of the principles of strong
writing. New writers gain this ability by practicing revision.

Some revisions:

I simply went to my knees...
I knelt...

I allowed my tongue to caress...
I licked...

Bob's face muscles tightened.
Bob grimaced.

He sent his tongue to guide his mouth down its...
He lapped...

My hand moved to his belt and zipper.
I unbuckled and unzipped him.

(With one exception, beware of body parts which seem to act of their own accord.)

Their lips touched and mouths opened.
They kissed.

Brownstonelike structures...
Brownstones, row houses, tenements, *or* town houses

fair, tanned skin
sunbrowned skin (hard to know what the author meant)

Ending up out here in the middle of nowhere with no car and no money...

"Here" is often redundant, and it is in this example. "Ending up" is misleading because the story does not end (on the contrary it is just beginning) and "middle of nowhere" is a cliché. "With no car and no money" can be stated positively by "without a car." The parallelism can be expressed explicitly by repeating the preposition "without." *Revision:* Stuck without a car and without money so far from anywhere I wanted to be...

I could only imagine that his chest was covered with the same luxuriant fur.

"Only" is misplaced. The speaker could do many things other than imagine, but he means that if he imagines he will imagine only one thing. "Luxuriant" is an overreaching adjective. *Revision:* I could imagine only that his chest was covered with the same thick fur.

I was sitting on the hood of my car, watching the new applicants gather outside the foreman's trailer.

The simple past tense is stronger than the progressive past. In this case there is no good reason to use the progressive past. The phrase at the end of the sentence is too far removed from the part it modifies. *Revision:* I sat on the hood of my car and watched the...

It didn't take long for my eyes to adjust to the darkness.

"It" is empty, standing for no noun in this sentence or in any previous sentence. *Revision:* My eyes soon adjusted to the darkness.

He let out a soft moan.
The verb is constructed poorly. Revision: He moaned softly.

I was in my bedroom, resting on my unmade double bed and wearing nothing but a pair of Jockey shorts.
The verb of the sentence is the puny "was" but two stronger verbs are available. "Nothing but" can be state positively by "only." *Revision:* In only a pair of Jockey shorts I rested on my unmade double bed.

Our first encounter was when he came to install my cable.
Use "encounter" as a verb to replace the weak "was." *Revision:* I first encountered him when he came to install my cable.

I'm responsible for keeping clean towels in the locker room, soap in the showers, and I also have to mop up the place and lock up after the pool closes.
The parallel ideas can be expressed in more nearly parallel structures. *Revision:* I keep clean towels in the locker room and soap in the showers. After the pool closes, I mop and lock up.

So much for the formalities, I thought to myself, trying to dispel the jitters.
Barring telepathy, all thoughts are to oneself. "To myself" should be deleted. How this thought might dispel the jitters is not clear.

Once settled, the lights went out and the curtains opened.
The phrase "once settled" can apply to nothing in the sentence. *Revision:* After we were settled in our seats, the lights went out and the curtains opened.

I could hardly believe how well it worked—no one had seen me enter.

"How well it worked" is restated or defined by "no one had seen me enter." A better punctuation would be to substitute a colon for the dash.

He had that classic swimmer's build, so finely chiseled, with the effortless, masculine grace of a dancer.

Here the author means to say something about the gentleman's physique and also about the way the gentleman moved. Unfortunately, the sentence he wrote says the gentleman's build was chiseled with grace. The author was not paying attention, as rereading would show. *Revision:* He had a classic, finely chiselled build, and he moved with the effortless grace of a dancer.

The barber whom I'd guessed was Clint from the name on the window of the shop wielded his scissors and comb.

This is carrying open punctuation a step too far. The barber is not wielding his scissors from the window. *Revision:* The barber, who I'd guessed was Clint from the name on the window of his shop, wielded his scissors and comb.

Some revised paragraphs.

The following are the first and last paragraphs of a published work of fiction as they were drafted. As an exercise, revise them. The published versions of the paragraphs follow immediately.

It's—it's just you go around, getting by however you do, and thinking you are beginning to get the hang of things. Then suddenly, something happens and you have to face the fact that there are great big forces, moving in the night. You can't call them good or bad, right or wrong; they are forces which can crush you in an instant and don't care whether they do or not. One of them opened a yellow eye in the dimness. And that was Les and Jesse.

Jesse, struggling back up the dune, I saw his head first, the open mouth and his hair stringy. And he hauled himself onto the dune. He hadn't buckled his trousers. He just clasped them up into the dripping red spot at his groin. The moon set behind him and stood there heaving dry heaves.

You get by however you do. You think you are beginning to get the hang of things. Then—suddenly—you realize something is out there in the darkness. A yellow eye opened in the dimness That was what was between Al and Jesse.

Only his head cleared the dune. He slid back in the sand. Then there was the flash and rust of Al's blade in Jesse's hand. Then his head and torso above the dune, silhouetted against the moon, facing the wind from the sea and clasping his shorts up against his groin.

Each word of a work of gay erotica is a spear for the eyes or groin or gut or heart of straight society. Make every word as sharp as you can.

5. *Techniques of Fiction*

Just as writing for publication differs from ordinary writing, the construction of a story for publication requires techniques beyond those needed in telling an anecdote among friends.

The power of suggestion.

Suggestion makes fiction work. Use suggestion in description, dialect, characterization: in every important aspect of the story.

When a cartoon character stands in front of a cartoon brick wall, only two or three of the bricks are drawn in. The two or three suggest all the rest of the bricks in the wall. The viewer has adapted his perception to the necessary conventions of cartoons. The viewer knows, (whether he knows he knows or not) that he must invest single lines with much meaning.

The cartoon character's eye is nothing more than a dot and an arc, his nose is a semicircle, and his mouth is a little squiggle. That is all the cartoon character has with which to represent the whole range of facial expressions. The cartoon viewer must be alert to very small differences in these, if he is to understand what the character's facial expressions represent.

If all the other bricks of the cartoon wall were drawn in, the viewer's powers of interpretation would be worked overtime to no good purpose. All those other lines really mean nothing; but while the viewer is discovering this, she is distracted from the subtle differences in the lines that do mean something. The two or three bricks suggest the wall as well without distracting from that little extra line in the character's forehead that means he is concentrating deeply.

Similarly, readers have adapted themselves to the conventions of prose. Conventions are necessary and reasonable. The reader does not analyze or even recognize conventions when he reads them. He accepts—until a clumsy writer mishandles something, overexplains, or deliberately exposes the machinery in an experimental work.

Few writers feel capable of writing a complete description of anything, and no reader would want to read one. Suggestion was fully developed before modern physics showed the inherent impossibility of describing anything completely, anyway.

To establish a medicine cabinet: An empty razor blade dispenser, a half bottle of mouthwash, a thermometer stood in a dusty glass. Complete catalogs of medicine cabinets have been written by Joseph Hansen, J. D. Salinger, and William Burroughs (I think). Whatever the purpose of those inventories, a medicine cabinet is as well created with three items as with dozens. The verisimilitude of the medicine cabinet does depend on the accuracy of the items.

The medicine cabinet is improved, not by adding dental floss and hemorrhoid remedies, but by saying that the mouthwash was amber and that the razor blade dispenser was for double-edged blades that would not fit the razor handle on the toilet tank. Naturally, such items are better when they contribute something to an understanding of the person who occupies the premises or contribute in another way to the story.

Some items, like Sherlock Holmes's Persian slipper, in which he kept his tobacco, acquire a life of their own. Not everything your characters use or touch has that quality. If your character has a place to live with a bathroom, and if he goes about in society without giving offense, we will assume that he has the usual toilet facilities and that he uses them. In other words, there may be no good reason to bring his medicine cabinet into it.

Similarly, you may show us what sort of person your character is by the way he acts in a few situations. We may or may not need to know the state of his relationship with his parents or his boss or the corner newsdealer. We do not have to have the history of his life, nor even a complete account of his daily activities to know what sort of person he is.

The radio-play theory of fiction.

Although the writer must avoid ambiguities that lead to confusion or nonsense, the ambiguity of language helps to create fiction. The writer describes something he sees vividly, something close to him, or something made of bits and pieces of things he has seen. Because language is ambiguous, the writer cannot describe the thing exactly. The thing the reader reads about becomes something close to the reader, something the reader has seen, or something made of bits and pieces of things the reader has seen.

Creative ambiguity is a key to fiction. The reader envisions the thing vividly, but he does not envision exactly the same thing the writer had in mind. The author who says, "But that was not what I meant," admits his incompetence or his ignorance of the principle of story telling. Like all powerful forces, ambiguity can be respected, controlled, and put to creative use, or it can be ignored, treated carelessly, and allowed to work destruction.

The writer needs to develop the ability to read his own work, not only recalling what he meant, but also ascertaining what the words could mean to others. To eliminate alternate readings is unnecessary, undesirable, and simply impossible. What is desirable is to remove the nonsense.

When a character is drawn with only suggestion, only a few details, ambiguity can work to the writer's advantage. This is the radio-play theory of fiction:

> Sandy blond, kinky hair, evident hard-on in his gray pants, bare-chested, some muscles but not too many, red fuzz on a little bit of belly. Stance saying "I'm just a regular guy and not too impressed with myself." He had stuck a rolled sandwich bag in the groove that curved between his torso and upper thigh. Through the silvery layers of plastic, I could see the bile-green herb.

"I could be mistaken," he said quickly.

"Oh?"

His erection arched hopefully—involuntarily, I thought—in the baggy gray fabric. "Nancy said you might help me."

I expect our narrator will help him. I expect many people would be happy to help him. But his description does not really tell us much about his looks. He could be any of the dozens of guys the reader has seen or known. He could be any curly-haired blond with a moderate build that the reader is interested in, that the reader wishes he could get hold of. That is the point. Or:

Mike's a real skinny guy. He's got little black hairs on his chest that kink up in knots. But the major impression is skinny. Until he drops his jeans. Which he doesn't do until about two seconds before he cuts off the light and hops in bed. While he was gone to class, I went into his dresser to look. This brand of underwear, I never heard of it, comes from a surgical-supply place. It has extra fabric in the crotch.

Later, in case the reader has somehow missed the point, mention will be made that Mike has a great big cock. Now, is Mike white or black? The reader will imagine whichever he pleases, because nowhere in the story that follows will the author say.

A character has to have a handle, something the reader can hold on to. Mike has a great big one. It could be a tattoo, an extremely prominent muscle group, a combination of hair and eye color, a way of dressing or of being undressed, a characteristic type of speech. Whatever it is, it has to be drawn clearly so that the reader can hang everything else he learns or imagines about the character on it.

In *The Bridge of San Luis Rey*, one of Thornton Wilder's characters had "a leprous affection on one cheek and a complementary adjustment of rouge on the other." Her red wig was askew, too, if memory serves. Having read that description, who is likely to forget the Marquesa de Montemayor? Naturally, something more attractive is desired for the lead in a work of erotic fiction.

Another example:

Jess claimed to be half Mexican. He had straight black hair but his body was light enough to freckle. He said "aunt" like a New Englander and couldn't tell if you called him a sonofabitch in Spanish.

He was about 6'4"—near enough to Al that they would stand back-to-back and ask who was the taller. If I could tell, I would not say. They measured their reaches against one another, standing at arm's length, patting each other's cheeks and pulling each other's sideburns—though the hair on Jess's face was sparse.

Now, is Jess broad-shouldered? Narrow-waisted? Well muscled? Smooth-chested? Brown-eyed? Well hung? More than likely he is all of that. He is a big, strong guy, and whether he or Al is the bigger and stronger is important to him. This last is indispensable to the story. The rest can be left to the reader's imagination.

Critic Stan Leventhal believes that detailed physical description is essential to a work of gay erotica. Since we know that the visual aspect is important in male sexual arousal, his theory cannot be dismissed. Having exhausted my modest library looking for something to steal for an example, however, I think the theory is not commonly put to practice.

Sometimes several paragraphs are devoted to describing one feature. In such cases the rest of the character's description is sketched lightly. Some authors continue describing their characters, bit by bit, throughout the story. The danger is that the author will put in something that contradicts the image the reader has formed. While each detail of description will add an appeal for some readers, it will also run against the tastes of others. Beauty is in the eye of the beholder. Leave it there.

In spare writing, the scene need not be set in great detail. If the weather does not matter, do not give it a whole paragraph. If it is a beautiful spring day, do not give us four or five paragraphs on the greenness of it all and the birds and the flowers without portraying the effect of the atmospheric conditions on the nether regions of your protagonist. If your character has taken off gloves, a hat, an overcoat, and galoshes, we will not need a mention to be convinced that the weather is frightful. If the weather is to play an active role in your story—for example, if your characters are to be stranded by it—more than a mention will be required.

Things that will be used may well be introduced in the setting. Lamps that will be turned off, fans that convey smells, and sources of background music will sometimes be better if they are established before they are used. Do not place a lamp for the sake of light alone. Readers will assume there is some source of light if your characters see each other. If you do introduce the source of the light, whether it is track lighting, a bare bulb with a string, a goosenecked lamp, or a fluorescent tube turning pink and flickering, let it not only give light but also tell us where we are, and if we are in an apartment, let it tell us whose apartment this is.

Plastic Tiffany-style lampshades. Antiqued mirrors. Flocked red-and-gold wallpaper. Scarlet carpet.

That—in two lines—is an apartment. Haven't we all had a regrettable experience in such an apartment? Didn't we know it was going to be regrettable the moment we saw the anthurium and bamboo bouquet in the entry? Why did we know there would be Beardsley prints and a bidet in the bathroom? Why do our mouths taste of cheap scotch when we think of it?

Remember where things are. Do not eclipse a gibbous moon or make a nearly new one rise at midnight. (These are astronomically impossible events.) If you write of a real intersection in a real city that your readers may have visited, put the bar on the correct corner. Quick: In which pocket does a right-handed man keep his change? If a nude person produces a twenty-five-cent piece, the reader certainly will be curious.

A good work of fiction meets the reader at his own level. The surface story can hardly be drawn too strongly. Characters must be clear on the surface. No essential aspect may puzzle the reader—that is, the situation must be understood, although it may be a situation involving a mystery. Suggestion can create the surface level because the surface details are drawn with heavy strokes. When you draw the whorish apartment, go lightly over the bronzed baby shoes on the dresser. Amid the red lava lamps, the leather sheets, and the sexual toys, they will go unnoticed by some.

A poet once wrote: "Uproar on the right; attack on the left." So it is with fiction. When the uproar on the surface is sufficient, you can cover many levels of meaning. Write "biker" or "cowboy" or "lumberjack," and you create in some readers an image so strong that you can contradict it safely in the rest of the story. This will amuse other readers and possibly provide them with some food for thought. A general once said, "When you have them by the balls, their hearts and minds will follow." This advice is a much sounder guide to erotica than to warfare.

All of this is to say that you cannot round a character unless you have established him well first. Deep in every cynic is a romantic; if he did not have his romantic streak, he would never have been disappointed often enough to become cynical. The attractive aspect of macho types is that they do have their softer spots; no one really wants to make love with a rock. But if you show us the tenderer spots first, we will not know that your character is supposed to be a macho type; and if we first find him in a pensive, romantic mood, we will not understand that you mean for us to see a hard-boiled, cynical detective.

In a way, suggestion is trickery. The object is not to fool the reader, but to entertain him. The craft of a sleight-of-hand magician is similar to that of a pickpocket. But the one has an audience while the other has victims. Try to make an audience of your readers.

As an exercise, add sufficient narration to the following dialogue to make an erotic story of it:

"Please don't hurt me."

"What makes you think I'm going to hurt you?"

"That look in your eye."

"Don't you know what that is?"

"Maybe. Please don't hurt me."

"If you thought I was going to hurt you, why did you come out here?"

"Don't know. Look, I don't have any money."

"Take off your shirt."

"What for?"

"For what you came out here for."
"I'm too skinny."
"You want me to contradict you?"
"That tickles."
"Shut up."
"No! What if someone comes out here."
"No one is coming out here."
"Look, this is a mistake. I'm going back in."
"No mistake."
"Let me go."
"No."
"Oh, don't. I'll lose it."
"Go ahead. That's what you came out here for."
"I won't want to do anything back."
"Then me first."
"No. I don't want to."
"Sure you do."
"Don't force me."
"Take it."
"Not like this. Not here. We'll go somewhere."
"I don't believe you."
"Okay. Just don't force me. I'll gag."
"Get to it, then."

"Why did you stop?"
"You were going to."
"Yeah."
"I don't... I can't..."
"Take it."
"Ouch. You're hurting me."
"That's right. Now get it."
"There. Are you happy now?"
"Yeah."
"No. Don't do that. Just hold on to me a minute."
"Let me have it."
"No. Please. Let me do it myself."
"Shut up."
"You're ruining it."

"Just lean back and shut up."

"Oh, just look. Look what you did to my shirt. I hate you."

"I'm here every Tuesday."

"Really?"

When this exercise appeared in the first edition of this book, a few editors accused me of being disingenuous, saying that they would have printed the dialogue as a story just as it was and that I must have known that it was a story in itself. This merely proves the point about suggestion. We have no idea what these characters look like and only a general idea of what they are doing. We do not know where they are, except that there is some possibility that they might be interrupted.

Yet I do not doubt that readers will immediately perceive this radio play as a story.

Now, when you have completed the exercise, check your work with the following questions:

What was the handle on the first speaker?

What was the handle on the second speaker?

Where does the dialogue take place?

Did you introduce any subtleties in characterizing either speaker or in describing the setting that goes against stereotype?

You may wish to review and revise this scene after considering the chapters on dialogue and on the erotic scene. At those times, revise the dialogue itself if necessary.

Needless to say, not every writer writes prose so spare as the radio play theory of fiction suggests. But no one can do without suggestion. Some writers do succeed who give lush—even purple—descriptions of their principal characters, but the only way such a writer can ever complete a story or novel is by suggesting other elements, by skimping on descriptions of incidental characters or the setting.

Climactic order.

The most important, interesting, and exciting parts of the work should come as near the end as possible. The high point of the work is the climax. The arrangement that puts the climax near the end is called climactic order.

The ideal of climactic order as taught in schools is often simplified. Tension is pictured as growing in a straight line to a peak, which is the climax. Beyond the climax, tension drops off sharply in the brief (one hopes) space between the climax and the end of the story. If we number the events in the story from the least dramatic (1) to the most dramatic (6), this simplified view of climactic order would have the parts of the story ordered: 1, 2, 3, 4, 5, 6,*; where * represents the little downward tail between the climax and the end of the story.

This simplified view may be sufficient for students who are studying the works of others; but as a model for construction of a story or novel, it is inadequate.

The first part of the work must be strongly interesting to persuade the reader to continue reading the story. This part is sometimes called "the hook," and commonly is second only to the climax in dramatic impact. Thus, a better model of climactic order would be: 5, 1, 2, 3, 4, 6,*; that is, with the second-highest level of tension at the beginning, and the highest level at the climax.

Even so, one further refinement is necessary to produce a working model of climactic order. Although overall the story should build up to the climax from a low point just after the hook, action, interest, and tension do not build up smoothly, but in a saw-toothed pattern. At each event in the story, things do not proceed directly to the next-higher level, but there is a little relaxation before the ascent to the next peak. This is most evident in novels, where each chapter reproduces, in miniature, as it were, the climactic order of the whole work. Episodes in a short story should behave the same way.

Climactic order, in other words, governs not only the work as a whole, but each of the parts and subdivisions. Climactic order should be observed in ordering words in a sentence (as far as syntax will allow), sentences in a paragraph, paragraphs in a chapter or episode, as well as in ordering chapters in a book or episodes in a short story. Climactic order is as important to ballads, lyrics, essays, and memos as it is to short stories and novels.

The writer, if properly advised, will often hear that stories should have a beginning, a middle, and an end. Most of the content of that advice is that stories should follow climactic order. Stories begin with a high point—a point of interest or importance. Stories have a middle in which tension, conflict, or interest build. Stories end with the dramatic climax: the resolution of the conflict introduced at first.

At the story or novel level, the climax may be followed by a little tail in which the loose ends of the story are tied up and the heroes ride off into the sunset. Such housekeeping must be kept brief. Sometimes the tail ends in a little stinger that points back to the climax.

The climactic order of the whole is reproduced in each of the lesser structures. Consider this passage from "Smuggler's Moon":

> What I recall: At one point, a body fell past the window. George made Al stop playing mumblety-peg, saying it would ruin Al's bowie knife. That might be so, but I expect George wanted to save his precious floor. Dan puked on the floor anyway—a good, explosive shot which surprised him as much as anyone. And one of George's blue antique bottles, which is what he calls anything he scavenges on the beach, was tossed out of the window.
>
> Afterward we didn't find the body where it would have landed—or the bottle, for that matter. What we did find, as things came back into focus, was Jess in Al's bunk.

The passage begins with a grabber: the body falling past the window. In another story, this might well be the most important thing, but not here. What is the most important thing in this passage? Jess in Al's bunk. It is right where it belongs. Not only is the most important thing at the end of the passage, it is also at the end of a paragraph and the end of a sentence.

In some circles, who wakes up with whom is not a matter of great significance. The author is telling the reader, whether the reader understands consciously or not, that this is a very important fact of the story.

The story is a tragedy in which the bowie knife plays a part.

Mention of the bowie knife is necessary in some early passage, such as this one, but too much attention is not desirable. The knife is placed right after the grabber, in the most inconspicuous spot possible.

Did the author really think about such things when he wrote the passage? Does the Queen Mother squat to pee?

Unfortunately, there are technical limitations in what can be done with climactic order and structure. One limitation is the shape of paragraphs on the page. A typewritten line becomes about two lines in a magazine column, but sets up as only about one line in a book. A reader is intimidated by a paragraph that sets up as many more than five or six lines. The first paragraph of the passage above would have set up as more than twenty lines in a normal magazine column: much too large a block of type.

Fortunately for the author, his editor was the ever-alert Aaron Travis, who had the story set in double-wide columns. The reader does not make the adjustment from magazine columns of normal size to double-wide columns or to book pages. Ten or twelve lines look gray and formidable, however wide they are. A speech of three or more lines looks like an oration. The principle of climactic order would be better shown if the paragraphs above were run together. But the appearance would be ungainly, even in double-wide columns.

On the other hand, a succession of short speeches which looks good in a magazine may appear on the book page to be fighting a losing battle against a blizzard of white.

English syntax forbids perfecting climactic order in the sentence. No doubt the charm of Caesar's Latin owes something to his putting the verb where it belongs, at the end of the sentence. The writer of English seldom can.

Introductory phrases such as "however," "finally," "on the other hand," and similar literary throat clearing, when not deleted altogether, ought to be pushed into the sentence so that a more important element can take first place:

However, the bullet missed Kyle's head by...
The bullet, however, missed Kyle's head by...
The bullet missed Kyle's head by an inch.

Frank anastrophe seldom achieves the desired effect. Do not resort to the passive voice for the sake of climactic order:

not: Kyle's head was missed by the bullet.
not: Red and slick with Bill's spit, it glistened.
not: The bullet aimed for Kyle's head, by a mere inch, missed.
okay: The bullet aimed for Kyle's head missed.

How much strain with the syntax bear before it snaps? Better to err on the conservative side because when it snaps, it thunders.

Plotting.

The analogy between climactic order and the history of a single sexual encounter is obvious. The beginning is interesting and sets up the problem of the story: one character is attractive, and the other is horny. The middle is building: a promising glance, a chance meeting, rising hope and desire played against the chance of rejection or worse. The end is the climax: the physical sex with its physical climax. The brief tail: they wave good-bye (or sometimes they move in together and live happily ever after). As far as the story line is concerned, even the most oblivious hack pornographer can hardly go wrong.

Similar formulas exist for other genres. The murder mystery begins with interest (at least for mystery readers): a dead body, usually found in perplexing circumstances. In the middle are the less interesting details: engaging the detective, her apparently fruitless inquiries, introduction of the romantic interest (which is a less-interesting detail in a murder mystery); and then the building tension as the detective's discoveries seem to be adding up to something: someone is accused whom the reader knows or hopes to be innocent; the character the reader most suspects is himself murdered; a new discovery wrecks all previously plausible theories. Finally the climactic moment occurs: all the suspects are gathered in the drawing room, and the detective reveals both the culprit and the reasons everyone should have known his identity all along. Then there may be the tail: the romantic interest results in bliss and exits quickly.

In a formula murder mystery, the characters might have explicitly described sex. But a sexual climax is not the climax of a murder mystery. The only possible climax of a murder mystery is one that untangles the mystery; but solving all the murders in Los Angeles will not suffice in place of the sexual climax of an erotic story. Sex is a necessary part of a coming-out novel, but the sex does not resolve the conflict—more than likely, it leaves the protagonist more confused than ever. Scenes of carnage may occur in the war novel, but most war novels turn on something other than the course of the battle.

In fiction what is important is what the writer makes important.

Certainly the defeat of Hitler was very important. In our story, however, what goes on between two wounded GIs in a hospital far behind Allied lines may be more important. Our GIs are not deciding the fate of Europe. They are deciding whether their affair is just one of those wartime things or whether it something else, something they should continue.

Should Joe go back to Akron, marry the girl everyone expects him to marry, although (naturally) he now realizes he never cared for her. Or should he go to New York with Tim? There is no question of coming out of the closet: it is 1944. Tim is, you know, a bit on the flamboyant side, obviously artistic and sensitive. If Joe brought Tim home, everyone would know. The sensible thing to do would be to go back to Akron, be a foreman at Dad's plant, and try to forget Tim. That would be sensible. But Tim is beautiful. And devoted. And good in bed. Besides, Joe really knows about himself now. It would never be the same with a woman. No one in Akron—at least no one Joe knows— is like Tim.

Remember Hitler and the battle for Europe?

A philosopher could argue that in their own way Joe and Tim *are* as important as the defeat of Hitler. The author does not need to believe that proposition; neither need he convince the reader of it. This is Joe and Tim's book. The climax does not occur in the Führerbunker, the climax occurs on the *Queen Mary* as the evacuees sail for America.

The book does not open with arrows on a map of Europe, it opens in a hospital smoking lounge. Tim is giving himself a manicure. He has to stop every few seconds so he can get the light right to see what he is doing with his uninjured eye. In Europe, Tim is so small that you could not see the speck on the map. But in the hospital smoking lounge, he is one of the most important things—one of the few human beings there. Because he is manicuring his nails in his pajamas and has adjusted his eye patch to a jaunty angle, he is one of the most interesting things in the room.

"I wish you wouldn't do that," Joe says.

"Why not?"

"I mean, I wish you wouldn't do that while the guys are watching."

"Nonsense." Tim looks up and focuses his good eye on Joe. "Lots of men groom their nails."

"Not any men I know of. They just clip 'em off."

Now what Göring is saying to Hitler is the most irrelevant thing in the world.

The story turns on Joe's conflicts about what people will think and what masculinity really is. The eroticism of Joe and Tim's relationship will be portrayed in smoking-hot terms. That will not be the end of the story. The comeshot does not relieve the central tension *of the story,* which is Joe's problem in coming out. In fact, hot sex only seems to make things worse. If the sex were not very good, Joe would not have to confront his homosexuality; he could rationalize it away as just another kind of masturbatory release. Then Joe would not be confronted with the choice between going back to Annabelle in Akron and starting a new life with Tim in New York. There would be no story because there would be no conflict.

Of course, the opening could easily be adapted to make this a formula stroke piece. Then, the question would be only how Tim can get the hypermacho Joe into bed. Tim has a chance because men who are really straight, though they might keep their distance in the shower, would not confront him for doing his nails. The real rubes do not know what a faggot is. Joe knows, and he knows that faggots do their nails. Perhaps Joe knows a bit more than that.

The sexual climax is the end of that story because the central question is whether Joe really wants to be done. Now, if Joe decides in the last line to go to New York with Tim, it is icing on the cake: an improbability too rich to be swallowed. The groundwork for that decision has not been laid. Akron and New York are as much beside the point as Berlin and London.

A plot structure can violate climactic order in several ways:

Failure to introduce important, relevant elements at the beginning.

Strong, interesting openings are important (and can often be achieved by deleting the first two pages of the manuscript). All creative writing teachers advise: grab the reader's attention. But the opening must have something to do with the story and, like every other part of the story, must point to the climax. If it were not so, every story might as well begin with a train wreck at a nudist colony.

If a story opens with a murdered corpse in a locked room, that is interesting and exciting. Also, it tells the reader that it is the beginning of a mystery story, not the beginning of a romance. The climax must reveal how the deceased met his death in such circumstances. Grabbing the reader's attention under false pretenses is worse than starting slowly. The reader whose attention is grabbed by the corpse may get off when boy gets boy. He will not be satisfied until he knows whodunit.

In a whodunit, surprise is a relatively important element. The author of a mystery may surprise the reader in many ways. The culprit may be someone no one would suspect. Perhaps all the suspects conspired in the murder. The corpse may turn out be someone other than the supposed victim. It might be suicide made to look like murder, or even an accident that left misleading circumstances. Possibly the death was an elaborate fake, and no one is dead at all. The surprise cannot be that the narrator wakes up and discovers it has all been a dream—at least not before we learn who was guilty in the dream and why.

Stories do not have to belong any recognized genre. All that is necessary is that the story's climax follow, by however tortuous a route, from the story's beginning. In particular, a tragedy must be a tragedy from the first paragraph, preferably from the first line.

A story that begins with the firing on Fort Sumter is fairly obliged to proceed to Appomattox courthouse. A story that begins with Private Grenville's part in the firing on Fort Sumter, on the other hand, may well leave off when he and the Yankee drummer decide that they are done with the war and ride off into the setting sun.

Just as the essayist limits his thesis in his first paragraph, so the fiction writer must tell us in the beginning what is important to his story and must avoid misleading the reader by making too much of minor characters and incidents that have little to do with the story.

Beginning before the beginning.

The crack-of-dawn flaw in gay fiction most often occurs at the crack of noon. For some reason, new writers think we will not know the sun is up unless we saw it rise, or that we will think the protagonist is asleep and naked unless we wake and dress him.

Oliver Twist begins with the birth of a bastard. But *Oliver Twist* is a weighty tome. In a short story, we should choose to begin a little nearer the action. (Of course, Dickens did begin near his action, for his novel is about the situation of orphan children.) We will take it for granted that all characters were born, to circumstances more desirable or less, and that they had the usual and perhaps some unusual traumas of childhood. In particular we know that a gay childhood in America is not likely to have been characterized by unbounded bliss.

It is not that a character should have no history, but that the reader should be spared having *all* of it.

Naturally, the past has influenced aspects of the character's personality, and some of her actions may result from causes that have long preceded. Some of these events may be brought in at appropriate times. But not many stories will turn on what the character had for breakfast a week ago Monday or put on her toothbrush this morning.

A particularly trying device is that of the character who wakes disoriented. Usually authors do this to have a chance to describe the character's usual surroundings as if the character were seeing them for the first time. Of course, this is not a flaw if there is a reason connected with the story that the character wakes disoriented—perhaps he has been drugged and removed to a strange place.

Neither is it wrong to wake a character at the crack of dawn, if what wakens him is a call from a friend who is in desperate circumstances. Even so, we must not dwell on the brightness of the light on the white bathroom tiles and our hero's normal toilet functions, but we must get him to the scene as quickly as possible to discover what the matter is. If he is not immediately arrested for indecent exposure, we will know he put on his pants.

Failure to resolve the conflict of the story.

A writer is not obliged to solve all the problems of the world with a single tale. Neither does it need to be the case that everyone lives happily ever after. The writer must solve the dilemma that gives rise to the story.

> Let Jerry be money hungry. Poor in childhood, hating his poverty, determined to have money above all else. Perhaps Jerry had difficulty making money: he gets a little ahead and wastes it on a long shot, harebrained scheme that everyone else realizes is doomed to failure. Jerry ends up broke every time. Then Jerry meets Karl. Karl is built and has a huge cock. They go home and have the hottest possible sex ever after. The End.

That is not a short story. It certainly is not a novel. What about the money?

To make a story of it, perhaps Jerry was not deprived in childhood. Perhaps Jerry wanted money only because he thought that with money he could get a cute boyfriend. Then Karl is the solution. Or perhaps Jerry decides to use Karl's looks to get money, but thereby loses Karl or almost does. Perhaps he has to choose between Karl and money. Does he want Karl badly enough to give up his lifelong dream of riches? Can he stop scheming for money even if he wants to for Karl's sake? The dilemma introduced in the beginning of the story does not have to be static. It can be developed, even to the point that the resolution no longer has much to do with the original problem. What cannot be done is to shift ground on the reader at the last moment and present him with a pig when he thought he was after a hare.

We may begin with the question: Who killed Sir Reginald? At some point, we may discover that Sir Reginald is alive, and the questions become: Whose body was found? And who killed him? Likewise, we may never answer the question of whether Jerry gets money or not, but to avoid doing so we must develop the more basic question of what Jerry really wants.

Needless to say, money is a difficult problem that many writers wish they could solve. Difficult problems lead to another kind of climactic disorder.

Plot abortion.

Various kinds of plot abortion have been recognized for a long time. They have in common the easy way out. Plot abortion is especially common in stroke fiction where plot, too often, is a vestigial part attached to explicitly described sex; but plot abortion is not rare in works considered great literature and in the works of the masters.

Deus ex machina is the sudden arrival of help from an unlikely quarter that extricates the protagonist from his difficulties with little or no action on his part. (It means "the god out of the machine" and is a stage device used in ancient Greek and Roman theater by which a stage deity is lowered into a scene and solves all problems. Curtain.)

Suppose Jerry wins the lottery. Or a previously unmentioned uncle leaves Jerry a previously secret fortune. These are miraculous solutions to the problem of poverty, and the most Jerry did for himself was, in one case, to buy a lottery ticket. Such solutions are unsatisfying for several reasons. We are not convinced that Jerry deserves such a happy ending. Many people are poor, but few win the lottery or discover rich, recently deceased relatives: we do not see much insight into the problem of poverty here. And here the problem is not merely that Jerry is poor, but also that he is so desperate to escape poverty that he squanders what little money he does have trying to get rich. Neither solution deals with this latter aspect of the conflict, and the one that requires Jerry to buy a lottery ticket would encourage this flaw in Jerry's personality.

Either one of these miracles is an example of deus ex machina when it is offered as the solution to Jerry's problem. Another story, however, might begin with a person like Jerry winning the lottery. After all, some people do win the lottery, and a profound change of fortune, even if it is for the better, is likely to produce the elements of conflict. Unlikely events are perfectly permissible in fiction. Most science fiction is based on the premise that people and ships can be made to move faster than light, which is not only unlikely, but also theoretically impossible. The flaw of deus ex machina is in producing the unlikely event at the *end* of the story to *solve* the problem.

"He suddenly realized," is another form of plot abortion. With a change of pronoun, it was once very common in confession stories. What is wrong with "he suddenly realized" is the "suddenly." Jerry might come to realize that money is not the most important thing in life. But this change of heart should not appear out of nowhere on page nineteen of a twenty-page story. Something has to shake his faith in money; we have to see his doubt emerge; he must want something and find money useless for getting it, his doubt must grow, and he may finally have to choose between money—or the false dream of it—and something real that he wants. Having done the groundwork properly, the author will resist writing: "He suddenly realized…"

The direct approach, although often successful in fact, does not produce good fiction. If instead of wasting his efforts and his little money on get-rich-quick schemes, Jerry works hard, saves what money he can, and invests wisely, then by the time he is fifty he is well-to-do and unlikely ever to be in want again. So what? That describes accurately how many middle-aged gay men have come to have good homes and big cars. It is no story. Neither is the extremely common formula piece that goes something like this: Biff is horny and hunky and has a big cock. Bill is hunky and horny and has a big cock. They spot each other and immediately head to the bushes and have great sex.

Such pieces work only when the writers exert exceptional effort in describing the sex act. Since there is no space for characterization or a real plot, the reader has no particular reason to care that either of these hunks gets off—any more than he cares about the very similar hunks in the next story. This is a fictional equivalent of a photographic model posed in front of a plain backdrop. Only a very striking physique can make up for the lack of context. In such a story, only very vivid writing can keep the reader from flipping to the pictures. This is specialty work. Not everyone can do it, and not every one who can, can be happy doing it. After a while a writer must repeat himself. If you would be happy to write the same story over and over, you certainly can sell it over and over to several periodicals in the market.

Killing off inconvenient characters is just another form of deus ex machina. If news arrives that the plant in Akron blew up, wiping out Joe's fortune, family, and fiancée, that settles it. It is off to the Big Apple with the flaming one-eyed manicurist.

Bumping off characters is fine in its place. Some conflicts can be resolved only by a duel to the death. In mysteries it is customary for the murderer or monster to strike again. In tragedy the properly-set-up death of a major character is inherent in the form. Sudden death can tie up a minor loose end if it is removed from the central aspect of the story. But it is unfair to remove the central tension of the story by sending a massive coronary from heaven to your antagonist or a crosstown bus to kiss off whoever else gets in the way. If an inconvenient spouse must be removed, do so before the story begins.

Superb writing and good characterization can overcome a poor plot. After all, there is no such thing as a threadbare plot, there is only hackneyed writing. Yet writing is so difficult that no one should undertake it with a flawed design.

Although writers go about it in various ways, plotting is the least mysterious aspect of fiction. The creation of a suitable plot depends upon several elements. The plotless, pointless literary ramble is dead. Contrary to what some authorities teach, a short story is not primarily a character study. Before it is anything else, a short story is a story.

(I mean, of course, the finished short story. The story in the writing may indeed begin with a character study or with a plot outline or with a few pretty sentences or with a scrap of dialogue overheard on a bus or, as sometimes does happen, may spring from the author's head fully formed.)

The writer must have confidence in his ability. Plotting begins with supposing. Suppose Jerry is money hungry. Suppose Joe and Tim are in a military hospital. Suppose Mike is kidnapped. Writers prevent themselves from supposing such things if they doubt their ability to create a money-hungry character, a smoking lounge in a military hospital, or a gay private eye. Real writers suppose first and worry about how later. Assume you can carry it off. It is much the same thing as jumping into cold water. It will be a shock. It will be a struggle. You may cramp. But you won't drown. Probably not.

Many beginners have an overly elaborate idea of what plot is. The murder mystery is supposed to be heavily plotted. Here, the beginner thinks he might create a mystery that cannot be solved. The beginner (and some masters) will not write "Chapter One" until the castle and all of its secret passages are diagrammed, the biographies of all the principals are written, and a working model of the blowgun is constructed.

On the other hand, many working writers claim that they begin a mystery without a plot. That is not entirely true. All murder mysteries have a plot: a murder is committed; a culprit is brought to justice (or at least is detected). The mystery writer may begin without knowing who has been murdered, who committed the crime, or how the guilty party was found out. He does know that someone has to get murdered in Chapter One and that the crime will be solved in the last chapter.

If you undertake a coming-out novel you may begin without knowing much about your protagonist. What you do know is that in Chapter One he is a naïf and in the last chapter he is out, proud and gay. As you write, you will discover the natural hair color of his kindly protector, what tattoo the blackmailing hustler has, and whether the best friend from high school turns out to be gay, too.

The essence of plot is tension. Tension arises from conflict.

This is conflict in its broadest sense and on virtually any scale; it may be intergalactic warfare or it may be a slight discrepancy in a single individual's values. At some point the writer must know what the tension is and who the parties (or what the poles) of the conflict are. The tension must be resolved. The conflict must have a winner. In murder mysteries, romance, coming-out stories, stroke pieces—in many forms, the tension and the resolution are defined by the form. Certainly a writer does better to choose a proven path rather than sit idly and bemoan his lack of ideas.

The mystery writer often commits the crime in Chapter One with no good idea of the solution. By Chapter Ten, once he knows his suspects and the methods of his detective, he may see that Chapter One must be redrafted to include an essential clue. Has the writer wasted his time? Of course not. He has written the novel. Whether it would have been more efficient to diagram the castle before he started is a matter of opinion. It is work to do the one thing and work to do the other. In any event, writing well is work.

6. *Dialogue, Dialect, and Diction*

Dialogue is not realistic.

Real people stammer, pause, interrupt, and are interrupted for no good reason, repeat themselves, digress pointlessly, use wrong words, and misunderstand each other. In fiction characters have speech problems only on occasion. Aside from the character who does stammer, characters stammer for a reason: they are nervous or rattled. Real people stammer—perhaps for reasons of the unfathomable psychological kind—but apparently at random. One of the complaints of writers first attempting dialogue is "My characters do not sound natural."

Of course they do not. They should not.

Dialogue requires the illusion of naturalness. In this the reader is the writer's ally. The reader is not an ignoramus; he knows he is reading a story or a novel. He wants the author to spare him the tedium of transcription. Naturally, in a modern work of fiction characters do not speak in Shakespearean iambs; neither is every character consciously witty or unconsciously silly, as in the plays of Wilde or Sheridan. Characters express themselves well within the confines of their intellects, backgrounds, and situations. The author does not report everything they say.

Characters preparing for a dinner party ask each other where their cuff links are in order to establish that they are going to a dinner party. The entirety of such real discussions is not reported unless the nature of the characters' domestic relationship is the point.

A conversational game played by men in boxcars consists of trying to discover whether in their travels they have known the same person. This game consumes many hours which is, no doubt, why it is played. As a bit of business in a piece of fiction, the game goes:

"Where you coming from?"
"Knoxville."
"Yeah? I spent some time there myself. Around Oak Ridge. Stayed with the Maxwells. You know'm? Five brothers. All red haired. Hard to miss."
"Naw. I didn't get out that way much. I had a room on Gay Street. Stayed around town mostly."

Which stands for several hours of dull talk. If the story turns on their both knowing a person, they must discover it very quickly, or a passage indicating the passing of time may intervene. The whole conversation may be represented within a couple of pages, although a transcript of a similar real conversation might easily fill a book.

Readers of mysteries have a right to expect a number of irrelevancies. The housekeeper is interviewed. She volunteers her opinion of the moral character of the deceased. She tells whom she suspects. She accounts for her actions and observations proximate to the crime. In the end, it turns out that this interview was a school of red herring.

Elsewhere in fiction, the reader wants to know why he is being told all of this. If the reader cannot place the relevancy of the material, he needs at least a guide to its significance. Dialogue should reveal character or advance plot, preferably both at once. Readers know that. Faced with dialogue that does neither, they become frustrated.

Transcribed speech is full of irrelevancies, and what is pertinent is seldom underscored properly. When real characters meet, by chance or design, with good intentions or ill, lengthy inquiries about friends and kin are commonplace. So are meteorological speculations and many similar types of discussion. Where such ploys must be represented in fiction, they are suggested. So are the ahs, hems, and haws, wells, and you-knows of common speech. Fictional characters do have speech mannerisms. But as in dialect, less is more. A character may have a tendency to begin his speeches with "Hey," or "Well, pardner, ah'll tell ya," but most of the character's speeches do not begin that way. Even a character who stutters, stutters less in dialogue than in real life. Giving characters speech mannerisms will not bring them to life unless they are also given speeches in character.

Attribution.

Do not avoid the "Bill said" and the "Jack said" (or try to vary it by inversion: "said Ty"). Attribution is a convention that is almost invisible to the reader, as by convention the black-clad stagehands of Noh dramas are invisible to the audience. However monotonous the "saids" seem to the writer, they should not be varied with "Jack remarked," or "Bill stated" or "Larry declared" for the sake of variation alone. If Jack remarks, his words must amount to a remark, which differs from a statement or a declaration. An inquiry and a question are not quite the same thing; do not ask an inquiry or inquire a question. In other words, "said" and "asked" are virtually invisible as they are. Do not use the less-transparent terms without good reason.

When characters are well defined and the situation understood, lengthy passages of dialogue can go unattributed (without "Jack said"). But do not set out to see how much unattributed dialogue you can stack up. The reader will become confused if one character is given a speech longer than a paragraph when the only indication that the speaker did not change is the absence of a closing quotation mark. If the roles in a dialogue are interchanged, so that the badger becomes the badgee, for example; if the transaction is complex, involving more than two speakers or one speaker who is given two speeches in succession; if the characters are not developed sufficiently that the reader knows Mark said it because it was what Mark would say— wherever the reader might go wrong, attribute the speeches.

Rounded characters sometimes say things they are not

expected to say; when they do, attribute their speeches. In a lengthy passage of dialogue you can sometimes throw the reader a line by letting a character address a speech: "God, Mike, what do you expect from me?" Now we know that the speaker is not Mike, but that Mike will reply. The number of times that two people in a conversation will address each other by name, however, is limited.

Adding an adverb to the "said" is not advisable. First it calls attention to the "said," making it visible. Second, there is a danger of committing a Tom Swifty.

Tom Swift was the protagonist of a series of adventure books for young readers. Characters in the series often "said haughtily" or "remarked off-handedly." This gave rise to a kind of alleged joke called a Tom Swifty, to wit:

"He was run over by a steamroller," Tom said flatly.
"Put the hay on the second floor of the barn," Tom said loftily.
"This is the worst August on record," Tom said heatedly.
"Stop right there!" Tom said haltingly.

Notice that although the speeches are contrived, the adverbs really are ones found with dialogue in second-rate fiction.

Third, the adverb on the "said" may encourage (or reveal) lazy writing. Do not write "Gordon said seductively," but make Gordon's speech seductive. If it is not evident that Phil's remark was sarcastic, it is too late to tell us by the time the place for the adverb comes along. A speech is not made exciting by telling us it was made excitedly (nor by appending exclamation points helter-skelter).

A good way of telling who gave the speech, advancing the plot, and giving the reader an idea of the manner in which the speech was delivered, is to place the speech in a paragraph with a bit of action by the speaker.

Jack unbuttoned his shirt. "It's been too long, Ray."
"Too long, Jack. Has it been too long?" Ray unfastened Jack's silver buckle.

The sentence or two of action has the advantage of allowing a speaker to make two speeches in succession without danger of confusing the reader.

"This is the man I want you follow." Agnes produced a large color photograph from the manila folder. "He's one of the most dangerous bigots I know of." She handed the photograph to Jim. "Although, to look at him, you might think it a pleasant assignment."

Do not make characters do something merely to tell who gave the speech. Reveal a character's mannerisms or mood, or advance the plot. Flower arranging, picture straightening, and toying with small objects should be reserved for a character who has such mannerisms.

"I hear you don't much care for old-fashioned girls like myself." Agnes touched the ornamental comb in her raven wig.

Action in a paragraph with a speech must be action by the speaker. The speaker must be the subject of any other sentence. *Not:*

"Are you going to stand in the hall all night, or are you going to come in?" He picked up his bags and stepped into Ty's apartment.

Eventually the reader may realize that the "he" of the second sentence is not the person who spoke the words of the first sentence. But the writer should not present the reader with little puzzles like this one. The writer knows what he means and he should tell the reader clearly:

"Are you going to stand in the hall all night, or are you going to come in?" Ty asked.
Cliff picked up his bags and stepped into Ty's apartment.

When a scene involves three or more speakers, attribute every speech explicitly or implicitly. Even in drama, where the identities of the speakers are obvious, having more than three or four speaking parts onstage at one time is unwise. Especially in print, mob scenes must be avoided. (Of course thousands of nonspeaking extras may be present.) The root of "dialogue" does not mean two; "monologue" was coined in error. But the writer does well to think of dialogue as essentially a two-character transaction. Scenes of three or four are for the minor housekeeping tasks such as making necessary introductions. Conduct business by twos.

The best dialogue is dialogue that is the action of the story right now. Dialogue which recounts past events, explains the present, or goes on too long about hopes for the future is weak. Especially to be avoided are Socratic exchanges in which one speaker is a foil so that the other may express himself. Doing is better is than telling. Good dialogue is what the characters are doing—that is, speaking. It is not the characters telling. Some of the things characters can do by speaking are seduce each other, hatch a plot, argue, reconcile, and lie. Otherwise, show us the action rather than let the characters stand to one side and describe the action to each other.

Dramatists have technical limitations. They cannot, for example, detonate an atomic bomb onstage. They have to have a character stand at a window and say, "Oh, look at the mushroom cloud on the horizon." In print, on the other hand, the writer can and should take us to the heart of the nuclear inferno.

Dialect.

In the hands of a master, dialect can enhance a work of fiction. When not handled properly, dialect can utterly ruin a story. The writer must have a sure grasp of dialect, or he must leave it alone.

Leaving dialect alone is a good alternative. A long-standing convention in plays, movies, and fiction allows characters' speeches to be translated to English. We know it is unlikely that native Martians on Mars speak English to each other. But in a science fiction novel, the author kindly translates without calling attention to the fact (although if Englishmen and Martians understand each other on first meeting, we are owed an explanation). In a movie, the U-boat captain talks to his mate in English, perhaps with a German accent to remind us that he is supposed to be speaking German. The writer is entitled to rely on this convention, if he wishes. Having exercised the option of rendering a dialect in standard American English, the writer must sure he is writing standard American English.

Readers and critics will always spot dialect gone wrong. They will seldom be bothered if dialect is not attempted.

For writers who believe they have the ear to handle dialect and think that dialect would add something to their work, a few suggestions may be made:

First, examine your motives for wanting to use dialect. Linguists tell us that the speech of rural Southern whites is objectively indistinguishable from the speech of rural Southern blacks. Yet Faulkner's blacks speak in dialect while his whites speak nearly standard American English, with few apostrophes, a slightly nonstandard syntax, and very few unusual spellings. The comparison of black speech and white speech, as Faulkner records it, reveals Faulkner's attitudes, but not the way whites and blacks in the rural South really speak.

New Yorkers do not believe they speak with an accent. Since many editors, publishers, and readers are New Yorkers, the attempt to portray a New York accent is pointless. When New Yorkers see "bird" in print, they think "boid." If you write "boid," they will not know what to make of it. In America dialect is reserved for blacks, Southerners, ethnics right off the boat, and other people deemed inferior by New Yorkers. For similar reasons, if you write about people on Fire Island, you are an author; but if you write about people in Houston, you are a *regional* author.

Many writers believe that they can render black speech simply by using the wrong form of the verb "to be." But dialects are complete languages, not simply standard English with random mistakes. The English verb "to be" lacks certain distinctions found in the corresponding verb of many African languages. Africans compelled to speak English adapted various forms of the crude English verb in order to express the refinements of African language. "You (be) beautiful" and "You is beautiful" are both well-formed sentences in some Afro-American dialects, but they do not mean the same thing. If you do not know the distinctions, you had better not attempt these dialects.

Gay people, of course, have their own dialect although few of us learned it as children. Not much is written in gay dialect, probably because we are still sensitive to the stereotypes (just as early black writers often adopted an elevated style of standard English). We know what it is when straight writers make gay characters say, "Oh, Mary" as an introduction to every speech.

While most of us have said "Mary" at one time or another and some of us say "Mary" quite frequently, one seldom refers to one's trick as "she." Bruce Rodgers reports the following malformation in a neophyte's mouth: "Some day she'll come along—the man I love." We know who is she and who is he and whom we call "Mary" and whom we do not. The straight writer thinks we just mix up our pronouns indiscriminately and that is how he composes our dialogue. We ought to bear this in mind before we attempt to write a dialect that is not our own.

In sum, the first suggestion is: reconsider attempting dialect. Beyond this, a little can be said.

One approach to dialect is phonetic spelling:

"Ah'm jes' uh good ol' boah, trahin' ta haf uh good tahm."

This system might work if English were spelled phonetically and the reader were used to translating letters directly into sounds. Since that is not the case, the switch from reading English to reading phonetics demands a lot, usually too much, from the reader. A few phonetic spellings are common enough to be easily understood:

"Ah'm just a good old boy, tryin' to have a good time."
"Ah hope y'all will hurry back now, y'hear?"
"C'mon. Just once. You kin do it back."

Naturally, when satire is intended, the more extreme the spelling, the better:

"Hey, yuse skies!"

But making fun of the way people talk is not very nice and, in the long run, not very funny.

As with much else in fiction, suggestion may be helpful. Suggestion is more effective in creating dialect than a detailed phonetic rendering could be. Effective ways of suggesting dialect are in careful use of variations in word choice, syntax, and idiom.

"I am just a good old boy, trying to have a good time."

"I should have such problems."

"At this point in time, our previous projections are well correlated with currently available data."

The reader knows very well which statement was made in New York's garment district, which in the Baton Rouge honky-tonk, and which in the Senate committee room. Yet every word in every statement is spelled in the standard way. We can make the good old boy utter the last statement: "Far as I can tell, things are working out just like I reckoned they would."

Word choice should be considered even by writers who otherwise are resolved to leave dialect alone. When your character goes out at noon, does he go to the grocery store or the deli? Does he wait in line or on line? Does he buy a soda or a pop? Does the clerk bag it or sack it? Does the character drink it with a poor boy, a hoagie, a submarine, or a hero? At noon is it his dinner or his lunch? When he returns to work at the candy store does he sell mostly bonbons or mostly cigarettes, gum, and newspapers? When he gets home, does he collapse on the sofa, the couch, the divan, or the davenport? Is his lover preparing supper or dinner? Will the wine come from the cellar or the basement? When he helps to clean up after the meal will he use a dish rag or a dish cloth?

If you do not know why these questions are posed, write about people like those who are very close to your home.

Syntax is the "I should have such problems." Every word is an English word spelled properly, and the words are all so basic to the language that they would belong to virtually any dialect based on English. It is the order in which the words are put together that makes them distinctive.

"Good old boy" is an idiom. These are English words. The syntax is as plain as that of "big green truck." But it is a fixed expression meaning "local gentleman." "One of a group of cronies" is not a native connotation of the expression.

For the sake of clarity in illustrating the use of word choice, syntax, and idiom, I have chosen examples that are crude and stereotypical. Unfortunately, such uses are too easy to bandy about when they do not represent actual observations of the ways people speak.

A Midwesterner thinks she knows what a "good old boy" is because she knows the stereotypical Southerner of motion pictures, television, and bad novels. When she reads "good old boy" in a story supposedly set in the South, her impression of verisimilitude is enhanced because what she reads reinforces her stereotype of the Southerner. We all like to have our opinions confirmed. When the Midwesterner writes her Southern novel, she is likely to throw in "good old boy" at every opportunity, convinced she is adding realism to her novel. Since there is some truth to stereotypes, she will do well for a while. But sooner or later she will use "good old boy" inappropriately. Those who know Southerners by stereotype will be none the wiser. Southerners and others who know how Southerners really speak will object.

The wisest course, if you elect to use dialect at all, is to stick with dialects you know thoroughly. Then you can move past stereotypes and record authentic usages. When you employ a dialect you are less familiar with, do not look for places to show off your ignorance. Confine yourself to a few characteristic uses of which you are certain and let suggestion do the rest. Dialect is an example of a situation in which, very clearly, less is more.

Point of view.

In some types of fiction, point of view is vitally important. In mysteries, some of the characters know things that the reader must not know. In suspense, the reader must know things— for example, that there is a murderous psychopath right outside the french doors—that most of the characters do not know.

Erotic stories are most often told in the first person. Fortunately the first person is easiest for beginners. It is how we tell our experiences to our friends. It is how most of us would record the events of the day in our diaries. When a story is told in the first person, the story has a natural order: the first thing that happened to *I*, what *I* did about it, the next thing that happened to *I*, what *I* thought about that, and so forth.

Do not cheat with the first person. You only cheat yourself of the natural advantages of that viewpoint.

> I called Kevin the next day. I thought then he was putting me off because he did not like me, but he told me later it was because he thought I was married to the worthless roommate I had at the time. What I didn't know was that my roommate was telling my friends that we were romantically involved so he could get them to lend him money.

The "he told me later" and the "what I didn't know" are cheating. Told in the right order, first-person stories naturally incorporate elements of suspense. *I* does not know what will happen next. The author, however, knows and sets things up properly:

> I called Kevin the next day, and he was very cold to me. I thought I had no chance with him at all, and I could not understand why his attitude had changed so quickly. I moped around. Finally I decided to go to the Y to work out and to forget about Kevin.
>
> While I was waiting for the train, I looked up and saw Rodger on the other platform. Rodger seemed very happy to see me. He yelled, "Congratulations! I am so happy for you!" The express train came between us before I could ask what he meant. It seemed so strange.

That mysterious encounter makes *I* even more depressed. How ironic, "Congratulations!" when *I* seems to have lost his chance for true happiness or at least for a hot date. Eventually we do find out that the worthless roommate was claiming that he and *I* were lovers. Kevin believed him, and that is why Kevin is so cold. It also explains Rodger's peculiar behavior on the subway platform. The business of I's discovering "what I didn't know then" is an essential part of the development of a first-person story.

An advantage to the first-person story is that I may lie or may report some things inaccurately. Even if I tries to be honest, everyone's perceptions are distorted to some degree by differences in personality, situation, experience, and so forth. Although some readers will believe everything I tells them and will never see any inconsistencies in I's story, other readers will be able to compare I's self-image of being a master seducer with I's fumbling delivery of stale, lame, pickup lines. If I is in love, her interpretation of her beloved's actions maybe somewhat at odds with what the reader sees from I's reports of the beloved's behavior.

For such rounding, sometimes stories will mean different things to different readers. A writer once composed a first person story in which the I referred to Thom as being straight. Throughout the story, Thom jacked off with I, it was revealed that Thom knew something about being fucked by I, Thom and I lived together and evidently had for a number of years, as I had an affair with a younger man Thom became more moody and cranky, over breakfast Thom took I to task because he had heard I say he loved the younger man. When the story ended, the younger man took off and Thom and I were shown in bed together for the first time. Some readers thought I had succeeded in seducing the heterosexual Thom. Others saw that Thom and I had been lovers all along and I referred to Thom as straight only as a concession to Thom's ego which would never let him come out of the closet. Readers of both kinds professed to like the story, perhaps because each reader could find in the story what he was best prepared to find.

In mysteries, I must not know everything or else I has nothing to discover, but most readers think it is unfair for I to lie about pertinent aspects of the crime or for I to turn out to be the culprit.

In the first person, the standard of diction is accuracy of the voice. If the voice is authentic and consistent, the writer need appeal to no other authority to justify *I*'s usage. The criticaster barks up the wrong tree if he criticizes *I* for saying "infer" instead of "imply," provided that *I* is a person who would not know the difference. An extreme dialect should be avoided for *I* because it is bound to wear on the reader who must listen to *I* far more than to any other character. In particular, it is not necessary and possibly not desirable for *I* to use the contractions he or she might use in conversation. The reader's eye will make the normal contractions and will make them properly so that the reader will never have to wonder whether "he's" means "he is" or "he was" or "he has," or whether "she'd" stands for "she would," "she should," "she had," "she could," or whatever.

The reader is supposed to feel a natural human sympathy for the first-person character which is difficult to create in some other points of view. Strong opinions and a healthy self-regard are endearing qualities in a first-person character when the same qualities might seem objectionable in a character described from the third person. First-person characters can express ideas of their own that would seem to belong to the author if expressed in the third person.

The first person has some traps.

Even if *I* is supposed to be enormously endowed or very attractive, *I* will always seem vain if he describes himself as such. A few *I*'s are vain, but many who are very attractive are also very modest. Getting *I* to describe himself at all is difficult: Please! no more lengthy self-assessments in front of a mirror. Let others react to *I* in a way that shows *I* to be attractive. Let others remark on *I*'s most striking feature. *I* may or may not dismiss these remarks modestly. *I* can refer other's proportions to his own, and so we may learn of *I* indirectly.

A beginner's problem is that of confusing *I* with the author. Many first-person stories are autobiographical, perhaps with the author rebuilt and the outcome altered. Many are the author's fantasies for himself. (Some, of course, *are* fiction.) Yet a character whose experiences differ drastically from the author's is a different character from the author. The experiences will shape the character into someone who is different from the author, and some experiences will not occur to a character unless he is different from the author. The author should be prepared to let the character go his own way.

An author who is consciously being autobiographical may know who he is and may assume the reader does, too. It is no sin for the author of a work of fiction to present an image that is not his own. The danger is that the author may present no image at all. When the author appears in a story as himself, he may forget or be unable to provide the characterization a first-person narrator requires.

In the early days of television situation comedies, movie stars often appeared as themselves. The roles were deliberately bland and inoffensive. Nonetheless, one star would appear to be a heck of a good sport, as intended, but another would seem flat and boring. The boring ones appeared as themselves. The ones who succeeded *played* themselves. The author may appear as himself or he may characterize himself.

Characterization, like stage makeup, requires an emphasis beyond the natural. The character must be clear to the audience in the balcony. The author must not merely show up and be himself, he must also do the things that show us who he is. He must, in other words, portray himself using the same techniques he would use to portray a first person character who was not supposed to be himself. A few people make their livelihoods from marketing their personalities or personalities they have created to market. Their books are merely among one of the ways the personality product is packaged. Authors of fiction need not go so far.

When the character is not supposed to be *I,* it may be helpful to play the character, at least mentally. Experience in dramatic improvisation may be helpful. Dramatic improvisation is very much what writing in character is; except that when you write, you always have the chance of going back to correct anything you get wrong.

Sometimes the narrator is another person who tells you his story. Naturally, he speaks in the first person. You transcribe what he says. I hear—as if remembering with particular clarity having heard them speak to me—many of my narrators, and indeed almost all of them who are not supposed to be me. Some writers are able to interview their characters.

The ear to hear characters is a gift that some writers never receive. Those who do not hear their characters can create their characters technically. Decide where the character is from, how old she is, what sort of person she is. Then list words and expressions that show the facts of the character's background and personality. Characters in fiction are composed of characteristics; or, in other words, all the reader knows is what the character does and what the character says, from which is induced what a character is likely to say and do. If you have enough examples of what a character says and does, you have, for all practical purposes, created a character; although, once you have created a character, it may be obvious that some actions and sayings do not belong to the character.

In practice, work on a character often goes both ways. From a notion of what the character is like at his unobservable core, you suppose some actions for him. From some of his actions, you alter your view of what the character is at his core.

However you create the narrator, you should eventually employ a style sheet of characteristic expressions and word usages, especially for a longer work. Be sure that your character uses words and expressions consistently, except where you mean for him to say something unusual.

The first-person narrator is not always the leading character. Detective stories are often told by the detective's associate. The detective then may have a good idea of the solution quite early in the story, while the reader is fairly kept in the dark because the story is told by a dim-witted Watson. In erotica, an off-center narrator, willingly or not, becomes a voyeur.

A story need not be the worse for that; indeed, the spying narrator is in a better position to describe the scene than either of the principals. However, unless the narrator has something to do with the story, unless his voice is a large part of the charm of the story, or unless voyeurism is rather the point, the writer should consider eliminating the narrator. Occasionally, especially in a history like Wilder's *Our Town*, the narrator appears only in the introduction and in the conclusion. In prose this provides an excuse for the third-person material, which forms the body of the story, to have a voice.

However handled, the off-center narrator requires a mastery of both the first person and the third person. The main chance for a beginner is in the ordinary first person, with a voice similar to the writer's.

True second-person narration is rare:

Late on a Saturday night, the bars are closed. You stop in an all-night greasy spoon. Two bums are holed up in a back booth, staying warm by taking advantage of the unlimited free refills of the horrible coffee. There's a drag queen at the counter camping it up with the cook, and some kind of character three stools down. You take a booth near the cash register. It turns out the cashier is the waitress, and she hands you a menu.

The little bells jangle and the cold wind hits the back of your neck. Someone is coming in. You look around in spite of yourself. It's him.

That is the second person. Most authorities say that the first time *you* does something the reader never would do, the reader will necessarily lose the essential "suspension of disbelief." At any rate, the second person is so rare that readers are not accustomed to conventions that are necessary to that viewpoint.

The second person does occur from time to time in gay erotica. The theory of writers who use the second person is that readers will become involved in the story and experience it as if it were their own. Nonetheless, the second person must be regarded as experimental: to be left alone by a writer who needs a sale.

The second-person pronoun does occur in stories that are not truly in the second person. Sometimes there are asides to the reader. Such asides call attention to the writing as writing. In modern works, whether addressed to *you* or to the *gentle reader,* asides are out of place. Especially to be avoided is the mannerism of short-circuiting description with "you know" or the equivalent:

Wrong: I decided to go into Sue's. You know how a preppy bar is on a Saturday night. Well, that's what Sue's is like every night.

If the reader is sure to know what a preppy bar on a Saturday night is like, then write: "Every night at Sue's is like a Saturday night at a preppy bar." If the reader does not know, then there is no reason to bring a preppy bar into it; simply describe Sue's as it is. Your narrator may have speech mannerisms, but avoid those as annoying as the gratuitous "you know."

A use of the second person which has met with some success is that in which *you* is not the reader, but is a visitor the narrator addresses. The pattern for this viewpoint is Browning's *My Last Duchess*. The visitor is unseen. The visitor's movements and remarks are deduced from the speaker's remarks in much the same way that comedians with telephone routines imply the remarks of the person they are speaking with on the telephone.

The narrator may say: "Here, let me fill your glass again." This implies that the visitor has finished his or her drink. The narrator says: "But of course, it is no imposition at all." This implies that the visitor has apologized for the circumstances of his call. In any event, the visitor says and does very little. The narrator's words are not set in quotes, and the visitor is never materialized.

The third-person viewpoint occurs in several forms. The best-known is the third-person omniscient, the god's-eye vantage. Most other forms of the third person arise from limiting or partitioning the god's-eye viewpoint.

All third-person narration should be as voiceless as possible. Diction should be transparent, standard American English. The writing is impersonal and dry. "Omniscient" is something of a misnomer. The writing should not reveal that it knows anything of the future. Events in the story may foreshadow the climax, but there are not asides such as: "He made this statement though he would soon regret it," "He hardly knew how that simple act would come back to him," "The outcome of this touching scene the reader will soon know." The reader may be distracted from some piece of evidence, or the reader's range of vision may be limited, but the reader must not be lied to.

Within these limitations, crafting a sympathetic story is difficult. Most writers seek cover in the head of a character. In the third-person single viewpoint, the writer gets into the head of only one character. In the sigma viewpoint—so called because sigma is the mathematical symbol for sum and, as we will see, the story is the sum of several viewpoints—the writer is in the head of only one character at time, but the character may be different from scene to scene or chapter to chapter.

Third person in a character's head is similar to the first-person viewpoint in that the reader can perceive only what the character can perceive and, of course, the character can be only in one place at one time. What the character sees in the third-person viewpoint, however, may be described in words the character might not use. The character's thoughts and impressions may be summarized for us, or we may be given a verbatim account of some of them.

Some writers set thoughts in italics (underlined in the manuscript). Others attribute thoughts like quotations, but do not use quotation marks. Whatever method is used for thoughts, it should be used consistently.

Thoughts represented directly:

Method 1 (italics):
The slapping sound of wet, bare feet on the locker-room floor drew nearer. *I hope it isn't Patrick. Patrick is such an asshole.* Jim looked the other way. *Don't let it be Patrick. Don't let him see me this way.*

Method 2 (attributed):
The slapping sound of wet, bare feet on the locker-room floor drew nearer. I hope it isn't Patrick, Jim thought. Patrick is such an asshole. Jim looked the other way. Don't let it be Patrick. Don't let him see me this way.

Thoughts represented indirectly:

The slapping sound of wet, bare feet on the locker-room floor drew nearer. Jim hoped it was not Patrick. Jim thought Patrick was such an an asshole. Jim looked the other way. He did not want it to be Patrick. He did not want Patrick to see him as he was.

Notice that in Method 2, having attributed the first thought, the writer has not attributed the successive thoughts because the thoughts are easy to distinguish from the narration. The indirect method of representing thoughts can be mixed with either of the direct methods, but the direct methods should not be mixed with each other. Given the general distaste for italics and the possibility that italics may be needed for another purpose, a mixture of indirect representations of thoughts and Method 2 is probably the best way of handling thoughts:

The slapping sound of wet, bare feet on the locker room floor drew nearer. I hope it isn't Patrick, Jim thought. Patrick is such an asshole. Jim looked the other way. He did not want it to be Patrick. He did not want Patrick to see him as he was.

The sigma viewpoint, because the writer must carefully establish whose head he is in at the moment, is better suited for longer works. For the café scene, get into the waitress's head before the principals arrive. Tell us what she thinks of them based on what she can observe. Give us only the dialogue that she can overhear. She does not know the story is about them; they are only a couple of customers to her. Stay in her head until they have paid the check and she considers the amount of the tip they left. For the erotic scene, let the voyeur with his telescope scan several other apartments before he notices that your protagonist's curtains are open. He cannot hear what goes on in your protagonist's apartment. He can only imagine what is said or what noises are made. The story is the sum of what the waitress overheard, what the voyeur saw, the observations of the bus driver or cabbie, and so forth.

Keeping things in order while you pop in and out of several characters' heads in the same scene is very difficult and can be done only from the fully omniscient viewpoint. If this is attempted, the thoughts in a paragraph must be those of the person who does the actions in the paragraph or who gives the speech in the paragraph. Put in the attribution, the "Jim thought" and the "she saw that" for each thought or impression. Avoid having more than two or three characters thinking in a single scene. In other words, handle thoughts very much like speeches.

In the third person, the narration must be objective. Do not write: "Patrick is an asshole." Show us Patrick and let us draw our own conclusions. If the waitress thinks Patrick is an asshole, that may be reported; but since the waitress, like many sigma characters, is on the periphery of the story, her opinion ought to be based on something she overheard, or the size of the tip Patrick left, or the fact that he sent the steak back.

Third-person writing must be stronger. If we cannot be told that Patrick is an asshole or that a painting is beautiful, you must be able to describe Patrick's behavior objectively so that we will know he is an asshole. You must be able to describe a painting so that we will conclude it is beautiful. For this reason, beginners usually find it easier to write in the first person. If Jim is the first-person narrator, he can say flatly that Patrick is an asshole. Then, from what Jim tells us about Patrick's actions, we can decide whether Jim is right or is overly sensitive to things that would not bother most people. Inside Patrick's head we will seldom find the thought "I am an asshole," but interesting results can be achieved by seeing things from the point of view of an asshole or a frank sonofabitch.

Whether the story is told in the third person or by an off-center first-person narrator, pronouns can be a serious hazard. When you write "he," which one of them do you mean? The worst examples occur in the erotic scene, where the writer wants, quite correctly, to proceed as directly as possible to his conclusion. But it is exactly in the erotic scene that the reader should not be made to stop to figure out what is going on.

Sometimes the writer can resolve this problem by redrafting the scene so that actions by one of the characters are grouped in a single sentence or paragraph. Whenever a sentence or paragraph begins with "he" the reader has a chance to go wrong. Here, more than anywhere else, the ability to read your own copy to see what it actually says, as opposed to what you know you meant, must be developed.

Characters still have to be called by name often. For that reason short, crisp, distinctive names are desirable. Major characters should not be given names that are confused easily, perhaps not even names that begin with the same letter. Beginners think that repeating names and other nouns is to be avoided. In fact, repetition is not as tiresome to readers as writers think and certainly is better than confusion. What if Lincoln had said, "Of the people, by them, and for them," or "Of the masses, by the electorate, and for the public."

Pronoun problems are another good reason for beginners to write in the first person, with the first person being one of the romantic principles. That eliminates the pronoun problem in the erotic scene, at least in twosomes, for the actors then are *I* and *he* (or in lesbian scenes *she*). Nonetheless, naming *him* (or *her*) occasionally is a good idea, and pronouns will still require attention in other parts of the story.

Write in the past tense.

The present tense appeals to new writers in the same way that the second person does. Again, the theory is to involve the reader in the action. The effect of the present tense, however, is often surreal or dreamlike (as, for example, in the lyrics of the Beatles' "Lucy in the Sky with Diamonds"). The surreal effect may sometimes be desired, but it is not what most writers who attempt the present tense hope to achieve.

The past tense is too deeply ingrained as a convention. Readers have more confidence when being told of things that have happened. Do not monkey with the present tense until you are certain of what you doing.

The simple past is more effective, perhaps because it is less wordy than the perfect tenses. The perfect tense can be avoid by shifting into the simple past once the time is established. The time can be established explicitly by mentioning the day or hour, a previous clause can establish the perfect time, or the facts can convey perfect time implicitly by recounting events described in immediately preceding text. Example:

Perfect tense: Dan had come over for an afternoon quickie.
Substitute simple past with time established explicitly: Last Wednesday, Dan came over for an afternoon quickie.
Perfect time established in a previous clause: Dan had tried to make friends. He came over for an afternoon quickie.

You may transport the reader across great distances by skipping an extra line. Try to do this with more art than "Meanwhile back at the ranch,..." but better "Meanwhile back at the ranch,..." than leave the reader wondering where you have taken her.

Do not make a habit of transporting the reader through time. The flashback is a poor device. It is made even poorer when it is formalized.

Very well, perhaps that is putting it a little too strongly. The flashback is overworked and often poorly executed. Beginners who know of devices such as the flashback are often overly eager to employ them. But the better policy is look for ways to avoid departures from a clear and direct chronological line.

A writer who has properly understood the importance of beginning his story with an important or exciting event may suppose that he should, once things have settled down a bit, flash back in order to explain the events which gave rise to the excitement in the beginning. In fact the flashback is not the only way and not the most desirable way of conveying necessary background information. Necessary bits of information can be fed to the reader as the story progresses. This may add an element of suspense to the story.

If, for example, we have to know that Jerry was wearing green suspenders at the time of the accident, we probably can find a way of slipping this fact in without flashing back to his dressing room. We may need to establish that hostility exists between Carl and Bob, but often their present behavior will show that and we will not need to recount the scene of their falling out. If we show the scene of their falling out, the reader will not wonder whether it was over money or jealousy or differences in housekeeping standards.

Little, informal flashbacks are sometimes useful. Joseph Hansen, author of the Dave Brandstetter novels, has a technique of jumping into the middle of the action and working backwards. It works for him. The writer sacrifices the suspense of the outcome of a minor matter. He hopes to equalize by arousing curiosity as to how the event came about. Begin by sacrificing something that would be difficult to make suspenseful anyway: sacrifice a point you are bound to lose.

The following occurred far too deep in "Dale and the Glory Hole," a short story that first appeared in *Torso*, September 1984:

Dale got stuck.

Whoever designed Sam's glory holes didn't have much imagination. It takes a lot of imagination to blow Dale.... And I'd thought it only seemed that Dale's cock got bigger even after it was hard.

Dale got stuck, and since he's about half-straight, that once was all it took. Now he won't go near a glory hole even if it's the size of a barn door.

Anyway, I'd gone around to the other booth.... It got bigger on my side and, more to the point, the part in my booth got bigger than the hole. He tapped this little tap on the partition, and I just thought he was enjoying himself....

"Come over here," he whispered...through the partition.

I thought the motion picture had inspired him to try something even more entertaining so I hurried over to his booth. I thought it was strange that he was still spread-eagled against the wall.

"I'm stuck."

"Just relax."

"If I could relax, I wouldn't be stuck."

The writer could not find a way to make Dale's getting stuck the subject of suspense. He thought the question of how Dale will get unstuck was enough suspense for this light story. Being stuck in a glory hole, however, is a curious situation, curious enough to support several paragraphs of backtracking. Once the subject of glory holes was established (in about 400 words too many) the writer wrote: "Dale got stuck." Then he did flash back. But he did not flash back to show aspects of Dale's childhood in order to analyze the psychic analogy between the glory hole and Dale's mother and how being stuck relates to Dale's subconscious feelings about his father. The writer flashed back only far enough to show how Dale got stuck.

If there is something essential to the story that can only be got at through a lengthy formal flashback, perhaps the story has not started at the right place. More likely, however, the author is overly attached to some bit of nostalgia which belongs in another story altogether.

Some figures and devices.

A complete discussion of figures of speech and rhetorical devices is beyond the scope of this book. Some of the main ones are introduced here, however, because the writer will employ them, whether or not she knows what to call them. Knowing what to call them may make it easier for her to organize her experiences. My object is not to encourage beginners to work in a device or a metaphor wherever possible, but to encourage an understanding of what such things are when they are encountered.

One of the most powerful devices of writing is parallelism.

Grammatical parallelism is simply the rule that constructions used in similar ways should be similar:

Wrong: We liked hunting fossils and to go horseback riding.
Correct: We liked to hunt fossils and to ride horses.
Or: We liked hunting fossils and riding horses.

As a literary device, parallelism is the principle that similar thoughts should be expressed in similar constructions.
This does not violate grammatical parallelism:

Joe was a top. Rick liked to be on the bottom. Gene was undecided.

But literary parallelism suggests:

Joe was a top. Rick was a bottom. Gene was an undecided.

A comparison of two situations each of which consists of two parts can be given in parallel form:

By day we were rivals; by night we were lovers.

This structure can be diagrammed:

A: by day B: we were rivals
a: by night b: we were lovers.

When the parts A and a are joined by a line and the parts B and b are joined by a line, we see that the lines between the comparable parts are parallel.

In this case, however, another figure may be more effective. When there is a contrast of two situations each of which has two parts *chiasmus* may be a striking way of presenting the ideas:

We were rivals by day; by night we were lovers.

Diagrammed:

A: we were rivals B: by day
b: by night a: we were lovers

This time, when the comparable parts are joined by lines, the lines cross, and this is how *chiasmus* gets its name.

Many figures of speech are, at their heart, metaphors. The central idea of metaphor is a departure from the literal meaning of words. A metaphor involves equating a thing with another thing that is dissimilar but which has some common aspect.

A metaphor: Joe's feet were blocks of ice.

Of course, Joe's feet were no such things. They were flesh and blood like everyone else's feet. The common aspect is what is meant here, namely that Joe's feet and blocks of ice had in common being cold. Unfortunately many metaphors, including this one, have been worked to exhaustion and have become clichés. Metaphors can be worked to death and, once dead, metaphors lose their figurative quality:

Joe is a stud.

Once this was a living metaphor in which Joe was compared to a stallion put to stud, the common aspect being that the primary usefulness of both Joe and the stallion was sexual. But most modern readers lack a rural background, and the expression is so common that many readers will understand the word "stud" to mean a sexually active man before they know the word has other meanings.

Some trite metaphors can be recast:

Trite: An hour of that night was a drop in the ocean.
Better: An hour of that night was a drop from a leaky faucet.

A *simile* is merely a metaphor in which the comparison is made explicit by the use of "like":

He opened his mouth like a baby bird waiting to be fed.

The dangers of mixing metaphors are usually taught in grammar school. Do not compare a cock to a glass rod in one breath and to a steel pipe in the next. Mixed metaphors often occur when one of them is dead or moribund:

His pale back was highlighted with a dozen small tattoos.

What went wrong here was that the author forgot that "highlighted" has a literal sense, and what is more, the literal sense is exactly opposite what the author means. Rather than being bright spots on the pale back, the tattoos are dark ones. Probably the author thought of the word "accented" and wisely discarded it as sounding too much like a designer's word. If he can think of nothing better, the word the author wants is "peppered."

Synecdoche is a kind of metaphor in which the whole stands for the part or the part for the whole:

The bare feet slapped the tile as they followed Jim into the locker room.

Of course, it is not merely the feet, but the whole person

they are attached to that has followed Jim. In some cases synecdoche can be as dead as any other metaphor:

All hands on deck.

What is wanted is all of the crew on deck, not merely their hands. But this figure is now dead because "hand" is now synonymous with "crew member."

Metonymy is a figure similar to synecdoche, but in metonymy some other close relationship besides that of whole and part is the basis of the substitution:

Watching him perform the bench press was a hard-on.

Here the effect stands for the cause. What is meant was that the sight was sexually arousing, but the result of sexual arousal is stated instead.

Shakespeare sometimes made Jeff weep.

Shakespeare could have done no such thing, since Shakespeare was dead centuries before Jeff was born. No doubt it was the sonnets of Shakespeare that affected Jeff so.

I wanted to punch out his lights.

This means I wanted to knock him unconscious, which would close his eyes and in effect shut off his sources of light.

Other figures and devices may be found (with these) in the brief glossary of terms.

Some miscellaneous advice.

In parallel structures, repetitive parts of jokes, and lists, three is the magic number. Once is an event. Twice is a coincidence. Three times establishes the pattern. If the writer errs and includes a fourth item, it will be forgotten. Churchill said: "...blood, toil, tears, and sweat." But the world remembers "blood, sweat, and tears."

Bartlett's does not reveal who first described a writing student as approaching a typewriter "determined to commit an act of literature."

Nothing, it seems to me, is wrong with wanting one's work to endure or in trying to write well enough that it might. Thucydides frankly admitted to writing for the ages. Twenty-four centuries later, we must admit he may have succeeded. And so I wrote when I wrote my most successful work, for I could not foresee the way it might be published while I lived. John Preston has reminded me, as I have reminded others, of Samuel Johnson's saying: "No man but a blockhead ever wrote except for money." Now I think that Johnson's statement is wise but overstated.

Writing for money and writing for the ages are not antithetical, but this spurious dilemma is promulgated by those who have comfortable means and who dare not try their masterpieces in the market. Some works are now more esteemed than when they were new. Occasionally old works of little merit are reprinted as curiosities. But generally what we now judge to be great literature and keep reprinting enjoyed at least a little success when first published. Dickens was a prodigious success from the moment he tried his hand at fiction, and he remained successful throughout his life. Although those forced to read it in high school may wonder at the fact, people once paid good money for the privilege of reading George Eliot's *Silas Marner*. Publishers never were, intentionally, pure philanthropists, but most books we think are great literature were first issued by hardheaded businessmen with expectations of profit.

What is wrong with attempting an act of literature is the method most students employ, which is to emulate a writer who is great or who is enjoying popularity: Salinger, Vonnegut, William Burroughs—for some reason, young writers once wanted to write as Thomas Wolfe did—the heroes vary from generation to generation, but the tendency of young writers to idolize their heroes and to try to rewrite masterpieces endures.

Do not esteem your betters too much. Respect is one thing, adoration another. Learn what the masters have to teach you, but then be appropriately impertinent. You cannot be sure your work will come to light. You can be certain only that it will not while you write in another's shadow.

To write fiction about being a writer, one's credentials as a writer ought to be in order.

The subject most often ignored in writing about being a writer is writing. Very little has been done about what it is that happens when a person comes to a typewriter with blank paper and experience and produces a story. Most writing about writing is about not writing: it is about not being able to write, not getting published, not making enough money, and not having an easy life. I am not sure that we need more fiction in this vein.

"Write what you know!" does not mean to write about writing. At least not until you do know about writing.

In a *Blueboy* editorial that appeared just as I was first thinking of writing fiction, M. J. Bevans influenced my opinion on this subject: forbear using a pen name for your gay erotica.

We ask general bookstores and newsstands to carry our work. We want our readers to show their faces to the clerks, at least long enough to buy our books and magazines. We trade upon a movement that cried: "Out of the closets and into the streets!" Not only is it politically incorrect for us to hide behind false names, but also it is wrong.

I acknowledge a few good reasons for using a pen name. A prolific writer may use different names to distinguish his several series of novels. A person who has some other position in gay publishing or the movement may fairly use another name for his gay fiction. A writer whose name is the same as another well-known writer's or whose name is so unusual that it is borne by only one other person may well alter the styling of his name or use a nickname. Everyone will understand if a writer whose name is Silvester prefers to work as Sly. For a John Smith to publish under his own name is hardly tantamount to coming out of the closet; he may wish to use something more distinctive.

Even in general publishing, some editors will react with suspicion when the name for the byline differs from the one for the check. Except where the reasons are obvious, editors may wonder: If this is his best work, why won't he put his name to it? If it is not his best work, why should I bother with it?

Naturally, I mean no disrespect toward my elders and betters who began working when conditions were very different. Today writers are not justified in using pen names. Those who adopt cutesy, obvious pen names insult readers.

Gay readers deserve a writer's best work. A pen name suggests that the writer thinks he might do better writing in something besides porn, that he has something better to do than to write for gay readers, that he is reserving his true name for work he considers more serious, and that he has spared some effort or talent in composing the work of gay erotica.

That is an affront gay readers ought not to receive with equanimity. It is an affectation that hardly endears a writer to his colleagues who are writing as well as they can and who are proud of their work.

Favor the use of common speech rather than blunder in the attempt to prove you know better.

This principle is owing to Fowler, who demonstrated the nonsense that may result from an overweening fear of splitting an infinitive, ending a sentence with a preposition, mistaking "will" for "shall," or using "who" where "whom" was called for.

In truth, a number of points that purists congratulate themselves for mastering are figments. The distinction of "will" and "shall" was invented by grammarians of the nineteenth century and has no basis in the history of English speech or writing. Purists cringe when "loan" is used as a verb. Only "lend" is the verb they say. But "loan" as verb, as anyone who consults the *OED* will discover, has been the Queen's English since at least the sixteenth century.

The wisest course is to learn the purists' prejudices and to follow them when it makes no difference. If you can write "to lend" as well as "to loan," then write "to lend." The purists will be pleased and no one else will know the difference. But if a character must say "to loan," then so be it. When the alternative to ending a sentence with a preposition is an ugly, twisted circumlocution, the purists will just have to lump it.

Answering critics is very poor judgment. Criticasters pan books because it is easy to do so. In writing bad notices there are many opportunities to display superficial wit, whereas thoughtful analysis and constructive criticism require knowledge and effort.

Sometimes a bad notice thoroughly misrepresents a work or suggests an author approves of everything her characters do or puts a character's speech in the author's mouth. A critic may depart from the text and may speculate about the author's personality. Speculation about the facts of a work's publication might be justified in the case of an ancient text; but while the author and the editor are still living, the critic could, if he would, make a couple of telephone calls and provide his readers with facts instead of speculation. In any of these cases, the author may be tempted to fire off a letter to the critic's editor. But the author cannot win in such a situation.

Adopt the attitude that there is no such thing as bad publicity. No one has shown that a bad review hurts sales (though a good one helps). The worst thing is to be ignored; that is what most hurts sales. When a book is reviewed, readers will recall the book's existence long after they have forgotten what the reviewer said, and many more people will recall the reproduction of the book's cover than will ever bother to discover what the reviewer wrote.

Stick to the main chance, at least at first.

In the front matter of *Big Shots* and *Beast of Burden* (both from Badboy Books, 1993) Aaron Travis describes his hyperthermal mode, which is what he calls the form of writing that appears in those books. It is third person, present tense, with uncensored fantasies, descriptions, and language, and sometimes has the dark melodramatic qualities of film noir. Clearly there are ways of writing successfully that are different from and even contrary to the methods I recommend in this book.

Aaron Travis is a very talented writer and editor who has worked in the gay market for many years and who, under another name, has a successful series of novels in the general market. His other works show that he has a complete mastery of more conventional styles. If you were Aaron Travis, I would say to you, "But of course. Strike out on your own. Explore the uncharted resources of the language. Do things that lesser writers dare not dream of."

But you are not Aaron Travis. If you are reading this book, I suppose it possible that you do not yet command the conventional forms of writing and that you do not have a well-established career in fiction. You are an apprentice. Do not mess with the spells in the master's book lest you invoke forces you cannot control.

You have been warned.

Murder your darlings. Another maxim.

I suppose no one knows why the passages, the figures, and the wordplay a writer loves best are the ones that must be cut from a work. Write them out if you must, but delete them before the final draft. In any event, an editor will never want to cut a mundane part, but only a great one.

Sometimes writers merely muddle through. Sometimes they are masters of grand designs. Nothing is wrong when a writer knows what he is doing. And nothing is wrong, really, with having a grand design. Except.

Except that a writer's universe may fit together all too neatly. In the period between World War II and the Vietnam War, many American writers suddenly discovered Freud and Jung. The psychological novel was upon us. Those fortunate enough to have avoided the onslaught can imagine how gay people fared in these books. Reality fared little better: anything longer than it was wide was a Symbol. Warped too, in their own way, are socialist realist novels, Christian short stories and, fast gaining on us, Politically Correct fiction. Certainly, if he wishes, the author may be a partisan. Fiction without an ax to grind is not worth reading, much less writing. The writer may be a Freudian, a Christian, or a Feminist. But the bourgeoisie is not the source of all evil, some of us were never particularly impressed with our mothers, Françoise Sagan was not a prophet, and not even the most devout Christian knows the mind of God. At the bottom of any good work, as in the real world, are forces the writer does not fully understand, things he cannot describe, and questions he cannot honestly answer.

You may know why Ronnie has a morbid fear of snakes, why Lester turned around at just that moment, and how Spyder got his carbon tattoo. But still there are things you do not know. You do not have to bring your ignorance to the surface and make a display of it. You need only avoid the pretense that you and your philosophy could explain it all.

Unless of course nothing is hidden from you, a condition known as paranoia.

Strunk and White wrote: "Do not explain too much."

My advice: Do not explain what you do not know. Do not write tracts.

Stick to novels and short stories. In other words, stick to forms that publishers and readers recognize. Novels are seldom serialized anymore; and, outside of gay erotica, there is little demand for story collections.

This is merely a reprise of the maxim "Know your market!" If you do not see much of a form you want to work in on the bookseller's shelves, do not be surprised if you have difficulty selling your work.

7. *The Erotic Scene*

Writing the erotic scene is both easy and difficult. It is easy because the reader wants the erotic scene, more than any other, to succeed. The reader invests his cooperation, his personal energy, and his furthest extremes of credulity. Not to put too fine a point on it, the reader is likely to have an urgent, palpable stake in the matter at hand and to hope feverishly for a satisfactory outcome.

The erotic scene is difficult because the writer wants, or ought to want, to make the scene as good as possible for the reader. The writer spares nothing to produce the desired effect. After all, no matter how well the rest of the story is done, how well crafted its frame, the erotic story will be judged by the erotic scene.

Literature is an art, not a science. However, some suggestions can be made.

Much of what makes the erotic scene work precedes it. Wherever possible, erotic tension should be introduced long before the erotic scene. To reach its greatest peak in the erotic scene, as it should, erotic tension must start at a very low level and be built up with increasing steepness.

A good story also erects other lines of tension. These may be played against the erotic to explore the eroticism more fully. They keep the story from collapsing before the erotic tension can be fully developed. And, since by masculine equation, other forms of arousal with varying degrees of efficiency can be transformed to sexual arousal, other lines of tension enhance the erotic tension.

As the heart of a work of stroke fiction—or of stroke nonfiction, for that matter—is the erotic scene, the heart of the erotic scene is the comeshot.

While I encourage the highest literary values in gay literature, especially in gay erotica, which is the principal historic form of gay literature, and while I aspire to the highest standards in my own work, I do not try to kid myself or anyone else about what stroke story is for.

Nine Rules for Comeshots.

I got a little fan mail from the first edition of this book. One of the fans who wrote me became my student. As often happens in such situations, it was I who was to learn more. My student's first piece was a memoir of his bathhouse experiences in pre-AIDS Florida. My student had been an advertising copywriter and tended to describe a foreskin as if it were a sort of matching handbag: "To complete the ensemble, Dick had a lovely, thickly veined..."

But my student took instruction well, and soon overcame that tendency and several other flaws in his writing.

I still could not get off on his stories.

I was puzzled. My student had hunky men on every page. His characters performed all the basic sex acts and quite a number of not-so-basic ones. Why didn't my student's stories work?

The answer was that he had not written any comeshots. Oh, his *characters* came enough. Sometimes four characters came within the space of a typewritten page. Sometimes one character came four times. They came in every position and combination. They drenched the sheets.

But there was no place for the reader to come.

The story was hot to my student because he worked from memory and his memories were hot. But what he wrote for a comeshot was "The hairy marine came on the redhead's chest." In the next paragraph, the redhead came in the blond's hand, and the blond came on the sheets. Then it was on to the next orgy. What the reader got was a box score, not a play-by-play.

To help my student, I gave much thought to what makes a good comeshot. I believe I have some answers.

I have written that however many orgasms occur in a story, one of them is *the* comeshot. Some readers will get off when the protagonist's feet are described or at the first mention of his studded black leather jockstrap. But most readers are looking for *the* comeshot.

It has to be there. The erotic writer has a contract with the reader. The reader will put up with the writer's literary conceits. In return, the writer will do his or her best to get the reader off. Which means, among other things, that the writer will let the reader know when to let fly.

Potent as the reader is, one comeshot per story or chapter is about all he can handle. After all, he must retain enough strength to get to the newsstand to purchase the next issue. But the reader is entitled to that one comeshot.

Thus the first rule: However many ejaculations there are in a story, exactly one of them is the *comeshot.*

Rule two: The comeshot is marked clearly.

The reader knows this is the one. If characters have orgasms before *the* comeshot, they are the throwaway kind, like those the marine, the redhead, and the blond were having. The reader doesn't want to get off, only to discover that the really hot stuff is on the next page.

Who gets *the* comeshot? Most beginners should write in the first person, so the comeshot is either "his" or "mine."

Rule three: Whoever is coming, we care whether and how he comes.

In most first-person stories we care about "I," so "I" can usually be given the comeshot. If "he" gets the comeshot, then "he" should have been in the story long enough so that we care about him. If the story is about "I" having the hornies, "he" may come to "my" sexual rescue in the last few pages. But the point of such a story is to give "I" the comeshot.

Some stories are of a voyeuristic kind, and we may observe the participants without having been introduced to them. Here interest is created by the visual and other clues about who these characters are. Elements of costume and set, nuances of observable behavior, and peculiarities of diction—if they can be overheard— are more important in stories of this kind. If, for example, the scene we spy out occurs in the bedroom of one of the principals, we should see enough of the objects in the bedroom to know whether its occupant is a college jock, a biker, or a longshoreman.

Rule four: From early in the scene, the focus is on whoever has the comeshot.

Say there are twenty hunks in a circlejerk and the redhead is to have the comeshot. Naturally the hunks and what they are doing are briefly described. But the key is on the redhead. If one of the hunks does something spectacular, the point is how the redhead responds. As the comeshot gets closer, more of the writing relates to the redhead and the hunks nearest him. Eventually, although the hunks are still there, only the redhead is seen.

Rule five: Warn the reader.

This is so the reader's hand has a chance to catch up with his eyes.
Example: "I can't hold out much longer," the redhead gasped.
A good length from warning to shot is about a typewritten page and a half. With any luck, the reader will not encounter the dreaded "CONTINUED ON PAGE 78" within this space.

Rule six: Cut the crap.

Fancy figures and coinages are best in the early parts of the erotic scene. Readers should not be given complex metaphors to puzzle through in the final lines. Language should draw in until, at the climactic moment, the diction is strong, direct Anglo-Saxon. This is difficult. The comeshot should be fresh and original. Yet simple, basic language is the most effective. Resolving this paradox is one of the things erotic writers get paid for.

When the reader is not hot, most descriptions of comeshots look silly. So the writer has to see that the reader will be aroused before he gets to the comeshot. Much of what makes comeshots work is in the writing that leads up to them. If handled properly, when the comeshot arrives, the reader will be in no mood for detailed literary criticism.

He will just be looking for the green light. This is no license to attempt to pass off inferior work, but it should be reassuring to a writer who does not find quite the same thing in a scene that he reviews cold as he thought he wrote when he was more in the mood.

Rule seven: Maintain the point of view.

If "I" has the comeshot, "I" can feel it as well as see it. But if "he" has the comeshot, it has to be conveyed to us through "my" senses. That is, "I" tells us what "he" does so that we know "he" is coming well. But "I" cannot tell us exactly what "he" feels. Be in "I's" head or "his" head, but not both at once. In films and videos, the model has to pull out so that we can see the shot. That is not necessary in fiction, although a writer who is stronger on visual description certainly may decide to use external comeshots. The writer should play to his strength.

Rule eight: Little or no dialogue.

Let the character's cock do the talking. The place for large amounts of dirty talk is earlier in the story. Characters who have to shout something should make it short and sweet. Trite and no-longer-erotic utterances should be avoided. One exclamation point per utterance is quite sufficient, and if you have not worked the exclamation point to death when it was not really called for, it will be at its most effective. (No "I'm co-o-o-o-o-o-o-m-m-m-m-i-ng!!!!!!!!") Biblical references are best confined to earlier stages of the story. ("Jesus Christ, what a horsecock you got on you, sir!") Several anatomical improbabilities may be allowed, but do not make a character enunciate clearly while something substantial is in his mouth.

Rule nine: Get out quickly.

As soon as the comeshot has flown, jetted, squirted, splattered, splashed, flooded, gushed, shot, popped, or whatever, everybody else in the vicinity comes in the next paragraph without further ado.

If it is the end of the story, it is ended. If it is not the end of the story, there is a prompt fade-out to the next scene. As video producer John Summers once told me, "Nobody wants to spend a lot of time looking at a cock that's already thrown up."

Do not take my word for these rules. Read through the stories you get off to—sometime when you can do so with a cool head. Notice that most really hot stories follow most or all of these rules. Plenty of other aspects of the erotic story offer opportunities for innovation. But until you have a few sales under your belt, do not tamper with this tried-and-true construction of the comeshot.

If you remember why they call them "stroke" stories, you can easily see that the comeshot cannot be handled in any other way.

I doubt that any except erotic writers are still with us in this chapter. However, many principles of the comeshot are applicable to other kinds of writing. The solution is the key moment of the mystery. The final battle with the monster is the key moment of sci-fi, etc. Check how well these rules work when they are adapted to other genres.

For example, the character we feel most strongly about should be present for the climactic scene. We will be most interested in how this scene affects the main character. This is analogous to rule four. The detective in a detective story will untangle many mysteries, but only one of these is the masterstroke by which he solves the case. This is analogous to rule one.

As an exercise, see how many of the rules apply to as many different kinds of stories as you can think of. Recast the rules in the form that best applies to each of the various kinds of stories.

Like all story elements, the erotic scene should conform to the reader's expectations. That does not mean that the reader knows precisely what will happen. It means that if a story begins with mentions of whips and chains, the erotic scene should make some use of them. The writer may contrive to surprise the reader, but the surprise should not be that the reader has been reading the wrong story. If the erotic scene is going to contain bisexuality or other distasteful elements, the reader should have been given fair notice early in the story.

In fiction, as in life, humor is often overlooked in the erotic scene. The protagonist and the romantic interest go to bed with miens so somber that one might think they were going to the gallows. Perhaps this is no time for nonsense, but sex is supposed to be fun, remember? Writers could do worse than to put the play back into foreplay.

For those not intimately familiar with the species: one of the most endearing traits of the supposedly straight trick is his peculiar sense of humor; the joking insults as a defense against intimacy express his affection in the boudoir as well as at the construction site. Self-effacing humor goes with the self-confidence of an enormous cock as much as Crisco goes with a knuckle enema. A giggle does no harm to the hard-on that knows what it is about. Lighten up.

Spontaneity in general is not compatible with good writing, but the appearance of spontaneity is. The erotic scene must seem to be, at its climax, both spontaneous and inevitable.

Sincerity covers a multitude of sins. A new writer is well advised to stick close to scenes that he himself finds irresistibly arousing. Even if that scene is a bit out of the ordinary, or not to a particular reader's taste, the writer's excitement will communicate itself as surely as a college boy gets horny when his roommate jerks off. Some writers admit to masturbating while they write their erotic scenes, but that is not done so easily by the touch typist. However, no erotic scene was ever harmed by being drafted when its author was exceptionally horny.

One writer I know of, to keep himself honest and to maintain a keen edge on the erotic scene, refused to write fictional erotic scenes until his career was fairly advanced. He adhered strictly to his own erotic experiences, although he recorded them in fictional stories. Yet, when he departed from this policy, he was able to write convincingly of scenes that he had never experienced in reality or in his own fantasies. However, he worked on the fictional scenes until they developed for him many qualities of a memory.

The erotic scene is the jewel of the erotic story. The writer may justify the effort of rewriting this scene many times. When a writer finds himself as much physically affected by the tenth draft as he was by the first, he knows he is on to something.

The writer must be as nude in his own way as the photographic model two pages back in the magazine. The writer must show his literary equipment. Coy clutching of the bedclothes over essential parts, the soft-focus lens of romance writing, the fade-out to a metaphor will not do. The reader cannot be expected to get off while the writer holds back like a five-dollar hustler.

Effectiveness is the criterion for the erotic scene. The rules given here are guides to effectiveness; but if the scene is effective, the rules are off. Make the reader want it. Make the reader wait. Then give it to him as well as you know how. All of it.

8. *The Market, Records, and the Sale*

Neither annual market books for writers nor monthly writers' magazines contain much information on the gay market. The writer of gay erotica is on his own. In many ways, this is not a bad thing. "Know your market!" is a sacred saying of the writing business. A mass-market writer may buy a market book and think that is all there is to it. That is a serious error, and one a gay writer, who has to buy issues to get the addresses of magazines, may avoid.

Build a market list of periodicals.
Step by step, this is how to build a market list of periodicals:

1. Get recent issues of gay magazines (or whatever magazines you think you may want to sell stories to), as many different titles as possible. Start with those around the house if they are recent. It is better to get a few different magazines each month than to subscribe to only one or two.

Naturally, as a writer, you carry a pocket-sized notebook and pens wherever you go. You are unlikely to be allowed to borrow recent issues, but many gentlemen will be happy to allow you to look at their magazines at their apartments, perhaps over cocktails. After you know what you are looking for, you can obtain the information you need in under ten minutes.

2. However you obtain the information, copy it into a large notebook you keep at your desk.

3. On a blank page in your notebook, enter the title of the magazine.

4. About two pages into the magazine is the contents page. At the bottom of the contents page, or in a vertical column on a nearby page, is the masthead. The masthead is a box containing the names and titles of the people who work for the magazine.

(Notice the number of names. Contributors are only freelances like you. Contributing editors are only contributors who somehow rate this entirely honorary title. The staff of a gay magazine is seldom as many as a half-dozen people. Compare this number of people to the number named in the masthead of a mass-market magazine like *Vanity Fair*, *Esquire*, or *Newsweek*. Think about this comparison when you do not get an instant report on your submission or when your story has not been edited perfectly.)

Look for the name of the editor in the masthead. Look for the person whose title is most nearly plain "editor." Write that name in your notebook. In truth, you will probably never receive a letter from the editor. (Writers deal almost exclusively with associate editors or assistant editors. "Editor" is used in later parts of this book to mean the person who is editing your work, but the title of that person usually is "associate editor.") But until you have a reply, address all your correspondence to the editor by name and title.

(In fact, anyone who works for the publication, including the publisher, may read the "slush." "Slush" is one of the nicer words for unsolicited manuscripts, including yours. Sorry.)

5. Under the masthead or at the bottom of the table of contents is a bunch of tiny type. Look there for the address of the editorial office, which may be different from the corporate address, the subscription address, or several advertising addresses. Write the editorial address in your notebook.

Read the rest of the tiny type. Is there a copyright notice?

Note if there is a notice.

All magazines say they are not responsible for unsolicited manuscripts. Note any stronger discouraging language. Almost all gay magazines have disclaimers regarding the ages of photographic models and the meaning of terms like "kid," "boy," and "son," and disclaimers regarding drawing conclusions about the sexualities of the photographic models. Become familiar with the standard forms of these disclaimers so that you can note any significant deviations.

Some mass-market magazines that say they never buy unsolicited manuscripts, in fact, do buy an over-the-transom (another word for "slush") submission from time to time. In the gay market, however, do not send your manuscripts where they are unwanted.

6. Look at the contents page. Does it list any fiction at all? A beginner will find it hard enough to sell fiction to magazines that use plenty of it. He hardly needs the disappointment that will result from sending stories to magazines that never or rarely print stories. Enter on the appropriate page of your notebook the number or the date of the issue of the magazine that you examined. Enter the titles of the short stories (if any) and the bylines of the stories. A few magazines do not show the bylines on the contents page; in these cases, turn to the stories to find the bylines.

Enter the approximate length in words of each story. To find the approximate length, count the words found in one inch of a column and multiply this number by the length in inches of all the columns in the story. If the width of the columns changes, of course adjust this procedure accordingly. Make an educated guess if the words in a column wrap around an illustration. This word count is for your own information and it will serve its purpose if it is accurate to within 300 or 400 words.

7. Read the stories.

For the moment, ignore the titles, the blurbs (editorial comments about the story meant to entice you to read it), and pullouts (excerpts set in large type).

With a little experience you can scan most stories instead of reading them word for word. Devise a shorthand way of recording the nature of the stories. For erotica, the personal-ad code can be used to summarize the kinds of people and sex in the story and a number of stories will fall into categories: biker, cowboy, frat house, and so forth. Some stories can be further classified according to genre: detective, one-night-stand, romance, science fiction, historical (specify the period), and so forth. Describe the story in a line or two.

If you work in other genres, of course you will need a different format to catalog stories. If you do not know enough about your chosen genre to devise a suitable scheme, you have not read enough of it.

Pay particular attention to stories that are difficult to categorize or that differ in many ways from the run of the mill. The magazines that run such stories are surely more receptive to really original work.

8. Now study the titles, blurbs, and pullouts. In confession magazines, these are always racier than any story the publication would consider running. The confession "I was a part-time mistress" cannot turn out to be the story of a prostitute, but is always that of a dutiful wife who plays the part of a mistress in enacting her husband's fantasies to save their marriage.

But, in most magazines, the story described in the large type describes the story the editor wished he could have run. There is always some discrepancy between the story described in large type and the story that is actually printed. But when the difference is very great, you may see the opportunity of providing the editor with a story that is more like the one he wanted.

9. If you wish, note features that pay for reader's experiences, jokes, or other fillers. By the word, fillers are the best-paying part of any magazine that does pay for them. Some writers specialize in fillers.

I do not suggest that you write fillers. Sometimes you will run across an item that is right for one of these features, or you will write a one-page fantasy that has no chance of going anywhere as a story but may do as a reader's experience. Few freelances are doing so well that they would not welcome a $25 check for a few minutes' work or for material that is otherwise valueless.

Fillers are sold on an all-rights basis and seldom carry a credit line. Sometimes even publications that do not advertise the fact will pay freelancers for readers' experiences. Be sure, however, if a payment is not advertised, that you arrange for payment first. Unless an editor has agreed to payment beforehand, he is entitled to use submissions to a readers' column free.

10. When you visit a newsstand, flip to the mastheads and the table of contents of familiar magazines. When the editor's name has changed, or there is a change in the pattern of the fiction, examine the issue more closely.

11. Include in your survey magazines you would not ordinarily buy as a consumer. Some magazines advertise in other magazines; order sample copies of the unfamiliar ones. For market magazines, you do not need the all-picture magazines that some magazines bill as too hot for their regular issues. These do not contain stories and naturally do not buy stories. Hard-core magazines sometimes contain considerable copy, but it is not bought from freelances.

Do not ignore magazines on pulp or those using only or mainly black-and-white photos. Some such magazines do not pay freelances well or quickly, but others are reliable markets. Production quality is not well correlated with treatment of writers.

12. Cross-reference sister publications in your notebook. Some magazines make a point of mentioning their relationship to others. When they do not, you can detect the relationship by looking for a coincidence of editorial address.

13. When you make a new entry in your notebook, write a letter to the publication—but not if it is related to a publication you have written before. Address the editor by name. Write: "If you have available prepared writers' guidelines, I would be pleased to receive a copy. I have enclosed a #10 SASE. Sincerely,..."

SASE means self-addressed, stamped envelope. A #10 envelope is an ordinary business-sized envelope, about $4^{1/8}$ inches by $9^{1/2}$ inches. Use #10 envelopes for all your business correspondence.

A short letter like this needs only two first-class stamps: one for the letter and one for the return envelope. Do not get the envelopes mixed up. Attach the SASE (folded into thirds lengthwise) to your letter with a paper clip. Record this transaction—the expenditure of two stamps—in your transaction journal. Show the date, the name of the addressee, the amount of the postage expended, and the purpose of the letter (in this case "request guidelines").

14. When you receive a response, staple the mail cover—your SASE—to the response and do not throw the response away, even if it discourages you from sending anything to the publication. Of course, you hope the response will help you prepare a submission that the periodical will buy; but even if it does not, it does help to prove that you are conducting your writing career as a business—which the IRS may ask you to prove.

Periodicals that most want freelance contributions respond quickly (that means within a month) and state what they want to buy, what they pay, and on what terms. Most likely, the guidelines will apply to all the related publications. If so, do not then request guidelines from the related publications.

Some requests for guidelines will go unanswered. Some publications that buy freelance work simply do not have prepared guidelines. But at first you should concentrate on publications that responded to your request.

If you follow the above procedure for a few months, you will have a better market list than you can find in any book and a better one than most of your competitors, including some who have worked in the market for a long time.

(In the gay market, however, there are serious drawbacks to thinking of other writers—especially the good ones—as competitors. Only a fraction of literate gay men buys erotica regularly. Although the market is small, it has plenty of room to grow and will grow if more good writers produce better gay erotica. Magazine and book publishers do receive many more manuscripts than they could ever print, but most of the manuscripts are horrible. Editors seldom complain of having to return too many great manuscripts, although the kinder sort of rejection slip seems to imply such a complaint. Not enough good writers are working to keep the magazines full of good stories, as a careful market survey should reveal. Good writers are always happy to see other good writers working in the market. As always, there is plenty of room at the top.)

Understand the market.

Although you should send for writers' guidelines and should read them, guidelines are seldom informative or accurate in describing the kind of stories a magazine buys. A better guide is the magazine itself.

A guideline might say: "We want stories that go beyond the usual formula stroke piece." Yet when you read the magazine— the stories the magazine actually bought—you may find the stories are all ordinary formula stroke pieces. If you do have a story that transcends formula, send it first to a magazine that is printing such stories.

Guidelines are better at describing stories a magazine does *not* want. Taboos vary. Magazines sometimes run stories that violate their taboos, but a beginner should not ask an editor to consider a story that lies outside the magazine's guidelines. Likewise, sometimes magazines run stories that far exceed the length requirements given in the guidelines. Such a story might have got read because the editor recognized the byline, or because the editor happened to have two good stories that were too short and he was looking for something longer to take up the extra space. But, on a normal day, if the editor picks up a story that feels too thick, he is very likely to shift it to the reject pile without reading it.

Many periodicals have a rapid editorial turnover: editors quit; editors are fired; editors are rehired and quit again. A new editor, even one who enjoys the confidence of the publisher, is frustrated in his attempt to change the direction of the magazine. The magazine he puts together today may not appear on the stands for six months. What the writer and the public see is his predecessor's product. Moreover, the previous editor has probably committed the magazine to an inventory of stories that the new editor is obliged to use.

Watch for indications of new directions in writers' guidelines and elsewhere. Editorial turnover is an opportunity for new writers (and a peril for frequent contributors). While many editors are happy to discover new talent when they can, the new editor is especially eager to develop a stable of freelances of his own.

Late payment occurs with several magazines that are otherwise good customers. Some magazines clearly never intend to pay writers on time, and that is the way they have done business for years. Other magazines have occasional cash-flow problems. Still others are on their way out of business.

Watch for sudden changes that suggest a financial problem. The *change* is the important factor. Some magazines have always been slim, some have always been printed on newsprint, and some have always had black-and-white photos on the inside pages. Those magazines may be quite healthy. But a magazine that changes suddenly from thick to thin, from slick pages to newsprint, from color to black-and-white, may be in trouble. You may not want to send stories to such a magazine until the situation stabilizes.

The magazines that always pay late are a fact of life. You may want to keep them on your list and to send them stories rejected by everyone else. After all, late payment is better than no pay-ment.

You should eliminate from your list slick magazines that do not pay freelances. A magazine that can find the money for slick paper and four-color photos but cannot find the money to pay writers clearly does not have its heart in the right place. You may want to eliminate some magazines for moral reasons: for example, trendy, new, slick magazines aimed at the gay market but which have virtually no gay content. Move magazines that did not respond to your request for guidelines to the bottom of your list, but do not scratch them off. You may want to send them some excess inventory from time to time, just to see what they are about. Just about at the bottom go low-paying magazines that use only formula pieces by the same three or four writers every month.

At the top of your list (and everyone else's) go magazines

that pay on acceptance or within thirty days of acceptance. ("On acceptance" does not mean there is a check in the letter accepting your story, but means when the accounting department gets around to cutting you a check, which amounts to the same thing as within thirty days.) Reserve a special place for magazines that may not pay well but often run innovative, well-written stories.

That you do not like the stories in a magazine should not necessarily commit it to the deep. Think what it is you do not like. If the ideas are stale and the stories poorly written, the editor knows that as well as you do and will welcome your fine work. (A few publications in the market do aim for mediocrity. This is the McPorno theory of publishing. Some publishers think that readers want a predicable product even if it is bland and boring. Be suspicious if a magazine never runs anything better.)

Perhaps all the stories in a magazine contain boots and whips, whereas you are the sort of person more likely to giggle at the sight of a studded jockstrap than to breathe heavily. While he was an editor at *Drummer,* Aaron Travis wrote to a contributor: "SM is ultimately about obsession, will, and imbalances of power; it can be represented by the crudely overt (Masters and Slaves) or by the exquisitely subtle." Titclamps and leather are the window dressing of the SM story. If you write well enough and can find something worthy of your talent in the complex dynamics of submission and defiance, pain and pleasure, and freedom and bondage, then you certainly may dispense with the cheap props.

If every issue of a magazine is a theme issue and the fiction always follows the theme, you are unlikely to be able to guess what themes will be under consideration when your story reaches the editor. Once you are publishing regularly, you may develop a contact who will tell you what themes are being considered.

Many magazines are themed loosely around the seasons. Learn to think in magazine time. If you write a ski lodge story in late October and it lands on the editor's desk during the second week of November, the editor will be working on the swimsuit issue for May or June. Many editors would be pleased to receive— in June—a cheerful little secular Christmas story. Note that both the December and the January issues are on the newsstand before Christmas, and both are billed as special gala holiday issues.

Some stories are set in any season. Some publications, and particularly those which are numbered rather than dated, take no notice of the changing of the seasons. Sometimes an editor will think a balmy, tropical-nights story a nice diversion for a February issue. But generally, when you send seasonal material at an appropriate time, you show a professional regard for an editor's needs. Editors notice and remember getting what they needed when they needed it.

Lead time of most gay magazines is about six months. Printing four-color photographs at reasonable rates takes that long (and it is the photographs that most magazines are about). If a story turns on some bit of news or a fad that is likely to be short-lived, the story will seem very stale when it appears. This drives article writers nuts—and it is also why articles in this market are interviews with timeless divas, and historical and travel pieces, rather than breaking news. If a story is based on prescience, the editor must share your foresight. Stories relying on things less certain than the changing of the seasons are risky. Risk is not a quality that editors are hoping to find in stories.

When magazines are dated, the date is usually when the magazine goes *off* sale. This doubles the writer's chances. A Valentine's Day story might go in the February issue, which says it is the February issue right on the cover, or it might go in the March issue that will be on sale on Valentine's Day. Publications that are numbered rather than dated usually will not be interested in seasonal material. They might buy a Fourth of July story, but that it is a Fourth of July story is less likely to be a selling point, and they probably will not try to put it in an issue that is available around the Fourth of July. And, of course, even an editor who is looking for a horrific Halloween story will not buy a horrible one.

I hope that no one has bought this book with the thought that he might sell a homoerotic story to *Harper's* or *The Atlantic*. James Baldwin could sell a story with homoerotic elements to *Playboy*. You cannot. Some crossover plays, movies, and novels have cracked the mass market. The following elements are accepted by general audiences: stereotypical drag queens, homosexuals from far away and long ago, discreet or insane lesbians, bisexuals (especially ones who are good parents), dead homosexuals, dying homosexuals, homosexuals who affirm nongay values, very unhappy homosexuals, silly homosexuals, psychotic homosexuals (especially if murderously misogynistic), guilty homosexuals, homosexuals who want families, old and harmless homosexuals, alcoholic homosexuals (better if also consumptive), homosexuals who never kiss, and the old standby, evergreen favorite: suicidal homosexuals (best if successfully suicidal). If it appears in fiction on the pages of *The New Yorker* it may be a homosexual; it is not a gay man.

Because homosexuals are amply supplied in the mass market, it is unnecessary to create them for the gay market.

Gay magazines throughout the market, kinky and vanilla, publish stories that are off their usual beat (far more often than, say, you would find a *Redbook* story in *Ms.* or a *Saturday Evening Post* story in *Commentary*). Sometimes a writer composes a story with one gay magazine in mind, gets the story back with a rejection slip, and then sells the story to a magazine that has never published anything like it before. Send a story first to the magazine most likely to buy it. But, if that fails, send it out again and again.

Every writer gets rejection slips.

New writers get more rejection slips. Part of the reason is obvious: Beginners' stories are often not so good. A large part, too, is that experienced writers less often write a story without some idea of where to sell it and more often send stories to the correct magazine. Fame is a smaller factor than new writers think.

Even good stories get rejected, even when they are prepared properly and sent to an appropriate magazine. When a magazine is overstocked, stories must be returned. A story may be good, but too similar to a story the magazine is already committed to. A story may be rejected by mistake or by quirk. Good stories can be rejected for many reasons having nothing to do with the quality of the work.

By the time a story comes back, the writer should be able to look at it more objectively. Read it again for typos. Revise it again if that seems necessary. Then send it out again.

The indispensable Aaron Travis advises: Never send a story back to an editor who has rejected it unless he has explicitly asked to see it after certain changes are made. A friendly editor who sees something promising in your work may take the time to jot a few notes on how a story might be improved. That is not an invitation to resubmit a story and, according to Travis, a story resubmitted under these circumstances almost never works out. Instead, send the editor who was interested in your work another story and the first story—whether or not you decide to revise it—to another editor.

(I have sold a story I resubmitted, but only to an editor who was already buying most of my work and after an exchange of many letters. The editor objected to it because it was one of the first safe-sex stories to appear in a national magazine and, for that reason, the effort involved in coercing the editor to accept it was worth my while. From a business standpoint, resubmission does not pay off.)

Naturally, do not hesitate to resubmit a story to a magazine that has changed editors. If an editor has bought some of your work, be sure to send him stories if he moves to another magazine in the market. When an editor buys one of your stories, send him another right away.

However, do not let a magazine that pays on publication acquire too large an inventory of your work until you have some experience in dealing with it. If it has agreed to buy two or three stories, do not send more until you are confident that the magazine meets its obligations. Sometimes a magazine will keep a story in inventory for a very long time—a complaint I hear more frequently these days from writers in the straight market. When a very great delay occurs (more than a year after the story was accepted, or more than several months beyond a scheduled publication date, if there was one) you may wish to write the editor to ask if the magazine is still interested in the story. If there is a new editor, he may offer to return the story. In theory, you should be offered a kill fee (a percentage of the agreed price). In practice, this does not occur in the gay market. If you continue to hear nothing about your story for many months, you may write again. Ultimately, you can send the editor a certified letter stating that you are withdrawing the story. Then you can sell the story to another publication, provided that you have a carbon or electronic copy of the story.

Free work.

As a rule, writers should not work for free.

An exception should be made for small, gay community publications or other community publications where no one gets paid or makes a profit. Not many holdovers from the underground presses of the sixties still exist.

Most local gay papers and certainly most local straight entertainment papers are profit-making ventures that can afford to pay something. Be realistic in your expectations of payment and do not insist on copyrighting material, such as a bar-gossip column, that cannot possibly be of any further value.

Adopt a local paper as home base. Few of the papers run fiction and, in general, journalism is not especially good training for fiction; but there are several advantages to having a pet local paper.

First, any kind of writing for publication helps you to demystify your own copy. Communicating with the written word is a tricky business. When your copy is read by an editor, you soon will learn the freakish interpretations that can be put to what you thought was direct English prose. You will discover that words do not always mean what you think they mean. You may also get the chance to see what happens when an editor alters a comma in a vicious, vain queen's copy.

Second, the experience of seeing copy transformed into print is very useful. At many little publications, everyone helps in the copy editing and pasting up. You can learn what printers understand and what they do not. You can find out what it is to have to shorten a tightly written story by several lines to make it fit space, come to understand the differences between copy and proof and, more importantly, the differences in what can be done with each, and gain the ability to look at a piece of copy and envision what it will look like in print.

Third, most such publications exchange issues with like publications elsewhere. As a member of the staff, you can pore over this material to keep in touch with what is happening in the rest of the country—usually while the news is still new. You can acquire the addresses of the papers while you are at it.

Fourth, you may get the opportunity to review books. The

reviewer may not get money, but he ought to get the review copies of the books he writes about. This is an inexpensive way of acquiring a nice library and a knowledge of gay book publishing. In reviewing books, it is desirable to actually read the books, to avoid panning the works of one's betters, and to make constructive remarks.

Do not agree to edit. Many of these publications sustain their precarious existences by burning out one editor after another. Beware of being caught up in the frenzy. Limit what you will do, but do that well.

The book market.

The book market is more reliably covered in *Literary Market Place* and *Writers' Market* than the magazine market. Once you contemplate writing a book, you will have plenty of time to research the market. Few publishers will want to hear from you until you have completed your manuscript—especially if it is fiction.

Most publishers have a particular flavor to their lists, but the books a publisher issues are much more diverse than the stories a magazine buys. Book publishers have fewer absolute taboos. Without being foolhardy, write the book you want to write, and then find a publisher.

At present, only one or two publishers in the country regularly issue frank works of gay erotica. A few others will issue anthologies of gay erotica and, rarely, a novel that is pretty hot. The shame is that none of the small gay houses still issues erotica—at least, not written erotica.

I except here the book factories that buy works for hire that are sold only in adult video stores and by mail order through little ads in the backs of gay magazines. Some people have a talent for producing these works and can turn out one in a week. Payment is about $400 for 40,000 words. If you wrote one of these every week and sold it, you would be making more money than 99 percent of all freelances ever make regularly. But you would not get your name on the covers of the books, you would never be invited to a book signing, and not even the sleaziest publication in the country would ever review your books. And, of course, you will never get a dime more for the work than what you were paid at first.

Even if you wanted to, you probably could not give up on selling your novel to a real publisher and sell it instead to one of the book manufacturers. Their guidelines are too strict to admit a book written with serious intent.

Real books come in three kinds:

Hardcover books which seldom sell for less than $20. I assume that every reader knows what a hardback book is. Hardly any gay erotica is issued in hardcover except one or two anthologies and soft-core picture books that are supposed to be art.

Trade paperbacks are paperbacks designed to be sold in bookstores. These are seldom cheaper than $12. They are put together like hardcover books and use a high-quality paper. Only a few works of gay erotica are issued in this form, although many namby-pamby issues of the gay presses appear in this form.

Mass-market paperbacks are the kind of paperbacks you see in wire racks at supermarkets. The paper is coarser than that used in trade paperbacks, and a variety of processes are used in the bindings. However thick these books are, they seldom sell for more than $10, and most for $6 or $7. Gay erotica, of course, does not turn up in many supermarkets, but most of it is issued in books of this format.

Aside from frankly erotic books, there are many gay books of all three kinds issued both by very big houses and by the smaller gay presses. Since erotica is out of the picture at the gay presses, there is virtually no difference between the sort of book that might appear on the gay list of a big house and the sort of book that might be issued by one of the gay presses. Thus you might as well submit your book where you are likely to get the most money, which is with a large house that issues gay titles in hardcover.

Records.

Records are an essential part of any business. For a writer, some records are an important part of the creative process.

Copies. The importance of keeping copies of everything you write cannot be overemphasized. Always keep a copy of any material you send out. If you work on a typewriter, keep a carbon copy or a photocopy. The trouble and expense of making such copies is nothing compared to the disaster of a lost manuscript. Writers who work electronically may feel secure because their material exists in disk files. But there is no security in a disk file that is not backed up. Indeed, one hears more often now of material lost through hard-disk crashes than of material lost in the mails—and the postal service has not improved.

Writers should make some provision to save false starts, sketches, and notes. Electronic writers should resist the impulse to send such fragments to oblivion. The writer with a typewriter should have little difficulty keeping a box for such odd papers, but the computerized writer will find it a little harder to remember to save a scrap to directory reserved for such items. Again, the electronic writer will have more difficulty going through his scraps, but the effort frequently pays off.

Many ideas age well. Sometimes, after six months, or even after several years, the writer's perspective on a scrap may change or develop. And a scrap may give a writer something to work with when he is staring blankly at a white page or a screen. I have got stories from a single line jotted on the back of a business card and from a few yellowing pages of typescript.

Plot lines, images, characterizing details, and authentic speech usages do not descend upon the writer like manna. Good fiction is based upon acute observation. Memory dulls observation. If you cannot record what you observe in a journal—and I, for one, find journals tedious—form the habit of jotting notes when you observe things of significance. What exactly is significant is hard to say: a peculiar way that someone uses a word that reveals his mental equation, how a shadow falls on the psi-shaped line that divides a beachboy's abdomen from his thigh, what he says when he has been fucked properly for the first time and does not know what to say, a curious graffito, a discarded item on the pier: what it is, why someone brought it, why it was discarded.

No one can command insight, but anyone can be ready when it comes. Being ready means having a stub of pencil and something to write on: Scribble, scribble, scribble. It is yours.

Even a computerized writer may keep a scrap box, for not many will take the time to enter every scrap into a file. Each little note goes into the scrap box to wait its turn to come to the top to be fit into a mosaic of fiction.

"Where do you get your material?" fans will ask someday. Then you must smile discreetly and avoid laughing in their faces.

Needless to say, completed works must be saved even if they have be offered in vain to every appropriate publisher. In time the right way to revise the material may occur to you, or you may wake one day to discover publishers who beg you to send them *anything*.

Correspondence. You should also form the habit of saving correspondence: originals of incoming mail and copies of your replies. Naturally, all items of business correspondence must be saved as business records: your requests for guidelines, the guidelines themselves, cover letters of manuscripts, queries of all kinds, even rejection slips. These records help to show that you are in business, even though a particular item, such as a rejection slip, is of no other use in itself.

Make and save copies of more personal correspondence. My very successful *Travels with Lizbeth* began with letters I wrote to Steven Saylor that he had the foresight to save. Those letters seemed trivial to me when I wrote them. But even letters that seem trivial may contain good ideas or fortuitous turns of phrase. In the literary business you are likely to acquire a number of very literate correspondents who will inspire you to write very thoughtful and literate responses. Whether you use your correspondence or not, save it. Your biographer will be very pleased to have such a wealth of material.

Transaction journal. The transaction journal is the financial record of your freelance writing business. You must keep such a record for tax purposes, and you ought to keep it so that you can use it for planning. The transaction journal shows that you are in business—a useful thing because, to many people, a freelance writer looks like a bum. If you are successful, it will show that, and you may be able to use it to establish credit.

If you keep the transaction journal properly, it will serve many purposes. Almost everything you do in the writing business costs money; so if you describe your transactions adequately, the transaction journal is a history of your activities. If you cannot recall how long a story has been on an editor's desk, you can turn to a well-kept transaction journal to see when you spent the postage to mail the story. If you keep your transaction journal up-to-date and you make detailed entries in it, you probably will not need to keep a card file to keep track of your manuscripts.

The transaction journal should be kept in a small book with sewn, prenumbered pages. Entries should be made in ink, with corrections made so that the originals are not obliterated, but are struck through with single lines.

Entries in the journal usually have the following parts: date, category, audit number, amount, and description. The date is the date of the transaction: the day you spent money or used a stamp, or the day you received a payment.

The category helps you to break out expenses at tax time. You may wish to keep records of business expenses that are not deductible or not fully deductible according to current tax law; be sure these expenses are recorded in categories of their own, apart from possibly similar categories of expenses that are fully deductible. Consult current tax forms to set up categories that will help you fill out Schedule C more easily. Some categories that might be useful for a beginning freelance are:

Commissions and fees: commissions you pay to an agent if you have one;

Depreciation: if you have chosen to depreciate equipment;

Legal and professional services: legal and accounting fees;

Office expense: if you qualify for the home office expense or if you keep an office apart from your home;

Repairs and maintenance: parts, and labor if you pay someone else to do the work;

Travel: travel, including local fares, you do for your business, and your meals while out of town on business; you may want to keep two categories of travel expenses, one for travel that can be supported as a 100 percent-deductible expense, and another for travel that you believe you do for your business but may not be fully supportable as a business expense on your taxes;

Vehicle use: for business use of your own car;

Meals and entertainment: this is for business lunches and so forth where you entertain someone else and supposedly conduct business, an expense that is not fully deductible;

Telephone: all long-distance calls you make in the course of your business and other business telephone expenses, but you cannot deduct the cost of local service to the first line to your home;

Equipment: equipment you buy that you choose not to depreciate;

Supplies: paper, ink, pens, staples, and so forth; technically, supplies are things that you expect to use up in a year or less, but inexpensive equipment items, like staplers or books, are often entered as supplies;

Postage: stamps as you expend them,

Printing and copying: for many businesses, this would be a supply expense, but because this is likely to be an especially important expense for your business, you may want a separate category;

Dues: this may not be a fully deductible expense under new IRS rules;

Publications: again, you may want a separate category for this expense because of the special importance of books and magazines to a literary business.

You are better off having more narrow categories than a few broad ones because it is much easier, if it is necessary to do so, to combine several small categories than to break out expenses from a general category. In particular, you should keep records of expenses which you feel reflect the cost of doing business even if those expenses are not deductible, but you want to keep these in separate categories that you will not claim on your taxes. Of course you must also have a *Revenues* category for payments you receive.

The audit number is merely a serial number. Call the first

transaction you record in a year 101, the next 102, and so forth. The audit number is used to identify documents that are related to the transaction. When you enter a purchase, copy the audit number on the receipt that is related to the entry. When you enter a revenue, copy the audit number to the payment memorandum that accompanied the check. File the supporting documents according to audit number. Then it will be an easy thing to provide the document that supports a given transaction if you are required to do so.

Some sample journal entries:

DATE	DESCRIPTION CATEGORY	AUDIT #	AMOUNT
1/10	SUPPLIES Mailer for return of Swamp Studs to typesetter; from Floydada Drug-store	105	1.09
1/18	POSTAGE Return galleys of Swamp Studs to typesetter by priority mail to Wm. Rubble & Co.	106	3.09
1/31	REVENUES Payment for "Hot Wax" from ManTime Magazines, Inc.; appeared in Nov. issue	107	(125.00)

Notice that the payment is entered in as a negative number (is enclosed in parentheses). In this particular bookkeeping system, revenues are entered as negative amounts and expenses are entered as positive amounts. Bookkeeping systems are beyond the scope of this book. The important thing is to make the record. If your business is small, you probably will not need a bookkeeping system. As your business grows, you may choose to learn bookkeeping, to employ an accountant, or to obtain bookkeeping software. Whatever you do, the transaction journal will remain the key document.

In this system you enter the postage expense when you actually use the stamp and the revenue when you actually receive the check. This is called a cash account. It is suitable for a small business. However, you should also make notational entries that have no figure in the amount column for other kinds of events involving money.

2/1	NOTATION 111—	Bought stamps at Floydada Station, $22
4/4	NOTATION 134—	"Guys in G-Strings" to *Blueballs*, $200. First NA Serial Rights, payable on publication to appear in October.

One of these entries shows the purchase of stamps expected to be used in the business. The other shows a sale, although the author does not expect to receive the money until October. Another entry might be the purchase of a computer which will not be paid for until another time. The amounts are not entered in the amount column because this is a cash system, and amounts are not entered until they are actually received or paid. A system in which debts are entered in the amounts column when they are incurred and income is entered in the amounts column when it is earned is called an accrual system. Accrual systems are difficult for freelance businesses and require a greater knowledge of bookkeeping than can be imparted here.

The Market Notebook. The market notebook and how it is constructed is described at the beginning of this chapter.

Blue Thesaurus. A recurring problem for the writer of erotica is that sooner or later you must get down to that same old thing. Bringing fresh prose to timeless acts can be very difficult. Unfortunately, writers often overreach themselves in the attempt to invent new figures of speech.

A blue thesaurus may be helpful. It is a loose-leaf notebook with dividers for various erotic subjects. Draw a vertical line down the center of the pages. On one side of the line, enter apt or effective expressions you find in the works of others. That side is for study. On the other side of the line, enter expressions you make up which seem promising to you. That side is for use. When you are stuck for a bit of description or an expression, look through your entries. Of course, writers in other genres will have differing difficulties: for example, new ways to describe gloomy old mansions.

Sometimes it is impossible to top a phrase you have read. Do not be discouraged. No one yet has bettered the *National Lampoon*'s Chris Miller, who wrote the immortal "throbbing, tanned, athletic penis."

The Sale.

Short fiction is not queried. That is, the author does not write the editor of the magazine to see whether the editor is interested in the story, but sends the manuscript whole with a return envelope and return postage. The manuscript should be accompanied by a cover letter.

I do not like to write cover letters, and seldom write them. But some editors, even some who never read cover letters, like to see that they are there. Since a cover letter is very brief, there is plenty of space on it for editorial notes, and that may be all that it is good for. (You never get the cover letter back unless someone makes a mistake.)

Here is the whole text of a cover letter: Enclosed is "Pro Jocks in Heat" which I hope you will find of interest to *ManTime* readers. I am sending photocopies because they are clearer than the originals, but this story is not under consideration elsewhere at this time.

I admire the production quality of *ManTime* very much,

and especially enjoyed the June center spread of Lance Thudd.

My first book *Swamp Studs* will be issued by GayBOOKS!!! this fall. Please let me know if you do not receive a review copy. It deals with coming out as a gay man in the gay ghetto of Floydada, Texas.

Typed single-spaced, this letter would take up about two inches in the center of a page. No cover letter should be more than twice as long.

Mention of publication credits, if you have them, is very useful. It tells the editor that someone else thinks you can write. Evidence that you have looked at the magazine before will be welcome; the editor gets many submissions from people who have no idea what the magazine is about. The photocopies are explained because editors do not like to read material that is under consideration elsewhere, and photocopies are suspect on that score. (Naturally, if you have sent photocopies, they are good xerographic photocopies and not copies you have run off on thermal fax paper.) If you are making a simultaneous submission, admit it in the cover letter. The editor will never forgive you if she has not been warned and tries to buy a story that has already been spoken for.

Likewise, if the story has appeared elsewhere, say so in the cover letter. With very few exceptions, major gay magazines will not buy second rights.

Most important is what does *not* go in the cover letter: bomb threats, accounts of your lifelong friendship with the publisher, detailed descriptions of your dog's starving to death—if only you could make a sale and get it something to eat. I do not exaggerate by much. Many would-be writers put many flaky statements in cover letters. However, if you have the body of death and are willing to do anything to get into print, stick an 8-by-10 of yourself in the envelope. Nude.

(New-writer paranoia being what it is, I ought to say immediately that business is *not* conducted that way. The 8-by-10 won't sell your story unless the story is passable. But it might get you a center spread.)

The cover letter, the story manuscript, and the sufficiently stamped, self-addressed return envelope are all clipped with a large stainless-steel paper clip (or some other rustless paper clip). Nothing is stapled or pinned. No brads, binders, or plastic covers. Address the envelope to the editor by name and title and affix sufficient postage.

After what seems like a very long time you will (usually) receive either your manuscript back with a rejection slip or an offer to buy certain rights in the manuscript. Naturally, you will not have spent all that time waiting by your mailbox, but will have begun work on something else as soon as you mailed the manuscript. In fact, it is a good habit to put two or three pages of the *next* work through your typewriter or word processor before you leave your desk with the finished manuscript.

You should allow three or four months for consideration of the manuscript, although most magazines will respond somewhat sooner. After that time (unless the magazine has stated in guidelines or in the tiny type under the masthead that it requires a longer time), write a polite letter to the editor inquiring about the status of your manuscript. If there is no response to that, you might as well consider the manuscript lost. (Always, always, always retain a copy of a manuscript you put in the mail.) When a manuscript is lost, nothing can be gained and much may be lost by writing nasty letters. Before you send the story elsewhere, write a letter to the editor saying that you presume the manuscript is lost and you are withdrawing it from consideration. You can send this letter through the regular mail. In this case, the magazine never agreed to buy the story. Unless an editor begs for forgiveness, move him to the bottom of your list.

Assuming the response is an offer to buy certain rights, you may accept the offer, you may write to clarify the offer, you may make a counteroffer, or you may decline the offer outright (which will win you no popularity points). When you send a story to a magazine that has stated terms and rates in writers' guidelines or market books, you should be willing to accept those terms and rates, at least for your first few sales. In the gay market, rates are absolutely flat at many magazines, and you will be offered no more and no less than I would be offered for a story. At other magazines, there is no such thing as a standard offer; but, in any event, an offer to an unknown writer for his first sale to the magazine is likely to be inflexible.

Except for short filler items, you should not be asked to sell all rights to a magazine. This was customary under the old copyright law, but is not the way things are done today. One magazine I can think of still operates as was common under the old law. It insists on buying all rights; but, as was done under the old law, routinely returns unused rights to the author upon request after publication. Rights are returned simply by a letter from the editor stating that he is returning the rights, but requesting that letter can be a pain if you are trying to put together a story collection quickly.

The editor should make an offer for "first serial rights" or "first North American serial rights." "First" means he gets to publish it first. "Serial" means he is publishing it in a periodical— or "serial," as periodicals are known to librarians. Of course, if you sell "first serial" rights, you must be sure that the story appears in no other publication first.

When a piece has appeared elsewhere first, you can sell "second rights." But it does not go to "third" and "fourth" rights. After the first publication, all other publications get "second rights."

"One-time" rights means the publication gets to run the piece one time, but you do not promise that they get the work first. Many cartoons and other features are sold on a "one-time" basis. You might sell one-time rights to several different regional publications at the same time. For the sake of goodwill, you should not sell the same piece to competing publications in the same region at the same time.

"Simultaneous rights" are unheard of in the gay market. You might sell "simultaneous rights" to publications that, by their nature, are not competitive; say, an inspirational piece to publications of different religious sects. In any event, the idea of simultaneous rights is that two or more publications get to run the piece at the same time.

Occasionally a magazine may ask for "exclusive rights." If you sell on that basis you will never be able to sell the piece again unless the magazine returns the rights to you. In this case, ask if it will take "first serial rights exclusive for two years." Then you will be able to sell second rights two years after the piece is published. Magazines that ask for exclusive rights usually are trying to be sure that you will not sell the story elsewhere until it has published it, and may settle for first rights if it is sure you understand that first really means first—you will shelve the story until you see it printed in the magazine.

In the gay market, it is not really very important what rights you sell so long as you sell some form of serial rights. There is almost no possibility of selling "second serial rights" in this market. You do, however, want to retain the book rights because there is a good possibility—better than that in the straight market—of selling a collection of stories as a book.

Because beginners are always interested in such things, I have explained more about rights than any fiction writer submitting short stories will ever need to know. If you receive an offer for "all rights," you must decide whether to accept the sale and worry about recouping the rights if and when you ever have another use for the piece. If you receive an offer for "first serial rights," then you have nothing to worry about so far as rights are concerned.

The letter of acceptance for the story usually contains the whole of the offer for the piece. If you accept the offer—and most often you should—you merely send an invoice to the person who wrote the acceptance letter along with any forms that may have accompanied the acceptance letter.

An invoice can simply be typed on a sheet of typing paper, or you can make up a form on your word processor. It looks like this:

Freddie Fumblefart
1878 Constitution Ave
Floydada TX 76969

April 17, 1998

INVOICE

TO: ManTime Magazine Inc.
     6969 Castro St
     San Francisco CA

DESCRIPTION DATE:	No. 146A	DUE
"Pro Jocks In Heat" short fiction		
first N.A. serial rights		$100
re: *ManTime* 3/99		
supplied on floppy disc		$25

TOTAL DUE $125.00

TERMS: Jan., 1999

MY SOCIAL SECURITY / TAXPAYER ID No. 123-45-6789

I warrant that I am the author and sole proprietor of this original
and unpublished literary work.
    Your patronage is deeply appreciated.

_____

Freddie Fumblefart

The invoice should state the name of the work. Do not worry
if the editor seems likely to change it. It should state the rights

you are selling. The "re:" line is a notation that in this case the editor said the story would appear in March. Some editors will not tell you when they plan to run the piece, but you still might enter the name of the magazine because the editor may be on the staff of several magazines. This publication pays you extra because in addition to the paper manuscript, you sent a disk file. "Terms" means when the editor promised to pay you. In this case, it is January. In other cases, the caption "on publication" or "on acceptance" might appear.

Although your social security number appears on your manuscript, include it here as a reminder. Some publications will still call you and ask what it is, and many will ask you to fill out a form that is supplied by the IRS.

Some magazines want the author warranty, and others do not. It does no harm to include it on all your invoices when it is true. You need not worry about entering ledger lines and such, but the word "Invoice" and the date are essential, as is retaining a copy of this document.

Unfortunately, payment on publication is a common practice, which means that you will be unlikely to see a check for about six months.

When payment is late—say more than a month or two after the publication of the magazine that contained your story— write a polite note to the editor. He probably knows that payment is late, and he probably has no control over the situation except to make a plea to bookkeeping on your behalf. Persistence is important in getting paid, but you should allow a reasonable time between letters, and you should not be nasty to the editor who will usually do what he can for you.

Legal action is a last resort. But if you actually sue, you will lose a customer whether or not the magazine was in the wrong. Unless you have made the mistake of extending too much credit to the magazine, the amount involved should not be enough to make a lawsuit worthwhile. Most magazines have been very late at one time or another. Naturally, you should not submit more work to a magazine that is late until the situation is resolved. While my sympathies are always with the writer, I do wonder about the sanity of writers who will allow a magazine to owe them for dozens of stories at a time. This is a difficult problem with no easy solution.

Book manuscripts are not mailed out whole. Write a query letter first. Such a letter should introduce yourself and should describe the book in under a page. I know it is almost impossible to describe a best-seller in under a page, but you must. Tell how long the book is.

Here are some sample descriptions:

Swamp Stud is a short-story collection. Most of the stories have appeared in magazines like *Blueballs*, *Yellowsnow*, and *ManTime*. All of the stories are explicitly erotic. Several stories deal with a central character who comes out in the watersports scene of the gay ghetto in Floydada, Texas. Several of the other stories investigate the erotic adventures of professional jockeys.

My novel is based upon my extensive travels throughout South and Central America and my five years' residence in Colombia. My central character is an attractive, brown-skinned young man who grows up in a small South American village. Because he obviously differs from the others he is sexually abused repeatedly by the bigger and older men according to the code of *machismo*. He verges on the brink of despair and possibly suicide until he is rescued by a kindly European traveler.

Certainly you should mention any pertinent credits. Mention any book credits. That will assure the editor that you are prepared to deal with proofs and other aspects of getting a book into print. If you do not have book credits, or even if you do, say why you are qualified to write the book: you grew up there yourself, you are experienced in the scene you are writing about, or whatever applies. If you are famous or infamous for something, mention that or anything peculiar about your life or writing that might make a publicity angle.

This really can be done in a page or less. Address this letter to an editor by name at the publishing house. Odds are good that your letter will be answered by someone else. The response may be a refusal to look at the book, a request for the whole manuscript, or a request for sample chapters and an outline.

If sample chapters are requested, send photocopies. An outline should give four or five lines to each chapter and should not exceed three or four pages. Aim for a two-page outline.

Whether you send chapters or the whole manuscript, address your correspondence to the last person at the publishing house who wrote you. Include a briefer cover letter mentioning that you have permission to be sending what you are sending. If the work is not under consideration elsewhere, be sure to say so.

Eventually you may get a letter offering to publish the book. This usually includes a summary of the publishing contract. In some cases, you will receive the contract itself. A first book contract is somewhat more negotiable than a first magazine sale. There may be an exchange of letters before the terms are clear and acceptable to both sides. When an editor offers to publish your book, it is not an act of charity on his part. He thinks the house can make money on your book. You may not get him to offer better terms, but he should not blame you for asking, and he will not withdraw the offer just because you ask for clarification.

If you did not get the contract to begin with, the editor will send you one when the terms are agreed upon.

For books it is customary and correct for the author to grant all rights to the publisher (but *not* "work for hire" or "outright purchase"). The book publisher is supposed to exploit the rights as fully as possible and to share the proceeds with the author in accord with the terms of the publishing contract. The book contract should provide for the return of the rights to the author if the publisher has not issued the book within a certain time or if the publisher allows the book to go out of print for a certain period.

The word "advance" is sometimes used in slightly different senses. A payment based on an outline, an idea, or a partial manuscript is an advance. That type of advance is out of the question for a first book of erotica—or for any other kind of fiction—unless the author is famous or infamous. That type of advance is sometimes offered to an expert for a work of nonfiction, to an established author, or to a celebrity for his or her memoirs (when a competent ghostwriter is lined up—and the ghostwriter should get all of the advance).

When a publisher has a complete manuscript in his hands and is planning to publish it, he should pay something for it right then. This, too, is called an advance. The author should insist on this type of advance and should take his manuscript elsewhere if he does not get it. Payment of the advance may be divided several ways: part on acceptance (as soon after the contract is signed as bookkeeping can get it out), part on publication, and possibly part thirty days after publication. In any event, when the contract is signed, the publisher owes the author the advance whether or not the book sells a single copy.

Either type of advance is deducted from the author's royalties, but is his to keep in the unfortunate event that royalties never amount to so much. (Of course, the first type of advance should be returned in the event that the manuscript is never completed.)

Most books never earn back their advance. That is, they do not sell so many copies that royalties ever exceed the advance, and the author never gets anything more than the advance from the work. In many cases, the author of a book to be issued in paperback cannot realistically expect to earn royalties beyond the advance. For this reason, authors always want larger advances. (And also because royalties, even if they exceed the advance, may not be payable until a year or more after the book is published, which will be something like two years after the contract was signed. The author will want the means to live in the interim.)

Terms of the subsidiary rights, which includes the motion picture rights, foreign rights, performance rights, and so forth are always negotiable, especially in a work of gay erotica in which these rights are more or less worthless. The size of the advance and the basic royalty structure are much less flexible. If the advance is to be paid in parts, you may negotiate to have more of it paid earlier. You probably will not be able to increase the overall amount by much or by any. If you really think your book will sell very many copies, you might negotiate for a larger royalty after the first ten, fifteen, or twenty thousand copies are sold. At that point, the publisher will be making money, and he could give you a little more. If he thinks your book will not do as well as you think, he might give a little on this point. If your book does sell forty thousand copies, he will be pleasantly surprised and will never miss the extra point or two of your royalties.

All book contracts provide for reduced royalties in case the book is remaindered and sold at deep discounts. Indeed, the author may get nothing on such copies. However, big chain stores are able to negotiate small discounts with the publisher for copies they sell. Unfortunately, many publishing contracts call for a disproportionate amount of these small discounts to come from the author's royalties. The author may not be able to remove this clause altogether, but perhaps he can limit the percentage of the copies sold at these small discounts.

Once you understand the publishing contract and agree to its terms, sign the contract and return it to the publisher. Sometimes you will return all the copies the publisher provided for his signature, and he will return a signed copy to you; but you should make a copy of the contract you signed to consult until your copy of the completed contact arrives.

I do not know of any writer who does not wish he could renegotiate his first book contract. Part of this is a trick of perspective. The first book credit changes a writer's relationship to the market. He forgets the position he was in when he sold his first book. He becomes jaded. He forgets the indescribable triumphal joy he felt when he first held his first book in his hand. It is good after that, but it is never like the first time.

I certainly do not advise anyone to give his book away. But the publishers of first books *are* taking a chance. I advise you to be firm in dealing with your first publisher, but I also know that you will be glad of whatever you get just so long as you get into print and that later you will have some regret.

It is much the same thing as learning you can get money for turning a trick. You regret what you gave away for little or nothing. In a way. But you had a good time, or you would not have done it at all.

9. *The Law*

Aspects of the law that pertain to writing sometimes have serious implications and some aspects do change from time to time. Nonetheless, writers do manage to work without the necessity of a lawyer looking over their shoulders. Writers need to understand enough of the law to recognize situations in which professional advice is desirable.

Libel.

You must avoid providing grounds for a libel action. Even when caution is exercised, suits are possible because characters must have names, descriptions, jobs, and places to live. Suits may result in settlements because juries believe that publishers and writers are wealthy, and thus fair game.

To avoid the avoidable, remember the following:

The disclaimer appearing in books and magazines about purely coincidental resemblances to real persons may discourage some frivolous suits and be a mitigating factor in others, but provides little real protection to authors and publishers.

Changing a person's name or superficial circumstances will not necessary eliminate the libel if the person is still recognizable. Though you set the book on Mars, if the jury thinks an average person would know who you meant when you wrote that Zibfritz was a golden-shower queen, your career has just been pissed away.

In the case of a private person, the fact that what you wrote was true is not an effective defense.

In the case of celebrities, in theory, truth may be a defense. Celebrities seldom sue and, evidently because writers and publishers appear to be underdogs in such cases, seldom win. The bad news is that homosexuality is the one subject about which a celebrity is likely to sue and to win. In his lifetime Liberace won a libel suit against a publication that had implied he was homosexual. The law will not necessarily recognize the obvious.

Publication of a statement that a person has a loathsome disease is a textbook example of libel.

Coincidences can be a source of libel actions. This could happen, for example, if you invent a gay cop and give him a name that happens to belong a real cop. Such accidents probably occur fairly often, the authors being saved by the compartmentalized nature of the gay market. Do not, however, rely on that.

One strategy is to give characters very common names. If you call a cop "John Smith," there will be so many cops named "John Smith" that no one of them will be able to establish that you libeled him in particular. Moreover, the reader may expect coincidences in the case of common names, and a real John Smith might have difficulty showing that any reasonable person thought that he and the fictional John Smith were one and the same.

The opposite strategy is to give your cop a name so unusual that no cop would be likely to bear it. Of course, if a real cop— or anyone else—does happen to bear the unusual name you chose, you may have great difficulty in a libel action.

The more particular your stories, the more research you should do to try to avert libel. If your story is set in a real city, check telephone directories, professional directories, and any other sources you can think of to eliminate the possibility that any real person could be mistaken for the character in your story. This is not a burdensome task. When, for example you check to see that you have spelled a street name correctly, check also that the house number you have given is impossible. Keep notes of any such research you do. It may be helpful to show that you did what you could to avoid the coincidence.

In theory, a libel does not exist if what you wrote is so absurd that no reasonable person would believe it. However, this is not a point of law to rely upon in your writing.

It once seemed written in stone that it is impossible to libel the dead. Yet several states now provide a libel-like action whereby survivors may recover damages in case the character of the deceased is defamed. Civil law is now tilted steeply in the plaintiff's favor.

You should not find this overly scary.

Romans à clef are written and published frequently and do not result in libel actions. So long as details do not define the principals too closely, you are safe in writing about people who are very like the famous and the infamous. You are most likely to libel a celebrity by letting a character mention him or her by name. Things gay people believe to be common knowledge are not always generally known to the public at large. Nor are they necessarily true.

You are generally safer commenting on the work a celebrity offers to the public for profit than on the celebrity's personal life. Whether you may write that Kolorinzikov *dances* like a drunken fairy is debatable; you certainly may not write that he *is* a drunken fairy. Your characters can watch a Jack Wrangler video, and comments about what he does on a video, if true, can hardly be questioned. He performed for the videos, he gave interviews to magazines in order to promote the videos, and he can hardly complain if your character says what he does on the videos. Whether he does the same sorts of things off camera is a dangerous area. It would not be playing the game, although it might not be actionable, if you mentioned the identities of his parents, supposing you knew.

A common type of work is a fantasy piece about this or that sex symbol. These stories are clearly labeled as fantasies and reminders are scattered throughout the text. None of these, to my knowledge, has ever resulted in a lawsuit. Nor should they. After all, such stars derive a good livelihood from providing the fodder for sexual fantasies. Fame, however, is fleeting, and those stars who do stick around for a while, do so by adjusting their images. A fantasy star-fucking story dates quickly—either no one remembers the star, or everyone now associates the star with roles that are incompatible with the fantasy.

While appearances by real persons in works of fiction have been in vogue in the mass market, they are iffy in gay erotica. The best solution is to write fiction. If you want to write about star-fucking, invent a star. Should you be privy to the peccadilloes of the rich and famous, you can write a better story than any of them has lived. That the reader thinks he knows who you mean will not save poor writing. Good writing does not need such a device.

Copyright.

New writers amuse the publishing world by taking elaborate precautions against literary theft, which is rare, while eagerly signing away rights in disadvantageous contracts, which is not. Time spent worrying that a manuscript might be stolen would be better spent making the manuscript worth stealing. Time spent understanding the terms of a publishing contract or negotiating for better terms is time well spent indeed.

Copyright exists in a work the instant the ink hits the paper. All rights in the work belong to the writer as long as he lives (and to his estate for some time after that), unless he allows the work to be published in an uncopyrighted publication or grants the rights to someone else. Those rights the author does not grant remain his.

In most cases, the grant of rights must be specific and in writing. One exception is letters written to publications that ordinarily print readers' letters. Magazines are entitled to construe a letter to a feature that regularly publishes letters as implying permission to publish the letter.

Except for letters features, all rights to letters you write belong to you. The person who receives the letter gets only the paper it is written on; she does not gain the right to publish the letters.

The words to watch out for in a contract are "work for hire" and "outright purchase." If you work on these bases, or if you produce writing for an employer as part of a job, you may lose all your rights in such work. The buyer may treat your work as his own. She may affix her name to your work, cut-and-paste the work with the work of others, use the work to line her bird's cage, or publish the work without acknowledging your contribution to it. You are unlikely ever to receive any more for your work than what you are paid for it in the beginning—and if you are on salary, you may not get any special payment for the work at all.

Another hazard to your rights is uncopyrighted publication. Many regional publications are not copyrighted. If you send work to such a publication, you must specify in writing that your own copyright notice is to appear with the work. Inadvertent omission of the notice can be remedied (as by a reasonable effort to insert the notice in undistributed copies). At present the law is inclined to recognize some fairly feeble gestures as sufficient notice of copyright; but if you do not ask for copyright protection before publication, it may be impossible to obtain it.

In submitting work to magazines that are copyrighted and to established book publishers, the author seldom needs to do anything. Copyright may be registered before the work is published, but only vain amateurs go to this expense and trouble when no special threat of infringement is evident. Registration is handled routinely by book publishers and magazines. The author does nothing unless an infringement is detected. Registration must be secured before an action for infringement can be brought, but under current law (the "new" law), registration has assumed its proper place as a minor bureaucratic procedure. Registration is just registration of the copyright. It does not create the copyright. The copyright, as has been said, is created when the work is rendered in fixed form, as ink on paper or blips on a computer disk.

When you sell a story to a copyrighted magazine, your copyright notice does not appear with the story. Instead, your rights in the story are protected by the copyright notice which appears in small type on the contents page or under the masthead. The notice is in the name of the publication. That does not mean the story belongs to them. What determines their rights in the story is what you wrote on your invoice to them or in other written agreements, such as their letter offering to buy certain rights and your letter accepting the offer. Which rights you should sell were discussed in the preceding chapter. If you sold first serial rights, you do not need to communicate with the magazine again in order to include the story in your book or to sell second rights to another magazine after the story has appeared, although you should always credit the first publisher of a work.

Some books advise you to include your own copyright notice on manuscripts. Such a notice would read as "Copyright 1994 by Lars Eighner" or "© 1994 by Lars Eighner." If used, the notice goes in the upper-right corner of a story manuscript or low on the title page of a book manuscript. When you submit manuscripts in the ordinary manner, this notice does not really afford you any extra protection. The object of the advice is to convince the editor that you know your rights and thereby to dissuade him or her from offering you disadvantageous terms. This rationale is dubious because professional writers, who really do know their rights, know the notice is unnecessary and seldom include it. The inclusion of the notice might make the editor wonder whether you are trying to imply that the work has previously appeared elsewhere.

However, if you submit manuscripts in some unusual manner, circulate copies among your friends, or display the work in some peculiar way, you ought to include the notice and to include the caption "All rights reserved," which is supposed to afford some additional protection in international copyright cases.

Once again, you are far more likely to sign away rights you later wish you had retained than you are to discover that a work in manuscript has been stolen. I have never heard of a clear-cut case of theft from a manuscript.

The kind of theft that is not rare occurs after a piece is in print, once there is no question of notices or registration. Sometimes a piece in a local publication is picked up without payment by a publication in a distant place. The offender, if caught and sent a sufficient number of increasingly threatening invoices, will almost always cough up a reasonable fee. The author cannot do much to avoid this happening, beyond seeing that the original publication is copyrighted.

Your ideas cannot be stolen because they do not belong to you.

Ideas and titles cannot be copyrighted.

If they could, then long ago I would have copyrighted the idea that a motorcycle cop stops a guy for speeding and then they have sex. If I could have copyrighted that idea, then every magazine in the gay market would owe me royalties—some would owe me more than they are worth.

For some reason, the public believes that the value of a literary work is contained in "the idea." A popular tragic figure is the struggling unknown writer whose idea is stolen by a famous-but-dried-up writer who makes a best-seller out of the idea. That is bullshit.

In human literature in general, and in the specialized gay market in particular, no idea can be both entirely new and entirely good. To be good, an idea must contain certain elements and touch on certain themes that were discovered long ago and have been used over and over by storytellers and writers.

What belongs to the writer is the particular literary expression of the idea. That can be and ought to be fresh and original. Nonetheless, charges of "stealing my idea" are common, which is one of many good reasons that established writers are reluctant to read manuscripts from aspiring writers.

You should not lift plots or anything else from other writers. You certainly may not lift characters—you may not write a Dave Brandstetter novel unless you are Joseph Hansen. You may write about *a* gay insurance investigator—and, owing to the conventions of the genre, all such characters will have some similarities. Likewise, you may not write a sequel to *Mr. Benson* without John Preston's permission—although you might try to write a very similar novel or you might name a very different kind of character Benson.

In the event that an idea really is stolen, the victim can sometimes recover by a lawsuit that is not based on copyright. Such suits sometimes succeed in the motion picture and television industries. To recover in such a suit, you have to show not only that you had the idea first, but also that the other person got the idea from your work and did not arrive at it independently. For practical purposes, your idea will have to have been expressed in a very detailed form, the other person's use will have had to have reproduced many of those details, where the details coincide there will have to be some peculiarities that would not have occurred to just anyone who had the same general idea, and of course you will have to show that the other person had access to your work. If some previous work exists with an idea similar to the one under dispute, the other person may claim to have got his idea from *that* previous work.

Moreover, no one has a special claim to facts. Perhaps another person does overhear that you are planning a biography of Gertrude Stein, and perhaps, because of that, the other person does decide to do a biography of Stein, too. This would be unethical, but it probably is not actionable. The resulting books are bound to have many similarities: to recount many of the same anecdotes and to quote many of the same documents. Both books may be similar in many of their conclusions because, given the same set of facts, many people will arrive at similar conclusions. Unless the other person has had access to your manuscript and has very nearly reproduced many of your expressions, you will have little chance of recovering anything.

The law recognizes a limited right to quote from the works of others. This is the doctrine of fair use. The statute does not specify exactly how much of a work can be used fairly, but lists a number of factors to be considered in determining whether a use is fair, most of which boil down to whether you have really impaired an author's right to enjoy the proceeds of his work.

The reason for the doctrine of fair use has mostly to do with nonfiction. No good new book on political economy could be written without extensive reference to previous works on the subject. A fiction writer is most likely to want to invoke the doctrine of fair use in quoting lines of a song. Do not do it. A song is such a short work that any recognizable portion will exceed the bounds of fair use.

Obtaining permissions can be a difficult and tedious process. Publishers may be skeptical of works involving permissions. Obtaining permissions is the author's responsibility, but a publisher may be unsure that the author knows how to obtain permissions correctly. Since many copyright holders will object to their property appearing in a work of gay erotica, permissions may be impossible to obtain.

The solution is to write fiction. Quote from fictional works if quotation seems in order. Write fictional lyrics and attribute them to a fictional fifties girl group. Let your characters be nostalgic about them. If you quote lines from *All About Eve,* which might be fair use, after all, you are trading on another writer's wit and another artist's performance.

Fair use pertains to direct quotation. By its nature, allusion is not direct quotation. You may allude as you please. You have also a fairly free hand to parody works, provided the parody is easily recognizable as such and is unlikely to be mistaken for the original.

Work in the public domain can be quoted safely, even at length. Ethics requires that credit be given unless the quoted work is so well known that everyone will recognize it. Works from the nineteenth century or before can safely be assumed to be in the public domain so long as they are in their original forms. More recent commentary, annotations, translations, and revisions may still be protected by copyright. Recall that letters sent to you remain the property of the letters' authors.

In fiction the game is not worth the candle. Do your own work.

Proprietary names.

Products and services often have names that belong to someone. Some names you might not think of as belonging to anybody are proprietary names. For example, "Ping-Pong" is a trademark for a brand of table tennis.

Writers are obliged to help protect the rights of the owners of proprietary names. The owners' lawyers are obliged to write nasty letters to authors and editors who are careless in the use of proprietary names. Unless a publication repeatedly abuses one particular trade name, things will not go past the nasty letter stage, but editors do tire of receiving nasty letters and may grade off when they detect carelessness in a writer's work.

On the other hand, the lawyers ask too much.

Lawyers for the StaHard company would like you to write

"Sta-Hard brand of easy-fastening metal cockrings" every time you refer to the product. They would be even happier if you could get the printer to insert a little ™ or a ® after the name. But characters do not say: "Jim, did you take the Sta-Hard™ brand of easy-fastening metal cockring off of my dresser?" They say, "Jim, what the hell did you do with the Sta-Hard? I'm sure I left it right here on my dresser." No character knows how to pronounce ™ or ®.

What you owe trademark owners is to capitalize their trademarks when you use them and to avoid using their names as verbs, a particularly touchy point around Xerox headquarters. Your characters can photocopy something, or zerocks it, or—as they do at Xerox headquarters—zero it. Just do not let them do that other thing.

In this book, I refer to college-sized dictionaries. Only the Merriam-Webster company may produce *Collegiate* dictionaries. Dictionaries can be useful in determining when words belong to companies, although as in the case of "collegiate" in the current *Collegiate,* a dictionary's word list may not always indicate when a word has proprietary uses.

Some proprietary names: Dumpster, Day-Glo, Realtor, Coke (when you mean the beverage), Dr Pepper (no period), College Board, Vaseline, Q-Tip, K-Y, Kleenex, Scotch tape, Crisco, A-200.

Obscenity.

This is ethical—not legal—advice.

Writers should take no notice of obscenity laws. In principle, it is every writer's duty to oppose every form of interference with the free expression and exchange of ideas, including that interference done in the name of Political Correctness. Writers have suffered and died for freedom of expression, and whosoever forsakes it is lower than the grubbiest, lousy, formula hack. As a practical matter, hardly anything helps sales in the long run so much as a brush with an obscenity prosecution. So this would seem a rare case of self-interest and principle coinciding.

However, the oppressive force of government does get smarter over time. Today ideas are suppressed without the heavy hand of censorship or the public airing of an obscenity charge in open court. Government suppresses ideas by using several statutes, supposedly meant to interfere with racketeering, to seize the publisher's property, or by using the Treasury Department's powers to tie up the publisher's assets. The McDonaldization of the retail book business has proceeded to the point that three or four major chains can determine whether a book or line of books lives or dies, and government or pressure groups can now exert a degree of pressure at the retail level that was impossible when almost all bookstores were independent enterprises.

Magazine publishers, especially those who hope to get their products through Canadian customs, have never exhibited much commitment to the principle of free expression. In the face of the new tactics of oppression, not many book publishers are willing to draw the line in the dust. To put the matter plainly, and in someone else's words, freedom of the press is restricted to those who own one.

At present, the idea that a person under eighteen might have sex is one hot spot. You need have no sympathy with chicken-hawk fantasies to understand that forbidding this topic makes it fairly impossible for serious writers to publish semiautobiographical work or work that accurately depicts the development of sexuality in characters. Society may have valid reasons for forbidding persons of certain ages to work as photographic models and for restricting some class of persons from certain kinds of literature for a limited time, but literature requires no underage models and does not necessarily involve the services of any minor for its production.

Many publishers will not consider stories with incest themes, even if the parties are adults. Other publications which encourage the most explicit descriptions of vanilla sex shy away from bondage, no matter how clearly the consensual nature of the acts is expressed. For a considerable period, most magazines in the gay market insisted on having only safe sex portrayed in stories, even when the stories were set in differing historical periods. Rape fantasies are forbidden, as if no one can tell the difference between fantasy and reality, and some periodicals profess to be unable to distinguish a brutal beating from an erotic spanking.

The proper auctorial attitude towards any sort of literary

suppression is defiance, although at present authors have few ways of expressing defiance except in attitude.

When attacked from the right, naturally one should seek allies on the left: the ACLU and other traditional supporters of free expression. However, the attack comes increasingly from the left; partly in the traditional leftist view that social planners know better how to run an individual's life than he knows himself, and partly from the socialist-realism-school of criticism, which holds that nothing unpleasant should appear in art unless blamed explicitly on the bourgeoisie. When attacked from the left, it seems, the gay writer has no natural allies. Dismal as this prospect may be, we must prepare for more—if anything of the future can be seen from the present.

Do not flout the taboos of a publisher. But if you write something that is taboo to one publisher, find the publisher who will print it, even if you take less money. Or even if you take *no* money—provided you are afforded the opportunity of withdrawing the work. Or even, if you must, circulate copies at your own expense so far as your resources will go.

A new writer may fairly stick to the main chance. Your duty to press hard against the taboos increases as you become established as a writer.

If you want advice on how to slither around just inside this taboo or that statute, you have bought the wrong book.

Taxes.

Tax laws and rulings change from time to time. Consult current IRS publications in regard to particular questions. When your income and your tax liability is large, consult an attorney or an accountant, and all the more so if large sums depend upon the interpretation of points that seem unclear in IRS publications. The pointers given here are meant to introduce tax issues you should consider and research for yourself when you write for publication. They are not meant to take the place of professional advice:

The IRS takes a suspicious view of freelance writing as an occupation, particularly when a writing business often shows losses that are used to reduce a writer's tax liability for income from other sources or when expenses that could be personal are charged to a writing business that does not show signs of life.

The most essential tax question is whether you are pursuing writing as a business; or whether writing, although you may make some money at it, is your hobby or pastime. You might pursue writing seriously in a literary or artistic sense and devote a lot of time and effort to it, but not be pursuing writing as a business. Not everyone who sells a story or a poem once in a while is in the writing business. I think it is desirable to approach writing with a professional attitude from the start. You may have that professional attitude—and probably should have it—long before you are pursuing writing as a business.

If you have large sales and large expenses, there are considerable tax advantages to pursuing writing as a business. But if your sales and expenses are small, the status of your writing activities will not make much difference in your taxes. Like all new businesses, a new writing business is likely to show a loss. But if a writing business shows losses year after year, doubt may be cast on whether it really is a business—that is, whether it really is conducted primarily for profit. For that reason, so long as your income and expenses are small, you may want to pursue writing as a hobby rather than establish it as a business that might show many years of losses, though they be small. On the other hand, if you are regularly paid more for your writing than you expend in creating it, there is no reason to avoid acknowledging the fact, if it is one, that you are in the writing business.

If your writing is a business, you are required to file the long form (1040), Schedule C (Profit or Loss from Business or Profession) or Schedule C-EZ (if your writing business is small and makes a profit), and Schedule SE (Social Security Self-Employment Tax)—although, if your profit is very small, you may not owe any self-employment tax. As a working writer, you do not file schedule E; the royalties reported on it are oil and gas royalties or royalties from copyrights to *other people's works*. Filing form 1040 in order to file Schedules C and SE usually will have no bearing on whether you should or must file Schedule A (Itemized Deductions).

On the other hand, if you are not in the writing business, you must still report any income you have from writing, but you report your income as "other income" on form 1040 itself. You cannot show a loss from your writing. You can only deduct your writing expenses as itemized deductions on Schedule A. Since not many filers will have enough itemized deductions to make Schedule A worth filing, you probably will not be able to claim your writing expenses at all.

Income from writing, whether you are writing for profit or not, is reportable and is reported (if it exceeds a certain amount) to the IRS by publishers. Most publications will not issue a check to you until they have your social security number and usually not until you have filled out an IRS form the publisher provides. Your social security number is an essential part of the heading of a manuscript (for tax reasons and for the reason that it shows you expect to sell the manuscript). The social security number must agree with the name that goes on your check, which will be the name at the top of the manuscript. Your pen name, if you choose to use one, belongs in the byline, not in the heading.

If you wish to have the tax advantages of being in business, much depends on your ability to prove that you are pursuing writing for profit. You must show that you engage in the business of writing regularly, that you pursue writing for profit, and that you have some reasonable chance of success. The IRS will not send a literary critic to evaluate your chances of succeeding, but you ought to keep records and documents that show you pursue writing regularly with an eye toward making a profit.

Save copies of your letters to publishers, including even the briefest requests for guidelines. Save publishers' letters to you, including printed rejection slips (write the name of the submission and the date received on the slip). If you have a telephone conversation with a publisher—not recommended as the way to introduce yourself—write a memo to yourself summarizing the conversation. Keep a log of writing-related mail you receive and writing-related meetings you attend. The value of these sorts of records is not limited to tax matters.

The IRS will not care to see your five-hundred-page manuscript. They want to see your queries to publishers and the publishers' replies that indicate you are actively trying to sell your manuscript.

If you show a large profit, the IRS will have little difficulty in believing that you are running a business. That you work at the business regularly, that you conduct business in the manner normal for the kind of business, that your income from writing is some appreciable part of your total income, and that you have had some success in writing or some related activity in the past can also help to show that you are in the business of writing. Some sales, even if they do not exceed expenses in a given year, will help to establish that you are professional writer; and that your sales are increasing, even if they are not large, may indicate that you intend to make a profit. A pattern of increasing profits, even if small, or even of decreasing losses may be helpful.

Although you will sometimes have larger equipment expenses and sometimes you will have expenses for projects that do not pan out, your expenses to make a given sale should be small compared to the amount of the sale; the price of a finished piece of writing is relatively high, compared to that of the ink and paper. You might spend several hundred dollars in researching a story that did not sell and still be in business. All businesses produce some products that do not sell, for some reason or another, or encounter unexpected expenses that result in a particular product selling at a loss. But if you expend $1,000 on a story that could not possibly sell for more than $200 and if many of your projects are like that, you are not really in business for a profit. No business routinely produces products that are projected to produce a loss (although if the ultimate goal is more profit, perhaps due to the public-relations benefits, occasional losing projects can be justified). You might, for example, send an occasional story to a little literary magazine that does not pay or write a gossip column that does not pay for a local publication on the grounds that the exposure, goodwill, or prestige of such work is helpful to your career, but this explanation will not make business sense unless most of your work is sent to paying publications.

Freelance writers who have established a writing business may expect to deduct most of the legitimate expenses of doing business. Properly documented expenses for the tools of the trade and supplies will seldom be questioned. The actual transportation expense, your meals, and lodging for out-of-town travel required by the business usually are fully deductible; but if the travel combines a vacation with research, the whole of the expense is not chargeable to the business. Deductions for business lunches and entertainment are being phased out. No doubt these are real expenses for certain kinds of writing and the writer should keep records of them to better assess the state of his business, but they cannot be fully deducted from the profits of the business for tax purpose. This raises the possibility that some marginal freelances may actually operate at a loss, while having to pay taxes on paper profits. You can deduct the expense of a writing office at home if certain precise conditions are met.

Good records are the solution to most tax problems. You must save receipts (not merely canceled checks) for writing expenses, and you ought to maintain an up-to-date written record of your expenses and income. You must maintain a rigorous separation between your expenses in the freelance writing business and your personal or household expenses.

An adequate journal of expenses obviates many other types of records. Keep the original in handwriting in a bound book, and keep it current. If the great majority of your expenses are supported by receipts, the IRS will often accept your journal entries as evidence of those minor expenses for which receipts are unobtainable or occasionally lost.

For example, when you buy stamps, buy them from a clerk at the post office. Ask for a receipt. The clerk is used to this request because all carefully run businesses require receipts. The receipt proves that you bought the stamps, not that you used them in your business. When you mail a manuscript, write a record of your postage expense, including the amount of postage you affixed to the return envelope. Your journal entry is evidence that you used the postage in your business. Save the letter of acceptance or your return mail cover and the rejection slip. This is proof that what you wrote in your expense journal was true. If you can prove most of these similar expenses, the

IRS will not doubt that some of your letters were unanswered. When maintained carefully in this way, your expense journal will also serve as a log of your outgoing mail, which will be very useful when you have more than one or two stories out at a time.

The rule of thumb for allowable expenses is "ordinary and necessary." "Ordinary" is relative to the enterprise; the price of a very extraordinary book on exotic poisons might be an ordinary expense of a mystery writer. Unfortunately, some rather ordinary expenses of a writer of erotica might not be allowed. "Necessary" is fairly elastic. A small writing business might exist without a fax machine, but if you buy one for your home office, use it in your business, and use it for nothing except your business, the expense probably will not be questioned. If you consider a trip to Cancún necessary to get the setting of piece of fiction right, however, you may expect to be asked to justify this conclusion. An article writer who travels to interview someone and who sells the interview at a profit will have an easier time justifying his travel expense.

When your profit reaches a certain surprisingly low figure, you will become liable for self-employment taxes. The self-employment tax is a form of social security tax, but the rate is nearly twice that at which social security taxes are withheld from paychecks: in a word, confiscatory. You may very well owe a substantial amount of self-employment tax even while you do not have enough income to owe any income tax.

Curiously, although you are in trouble if you do not pay this tax, you must be able to prove you are *entitled* to pay it. Evidently, joining the social security system was once considered a great privilege. You may (and must) pay self-employment taxes only on income from a business in which you are regularly engaged—you do not pay them, for example, on a Las Vegas jackpot, unless you are a professional gambler.

Self-employment taxes are likely to constitute a large part of your tax liability, and you must consider them in your personal budget. At present you can and should use a portion of your self-employment taxes as an adjustment to your gross income, but the taxes are not a deductible business expense. Like income taxes, self-employment taxes are paid only on profits, not on gross receipts.

Everyone must pay federal taxes on income as the income is earned. When you work for someone else, this is usually done automatically by your employer, who withholds an amount estimated to cover your tax liability from your paycheck. When you have income from your own business, you must arrange to pay taxes on your business income as you earn it.

This can be done in either (or both) of two ways:

If you also work for someone else, you can get your employer to withhold more money from your paychecks, or

Whether you work for someone else or not, you can pay estimated tax.

If enough is withheld from your paychecks to cover your tax liability for your income from all sources, you do not have to pay estimated tax. If you pay enough estimated tax to cover your tax liability from all sources, you may ask your employer not to withhold taxes from your paycheck. For most beginning writers, it is much easier to have more money withheld from their paychecks at their regular jobs.

But if you do not work for someone else, or if your writing income is large, you must pay estimated tax. Estimated taxes are due at four times in the year. You should request an estimated tax form from the IRS very early in the year. Once you are paying estimated taxes, the forms are sent to you auto-matically.

Freelances often have great difficulty estimating their taxes because they have great difficulty estimating their incomes. At present you can avoid penalties and interest by paying at least as much in estimated taxes this year as you paid in taxes last year. However, if you know that your tax liability will be significantly greater this year, you may want to pay more estimated taxes so that you will not have to come up with a very large payment at the end of the year.

If you are paying self-employment taxes for the first time, you should realize that a small increase in income from your business may entail a large increase in tax liability.

"Inventory" on Schedule C means, for present purposes, merchandise. It does not include the rights to writings, the manuscripts themselves, or your writing supplies. Unless you are self-publishing or are selling copies of your book yourself for some other reason, you probably have no inventory.

If you enter your expenses when you actually spend the money and your revenues when you are actually paid, your accounting method is "cash." If you know how to handle other accounting schemes, you do not need any advice I have to offer here.

Break out your business expenses according to the categories on Schedule C and use the "other" categories for any that are deductible but cannot be made to fit the IRS's scheme. It is much easier, of course, if you set up your books according to the previous year's categories—your categories will usually not vary much from year to year.

After any occasional equipment expense (and commissions, if you have an agent), postage expenses and supplies will be a writer's major expenses. These are also likely to be where the writer loses the most of the deductions she is entitled to. Pens and envelopes are likely to get lost among the writer's personal expenses, and the postage expense may be forgotten once a business letter is answered. The habit of keeping receipts and making records must be formed while the amounts involved are still relatively insignificant.

Although sales taxes on items you buy for your business are no longer deductible as a separate expense category, they still can be deducted as part of the cost of the items. Many other state and local taxes, if incurred because you are in business, are deductible.

If you pay interest on installment purchases of equipment used in your business, the interest may be a deductible expense of the business, even though the interest would not be allowable as a personal deduction if a similar item were bought for personal use.

Your journal should serve your purposes as well as those of IRS. You should have expense categories for expenses that are deductible on Schedule C and for expenses that are partially deductible on Schedule C. If you feel you have expenses that you incur because of your business but believe they are not deductible, you should keep records of them anyway. You should keep nondeductible expenses in categories apart from deductible expenses so that you will not claim them inadvertently on your tax return.

Your expense journal is not your tax form. If you really went to Hawaii after a story, and you would not have gone otherwise, you may want to enter that expense in your journal. This may give you a better idea how your business is doing, and it may help you to make a better decision the next time you consider a trip. Of course, if you cannot support this expense for tax purposes, do not report it as an expense on the tax form.

If you are honest, you are as likely to err in favor of the IRS as you are to err in your favor, An accountant or even an IRS auditor may discover that one of your nondeductible expenses is allowable after all, or rulings may change in your favor. They will benefit you only if you have maintained complete records.

You probably can deduct the full price of equipment you buy in the year you buy it, but you will have to ask the IRS to send you the form for the equipment expense because it will not come with the others in the 1040 package. The amount you are allowed to deduct in a given year exceeds any probable equipment expense of a single freelance writer. However, if you expect that your income will rise, you may want to investigate depreciating equipment expenses in order to preserve a part of the deduction for years in which you expect to need deductions more.

Equipment used partly for personal purposes is not fully deductible as a business expense. Equipment installed anywhere except a home office will be presumed to be used, at least partly, for personal reasons. You may, however, be able to reclaim part of the value of an item bought for personal purposes if it is converted to business use.

Technically, anything that is durable could be equipment. But, as a practical matter, inexpensive items such as staplers are usually entered as supplies.

Travel expenses are best supported when you can show you had an assignment (which a fiction writer will rarely have), or that a sale resulted from the travel. Travel, however, includes local travel and thus includes trips to the library to research a historical piece. Fares, when you get a receipt, are easy to document. If you travel in your own car, you must keep careful records of mileage.

Lodging in ordinary hotels is deductible, if the trip is for a business purpose. Usually, lodging in resorts is not deductible, but a travel writer might be able to claim it.

Taking the home-office expense is an extremely effective way of inviting the IRS to hold an audit. But an honest taxpayer has little to fear from an audit, and the home-office expense can be a large deduction, if you qualify for it. For the freelance, the main qualification is that you have a room in which you do your writing business and that you do not use that room for any other purpose. A freelance writer who meets this criterion will probably meet the others and then be entitled to deduct a portion of his utilities and a portion of his rent or the fair rental value of the space if he owns it. You cannot use your home office expense to create a loss in any given year, but you may be able to carry excess home-office expenses forward to offset a profit in the following year.

This deduction is very reasonable and useful for someone who really is in the writing business and who really does maintain his office at home. It is not allowed for the writing hobbyist who has a typewriter in his den. Unfortunately, the home-office expense is also not allowed to struggling writers who, like Margaret Mitchell, set up a typewriter in a kitchen alcove, although the IRS will expect its cut of the royalties if such a writer produces a book like *Gone With the Wind*.

You may deduct the long-distance phone calls you make in connection with your business, regardless of the telephone you use to make the calls. But you may not deduct the cost of local service for the first line to your home.

As sole proprietor of a freelance writing business you may not pay yourself a salary, and you may not deduct the value of your own labor in making repairs or providing other services to your business. You may deduct sales commissions you pay to agents and fees you pay to attorneys, accountants, and other professionals you consult in regard to your business. You may deduct wages you pay to employees, if you have any.

Recall that if you have employees, you will have to withhold taxes from their paychecks and pay a part of their social security tax yourself. You will not have to do this in case of commissions or amounts you pay to independent contractors. But you may have to send Form 1099 to recipients of such payments and provide the IRS with a copy.

In truth, a writer is never off duty. Many vacations or other recreations have resulted in profitable short stories. Virtually anything a writer does is grist for her mill, and any experience is liable to be reflected in a paying work of fiction. Unfortunately, the IRS remains unconvinced of this reality. But it is also true that any honest writer can distinguish perfectly well between business and personal expenses as the IRS defines them. Someone who once wrote a story for the school paper who tries to deduct as research the expense of a three-week vacation in Hawaii cannot expect a sympathetic hearing from an honest professional writer.

10. *From Manuscript to Print*

Your manuscript conveys your story to the editor and, if all goes well, to the typesetter. No story was ever sold because the manuscript looked good, but many stories are rejected because the manuscript is faulty or offensive in some way.

The ideal manuscript looks as if it were typed by a perfect typist on an IBM Selectric typewriter with a carbon-film ribbon and the Courier 10 typing element. This is the ideal, in the sense that such a manuscript is nearly universally acceptable. Some—or even many—editors will like manuscripts with other appearances, but no one will be offended by a perfect Selectric manuscript.

But not many writers are perfect typists and IBM no longer produces Selectric typewriters. And no one who has worked on an electronic word processor will willingly return to a typewriter. Nonetheless, the Selectric appearance is what to aim for.

My first draft of *Travels with Lizbeth* was typed on an upright manual Royal typewriter by the light of three oil lamps. I remain unconvinced that the choice of the right word-processing system is the key to writing success. I still think, as I wrote in the first edition of this book:

> A writer who begins working with a typewriter need not feel he is at a disadvantage. Most working writers learned their craft on a typewriter. Computers are the least help for the things a beginner most needs to learn.

If you own a typewriter which produces acceptable copy, begin with that.

After a discussion of the ideal manuscript, we will return to the issue of what to use to produce it.

The manuscript.

Something more than half of the beginners' manuscripts I see are seriously defective in form. Some are so badly misshapen that they could not possibly go through the publishing process, even if an editor were willing to look at them. I no longer see much erasable bond—the unusable paper immortalized in Stephen King's *Misery*—because that is a mistake only someone with a typewriter is likely to make. I see more and more manuscripts produced in camera-ready form or with other errors that can only be made with expensive desktop publishing systems.

Odd typefaces are unacceptable. Courier 10 is available on many word processors, and it is what should be used if it is available. The ordinary pica face of typewriters without interchangeable typing elements is acceptable. Elite typefaces such as the old typewriter Elite and Prestige are second-best to a pica face, but are acceptable.

Unacceptable faces include script, Old English, Orator, or any other face lacking a true lower case, faces smaller than elite (more than twelve characters per inch), faces with unusual curlicues such as Contempo, faces in which the tails of letters like *g* and *y* do not hang down from the line, and old dot-matrix faces in which the individual dots that form the characters do not connect.

Sans-serif typewriter faces such as Tempo and Letter Gothic are probably acceptable. Many editors will read, and some prefer, proportional typefaces like Times Roman. Proportional spacing, however, may pose problems for some editors who use certain formulas to estimate how much space a story will require when set in type. As the object is to make your manuscript as widely acceptable as possible, proportional faces are not recommended.

A good way of discovering whether a word-processing program was really devised for professional writers is to see what its default typeface is. If it comes up in Courier 10 or a similar pica face it really was meant for professionals.

The manuscript should be exactly double spaced.

The whole of the manuscript should use the same margins and tab settings. These should provide a sixty-space line centered on the page or with slightly more space on the left, and paragraph indentations of five spaces. Most fiction writers will not need other tabs, except for one in the center of the page if the machine does not have automatic centering.

Allow margins of at least one inch (excluding headings) on all sides of the text, including the top and bottom. The theoretical maximum number of text lines per page is twenty-seven, but when headings (headers) are used, as they should be, the manuscript is more attractive if it uses twenty-five lines for text and allows extra space between the header and the text.

Except for the first and last pages of a chapter or story, every page should bear the same number of lines, counting embedded blank lines. If the manuscript is typed, however, retyping is not necessary if a page or two are a line short or a line long.

The manuscript should be typed ragged right. (The right margin should *not* be made to come out even, or nearly so.) Features which automatically hyphenate words, return the carriage when a hyphen is struck near the end of a line, or insert spaces of varying size must be turned off. That is, the manuscript is left-justified only. The left side is even except for paragraph indentations.

Never end a line with a hyphen. If a word or an expression contains a hyphen, carry the whole expression to the next line no matter how uneven this makes the right margin. To do this on an electronic word processor, consult the documentation to learn how to enter a *hard hyphen*. Use hard hyphens only and turn off features that automatically insert hyphens in words at the end of a line.

Manuscripts must use only one side of the paper. Nothing may be entered on the back of a page.

Do not make extra space (do not double-space twice) between paragraphs. If you wish to indicate a break in a story or a change of scene by having extra space ("leading") in the printed version, center the pound sign (#) on an otherwise blank line.

Make no attempt to get paragraphs to come out even on a page. Carry the last two words of a paragraph to the next page, if the typing comes out that way. For those with word processors, this means: turn off widow- and orphan-control features and protect block features.

Center your title and capitalize important words in it. Use exactly the same typeface that you use for text, and do not underline your title. Do not use all capital letters for your title unless the title is an acronym, or there is some other special reason for the unusual capitalization.

Every page of the manuscript except the first should have a heading line (also called a header or a slug line). This line should not vary in form. The header for a short story should be in this form:

Eighner/Elements/page x

That is, your surname, slash, a very short form of your title, slash, the word "page," and the number of the page.

The header goes in the upper-left corner of the manuscript, and its form and position should be the same on both odd and even pages. If you wish, you may use a slightly smaller typeface for the header.

In a book, the short title is the abbreviated title of the book and does not vary from chapter to chapter. Page numbers for book manuscripts should not be entered in the header, but should be entered without the word "page" in the same line as the header in either the center of the page or in the upper-right corner.

There is much disagreement about whether book manuscripts should be paginated at the center top or at the top right. My best suggestion is that novels should be paginated in the upper right corner. But in story collections or any other book in which whole sections or chapters may be rearranged before publication, put page numbers at the center top. The purpose of putting page numbers in the center is so that when the final order of the book is fixed, the editor can more easily renumber the pages, using a stamping machine designed for that purpose.

When a page must be inserted between page 123 and page 124, number the page 123A. Make a circled note near the page number of page 123: "Page 123A folos." Make a similar note on page 123A: "Page 124 folos." If necessary, page 123B may follow page 123A, and so forth. Never insert slips or tape or clip insertions to a page. Insert only standard-size pages even if the inserted page bears only a few lines.

A few insertions are acceptable in a book manuscript, and many books will have insertions by the time the editing is complete. A short story produced on a word processor, however, should not have insertions.

The journalistic practice of typing "—more—" at the bottom of each page except the last is not used in fiction manuscripts, unless there is some special likelihood of error, as when a page of a few lines is inserted in the manuscript. All such notations, when used, should be circled in pencil.

Chapters should always begin on a new page. Writers using word processors should look up the keystrokes for a *hard page* command, which will force the word processor to begin a new page. Leave an inch or two of extra space at the top of a new chapter. Center the chapter title on a line and skip an extra line before beginning the text of the chapter.

How the dash and the ellipsis should be entered in a manuscript are matters upon which some editors disagree sharply. This is my best advice and if you run into an editor who tells you differently, simply say, "I'm sorry, I was ill-advised."

Make a dash by entering two or three hyphens. I use three hyphens, but whichever you use, use them consistently. If you use a word processor, make the dash out of hard hyphens. Do not use the dash special character that your word processor may provide; it is too small for editors to mark up the dash, as they must.

Do not leave a space before the first hyphen or after the last one, and do not put spaces between hyphens. Do not end a line with a dash, but carry the word that precedes the dash to the next line if necessary. (This will happen automatically on word processors if you have entered the dash as I suggest).

Form the ellipsis with three periods separated by spaces. Space before the first period and after the last one. If you work on a word processor, enter *hard spaces* between the periods to keep the ellipsis from being broken at the end of a line.

Make a note of any editorial static you receive on these points. If you have entered dashes and ellipses as I suggest, and you work on a word processor, you should have little trouble in using your search-and-replace function to tailor your manuscript to fit the demands of editors who prefer different forms of the dash and ellipsis.

Do not use large or ornate typefaces for the first letter of a paragraph. Do not set the first few words of a paragraph in small capitals.

Editors may decide to do these things to improve the appearance of the printed work, but the author has no business suggesting such things.

Do not indicate italics by using an italic typeface. Indicate italics by underlining. Do not call upon boldface, small capitals, or other typefaces.

Why does a dog lick its dick?

Because it can.

Because they can is probably the reason that some new writers send their computer rodents to get an italic face, turn on their automatic-hyphenation devices, right-justify their manuscripts, and enter whole passages in Barnum & Bailey type. Editors speak to them as we speak to dick-licking dogs: *"Stop that this instant!"* New writers who persist in doing such things as sending out camera-ready versions of manuscripts never get to be old writers.

Have a good reason to request special typography. Authors have a right to call upon italics. Harry M. McNaughton has advised the reader of his *Proofreading and Copyediting:*

> The use of italics for emphasis is not controlled and our novices can be allowed to wallow in them. Used sparingly the practice has some value and is quite proper but it tends to insult readers' intelligence and sound homosexual.

My goodness, Miss Agnes! Some editors of gay periodicals agree that italics are not butch enough and will change italics to all capitals or delete the italics. Frequent requests for italics, especially for single words or phrases, indicate that the writer has doubts about his ability to place the emphasis in its proper place. Many gay magazines are set in gothic faces that do not show italics well.

(Forget the popular misconception, if you have it, that "gothic" means something like Old English or German Text. In the printing and publishing business "gothic" means a sans-serif face similar to what is taught as printing in the primary grades.)

Magazine editors want control over the general appearance of the book (as they call their magazine) and think the use of many unusual faces is a complication they do not have time to be bothered with. They will often have special uses for boldface and small capitals and other variations in type, and they will not want to use these inconsistently simply because you think they would look neat in your story. As an attention-getting device, unusual typography loses its effectiveness quickly and calls the reader's attention to print as print, breaking the spell that a work of fiction should cast.

Occasionally there are good reasons for unusual typography. In some editions of *Dracula,* different typefaces are used to represent the different handwritings in the documents which are supposed to compose the novel. I have asked, with varying degrees of success, for specimens of business cards to appear in a work of fiction. In *Classified Affairs* (Boston: Alyson, 1984) John Preston and Frederick Brandt had far more call to do this sort of thing, and I defer to Preston on the point: Announce a change in type style with a centered notation enclosed in brackets. Like:

[All that follows should appear as a classified ad.]

The bracket announces a message to the editor.... Then another centered bracketed notation announces the end of the instruction.

Between the brackets, of course, enter your text in the normal body type of your manuscript. In most fiction, there is no real necessity for reproducing leaflets, newspaper articles, and documents as they might have appeared. Novices should find another way of handling such material.

Authors should feel entitled to call upon any character used in the boldface entries of an American dictionary (but not, of course, the special characters of dictionary printing that are found in the pronunciation guide). Magazines do not always have all of these characters, and even some book publishers who have them will not bother with them.

Accents—both acute and grave accents occur in words that are now English. On a typewriter, do not use the apostrophe key to form accents because it will not make it clear which accent you mean; enter them in black ink by hand if necessary. Consult the documentation of your word processor to learn how to enter accented characters.

Cedilla—an acceptable substitute can be formed at the typewriter by overstriking *c* with a comma. "Façade" and "curaçao" are fairly common English words that require this character. On some word processors, you can compose special characters using a special command and the same keystrokes you would use to form the character at the typewriter. For example, in WordPerfect 6.0 you use Ctrl-a, which is the compose command, and then c and a comma to form the cedilla.

Umlaut—an acceptable substitute can usually be formed by overstriking with the double-quote key. The old saw was that "Brontë" was the only English word or name requiring the umlaut. But "Führer" is now in the main word list of the *Collegiate* and no doubt there are others. In its alter ego, the dieresis, the umlaut is appearing more frequently in highbrow magazines like *The New Yorker* where it serves to remind readers when adjacent vowels are pronounced separately, as in the word "coöperative."

Tilde—common in Spanish names and in words adopted from Spanish such as "señor." Enter it by hand if necessary.

Macron—the bar that indicates a long vowel sound. It is not required by any English word I know, outside of trade names. At the typewriter, a raised hyphen will work.

Circumflex—still used in some words and expressions from French such as "tête-à-tête," but no longer commonly entered in words like "rôle." Enter it by hand, if necessary.

Do not attempt to enter characters from Greek or Arabic or any other language that does not use the Roman alphabet or mathematical symbols in a fiction manuscript.

On old typewriters, lowercase *l* is used for the figure 1, but a circled marginal note should name any character when there is a genuine danger of confusion. The names of letters are spelled phonetically: el for *l*, oh for *o*, em for *m*, and so forth. On old typewriters, the exclamation point is formed by overstriking the period with the apostrophe. This last is a good way to form the exclamation point if you tend to overuse it, because you may reconsider in the time it takes to make the extra keystrokes.

Although left and right quotes look different in print, use the same double-quote key to enter either the right or left quote. Use the apostrophe key for apostrophes and right or left single quotes. If your word processor does have left and right quotes and different keys for the apostrophe and the single quote, you may want to enter the correct characters; but if you are using Courier 10, as I have suggested, the distinctions between these characters should not be evident in the printed copy.

Paper used for manuscripts should be white, opaque, $8^{1/2}$" by 11", with edges as smooth as possible. This last is directed at those tempted to use the cheapest kind of tractor-fed paper which leaves nasty nubs whenever it is torn apart. Copier-quality papers are now universally acceptable. Papers of 16- and 18-weight are acceptable, but many people prefer the feel of 20-weight-paper.

Erasable paper, onionskin, colored paper, the paper sold in drugstores as typing paper, and newsprint are unacceptable. Letterhead paper must not be used for manuscripts. You may want to have a nicer kind of paper for letters that you write in your business, and that paper might be off-white or natural. I suggest that a letterhead, if used for letters, contain only your name, address, and phone number, and that you avoid quill-pen logos and titles.

However formed on the paper, letters must be black.

No other color is acceptable. Ink ribbons, if used, must be retired to draft work once they begin to form gray characters. Since a writer wants only black, multicolored ribbons are wasteful.

The first page of a short story should contain the author's true name, address, and social security number in the upper left corner. In the upper-right corner should be the caption "fiction," the approximate word count of the piece, and the rights offered if not the standard first-serial rights, each on a separate line. The first page is not numbered. The author's title, in ordinary body type with important words capitalized, is centered on a line about a third of the way down the page. On the next double-spaced line is centered the word "by" and the name under which the story is to appear. The next double-spaced line is skipped. The story begins on the following line.

The title page of a book manuscript is much the same as the first page of a short story, except that no text is on the title page, and the caption "fiction" is replaced with an appropriate caption, such as "a novel" or "a story collection."

The other special pages of a book manuscript are discussed later in this chapter.

Equipment for producing the manuscript.

There are three options in equipment for producing the manuscript. The best one is probably the one you have already. If you have one of the machines that will produce acceptable manuscripts, begin writing with it. If you do not have one that produces acceptable manuscripts and you cannot afford any of them, write longhand until your circumstances improve.

The typewriter.

A serviceable manual typewriter can be obtained secondhand for twenty or thirty dollars. Electric typewriters are more expensive, but you should not pay extra for memory typewriters or spell-checking typewriters. These features are not powerful enough to provide the advantages of real word processing.

Watch out for unacceptable typefaces, the inability to double-space (some will only one-and-a-half space), and special ribbons and typing elements which may no longer be easy to find. Be sure, of course, that all the keys work.

Typewriters with separate lift-off correction ribbons are acceptable. When the correction ribbon is part of the ink ribbon, the typewriter is unacceptable because the supplies will be excessively expensive. If you have such a machine, however, you may choose to use it.

While typewriters can be used to produce perfectly acceptable manuscripts, they cannot produce disk files. A few magazines require disk files, and many prefer and pay extra for disk files. (But all still want a paper—or hard copy—of the manuscript, too.)

Small dedicated word processors.

Dedicated word processors are computers that are designed only for word processing. They are smaller than a general-purpose computer, and in some, the typewriterlike printer, the computer screen, and the keyboard are built together in one piece. The price of such a machine runs between that of an electric typewriter and a modest new computer system. Such a word processor may or may not produce disk files that are acceptable to the magazines that want disk files.

I do not recommend buying a new dedicated word processor. For the same money, you can buy a fully functional computer secondhand. Computers made just a few years ago are now considered obsolete and are being replaced by their owners. But many of these so-called obsolete systems are more than adequate for a writer's needs. Consult a friend who knows about computers to assist you to be sure you get everything that ought to go with the computer. Your friend, if a real computer buff, will probably want you to get a new system or a bigger and faster computer than you really need. Insist that you just want something cheap that you can process words with.

With the secondhand computer you should get the operating software and a word processor that is appropriate to the system. Insist on this. Newer versions of the operating system and word-processing software may be too big to run well on an old machine, and you may have difficulty finding the older versions elsewhere.

In used computers, look for kinds that are still represented in the new computer market: either a PC-type machine or a Macintosh. Beware of evolutionary dead ends, such as Texas Instruments and the Tandy machines using floppy disks the size of LPs. Look for a machine with a hard disk drive, even a small one. Be sure that the printer can produce acceptable copy. Some 9-pin printers can produce good-quality print, but these were relatively expensive in their day, so the chances are that a secondhand 9-pin printer is not acceptable. Ask to see a sample printout. Check to see that characters really seem to be formed of lines and curves, and that individual dots are not visible.

Computer systems.

There are two viable sorts of computer systems available:

1. PC-type computers, based on personal computers originally developed by IBM but now supplied and supported by very many companies, many of which produce machines superior to those offered by IBM; and

2. Macintosh computers, all of which are made by Apple or its licensees. There are a few computers which belong to neither class (such as Amiga), but they seem to be evolutionary dead ends and should be avoided by someone who knows little about computers and wants primarily to do word processing and to produce disk files that can be widely read. Beware of machines sold by electronics hobby shops. These may claim to be PC-compatible, but some of them are not very compatible.

Macintoshes are easy to learn to use—or so I am assured by everyone who has one. The drawback of Macintoshes that most bothers me is that once you are committed to a Macintosh, you are committed to one supplier: the Apple company. You may see what I mean if you pretend you need a new or better printer for your Macintosh. Look at the ads in the newspapers and see how many choices you have.

I do not pretend the following is objective. This is the advice I would give a friend who was going into the writing business and who had the money to spend:

For about $1,000, you can get a new PC-compatible computer without a printer. You can get an excellent 24-pin printer for less than $300 or a laser printer for less than $800. If you cannot afford a real laser printer, get a top-of-the-line 24-pin printer. Avoid printers with "jet" in the name. Jet ink never really dries. (If you own a jet printer, you can live with it for a while. Make xerographic copies of your manuscripts to preserve them.) A good 24-pin printer will produce copy that looks about as good and which will remain on the page. Most new PC-compatibles come with Windows. If you are afraid to delete Windows, at least disable it. Get WordPerfect 6.0 for DOS and install it. This will cost about $600 if you do not already have a WordPerfect license. You may want to get a fax/modem that is compatible with WordPerfect so that you can send faxes from your computer. When business picks up, you may want a spreadsheet and a data base. Ignore the Microsoft programs that claim to be spreadsheets and data bases. Get Lotus and dBASE.

That is my advice. Of course, I am the sort of person who likes computers, who reads documentation and runs tutorial programs, and who is not afraid to experiment with different options until I discover how to do things they way I want them done. If you are not that sort of person (and many people who are attracted to writing are not), you may want to get a Macintosh, or you may want to run Microsoft Word under Windows. In the latter case, be sure that your machine has enough memory. Windows can be installed on a machine with as little as two megabytes of memory, and some systems come this way. To run Windows effectively, you really need at least eight megabytes of memory, and more is better.

In any event, unless you have someone to set the system up for you, you will have to learn something about computers in order to produce a manuscript like the ideal one described above. The machines which are easiest to use—Macintosh and PC-compatibles running Windows—make it easy to do the things that most people want to do. Unfortunately, most people do not want to produce professional-looking manuscripts. Most people want to write notes to their friends in Barnum & Bailey type with flowered borders, and this is all too easy to do with a Macintosh.

The best computer, of course, is the one you already know how to operate. If you have experience with a PC-compatible or a Macintosh at work or school, you will probably be happiest with a machine of similar kind, and the advantage of familiarity might be great enough to justify getting an Amiga or a Tandy. Likewise, the best word-processing software is the kind you know how to use.

Corrections.

Corrections in a short-story manuscript should be made electronically. For many corrections, it will be possible to reprint only the page with the correction—be sure the new page starts and ends where the old page did, and simply insert the corrected page in place of the old page. If there are many corrections on many pages or if a correction seriously affects the appearance of a page—making it much too short or too long—running out a complete new copy of twelve to twenty pages should not be too great a burden.

No one will expect you to run out a new four- or five-hundred page book manuscript to accommodate a few corrections. If the corrections cannot be made by reprinting single pages, new pages can be inserted, as has been described.

Corrections to a typewritten manuscript can be made by covering the error with well-thinned Wite-Out and typing in the correction, when the correction will fit the space. (Do not use powder tapes to cover over mistakes, and never strike over an error without covering up or erasing the error first.) When the correction does not fit the space, minor corrections can be made by hand.

Even a writer who works electronically should know how to enter corrections by hand because one day he may get to review edited pages of his book.

Use a dark pencil to make corrections. If you *are* working with edited pages, use a dark color that differs from the colors the editors have used. But if you are entering corrections on a manuscript that has not been edited, use an ordinary No. 2 pencil. In any event, make corrections firmly.

Indicate all corrections within the typewritten lines, which are what the typesetter's eyes will follow. (Later, if you work with proofs, you will have to make a mark in the margin to indicate every correction. In correcting copy, which is what you are doing now, only some corrections will require marks in the margins, but all must be indicated in the line.)

Do not obliterate material you want to delete. Draw a single firm line through material to be deleted. When a large block is to be deleted, draw single lines through the material and draw a closed line around the whole block. To delete a single character, draw an oblique slash—like a solidus—through it. If the character is to be removed, put small arcs, like sideways parentheses, at the top and bottom of the slash. If the character is to be replaced with a space, make a number sign (#) at the top of the slash, using the slash as one of the legs of the number sign.

To restore deleted material, put dots under the material to be restored, write "Stet" in the margin, and circle the word "Stet."

To add italics, underline the material once and write and circle the abbreviation "ital." in the margin. To remove italics, hang little slashes, like legs, from the underlining so the result looks like a skewed comb missing most of its teeth.

To insert material, draw a vertical line through the type line at exactly the place the insertion is wanted. Commas and periods are indicated in a caret below the line. A period is indicated by a small circled dot. Other insertions are indicated in an inverted caret or bracket above the line. Several words may be written in a long bracket above the line, but they must not bend around corners or run down the margins. Do not paste, staple, pin, or otherwise attach insertions. You may have to retype.

In making handwritten corrections, a hyphen that is to appear in print (a hard hyphen) is represented by two short parallel lines that resemble a short equals sign. This symbol can be entered in a caret above the line if only the single character is wanted, and should be used for the hyphen in any longer written insertion. The number sign (#) represents a space. To insert a space, use the vertical line that indicates the place of the insertion as one of the legs of the number sign.

To change a single character to another, draw a slash through the character and write the correct character over the slash (unless it is a period or comma).

When adjacent characters or words are simply transposed, the material to be interchanged is enclosed in the arms of a long sideways s. Whole phrases within the same line can be interchanged in this way, but this cannot be done when three elements are in the wrong order. Circle the notation "tr." in the margin.

To change a capital letter to lowercase, put a slash through the letter and circle the notation "l.c." in the margin. To change a lowercase letter to a capital, underline it three times and circle the notation "cap" in the margin.

Small capitals are represented by double underlining, and boldface is indicated with a single wavy underlining. Do not enter these indications on your manuscript; but if you have edited pages, you may need to know these marks to see that these indications have been used consistently. For example, if the editor has indicated small capitals for the abbreviation AWOL in most places, he surely meant for it to appear that way in all places in the text, and you should double-underline any occurrence of AWOL that he missed.

Circling material indicates that it should *not* be set in type. All notes to the editor and to the typesetter should be circled. A circle around a figure like 7 in the line of typewriting means that the number should be spelled out, and circles around abbreviations and contractions also mean they should be spelled out. On the other hand, a circle around a spelled-out figure means it should be set as a figure. In your manuscript, you do not know the editor's policies regarding figures and abbreviations, so do not circle such things.

The number sign (#) you used to indicate where extra space was wanted between paragraphs will be circled in edited pages. That does not mean the editor has decided not to allow you the extra space. It only means the number sign itself should not be set in type.

Arcs or bow-shaped marks indicate material is supposed to be skipped over and that the space it occupied is to be deleted. Deletions should always be struck through, but sometimes the bows are added, too, to guide the typesetter's eyes and to indicate that the next part should follow immediately. Little arcs above and below the line are used to remove small unwanted spaces, such as the ones some writers will put around dashes. When words that have been typed separately are to be set as a compound word, the small arcs, top and bottom, are use to remove the unwanted space (to close up).

A curved line from the end of a paragraph to the first letter of the next paragraph indicates that the paragraphs should be set as one, and sometimes the notation "run in" or the symbol "no ¶" is circled in the margin. The notations are also used in case the material to be joined is on the following page.

The paragraph symbol ¶ is used in the line of typewriting just above the point that a new paragraph is wanted.

Although the proofreading marks given in a table in every standard dictionary are not exactly the same as copyediting marks, some editors use the marks more or less interchangeably. This table may clarify any indications you see on edited pages.

Do not mark up your manuscript for typesetting.

Any very complicated or extensive error should be corrected by retyping. Retype the first few pages several times, if necessary, to make them as neat as possible.

Parts of the book manuscript.

All pages of a book manuscript, except the title page, should bear a heading line, described previously. The first page of text is page one; the pages that precede it are not numbered. The forms of the pages composing the front matter should make it immediately obvious what these pages are. If one of these preliminaries goes on for more than a page, enter a caption in the heading line like "contents—page 2," "acknowledgments—page 3," and so forth.

The copy supplied by the author for a book of gay erotica or for most other kinds of fiction is:

The title page. The title page is mandatory. Do not include blank cover sheets or half-title pages. The author's true name, address, and social security number go in the upper left corner, each on a separate single-spaced line. In the upper-right corner goes a descriptive caption like "a novel," "a story collection," or "two novellas." Below that goes the approximate word count. (This estimate can be made by counting five typical pages, dividing by five, and multiplying by the number of text pages in the manuscript. There is no point in making this an exact number. Round the word count reported by your word processor if you have one.)

Centered on the page go the author's title, with important words capitalized, the descriptive caption again, and the byline, each on a separate, centered, double-spaced line. The author's pen name, if used, goes in the byline, but his true name should appear in the heading. If the author wishes to include a copyright notice it goes in the lower left portion of this page.

The acknowledgments page. Acknowledgments are mandatory, if they are applicable. This is not the wordy expression of gratitude, sometimes called "acknowledgments," that really belongs in a preface or an author's note. This is the record of the previous publication of material that appears in the book. In the printed book, this information usually appears on the back of the title page in tiny type, but in the manuscript it is entered on a separate page under the centered title "Acknowledgments," and is double-spaced in the same typeface used for the body of the work.

If the author has sold only serial rights to magazines in which the material has appeared previously or if magazines that bought all rights have returned the unused rights to the author, then the author has the book rights to the material and the acknowledgment notices take the form:

"Lesbian Nuns on Bikes" first appeared in *Leatherdyke Magazine,* November 1999.

"Jocks" first appeared in *ManTime Magazine,* March 1999, as "Pro Jocks In Heat."

Portions of chapters one and two first appeared as "The Confessions of Lance Thudd" in *Blueballs Quarterly,* Spring 1999, in slightly different form.

But if the works of other people are used, or if you do not have the copyright to material of yours that you have included in the book, then each use of such material requires a full recitation of the owner's original copyright notice (and you will have to provide your publisher with properly executed permissions to use the material).

If you have material of both kinds in your book, remove the citations of works requiring permissions to a separate page. And, of course, if none of the material in your book has ever appeared in print before, you should have no acknowledgments page.

Card page. This is the list of other books you have written. Some publishers are mean enough to list only the books that they have published: "Other books by Freddie Fumblefart from GayBOOKS!!!" It makes it appear that these are all the books you have written. Of course, if some of your other books are very well known and highly regarded, the publisher will want to list them so that the reader knows you are that same famous author.

In the finished book, the card page may go in any of several places. Often it comes before the title page. But, in manuscript, nothing comes before the title page. Simply type "Also by" and your name and list your previously published titles on separate double-spaced lines.

Dedication. The dedication is optional. Some publishers will squeeze the dedication onto the back of the title page. In the manuscript, center the title "Dedication" on the first text line of the page and enter the dedication below it. The fashion is to make the dedication as simple as possible, perhaps no more than the word "to" and the name. Recall that the book will almost certainly not appear until at least a year after the dedication is written and that the dedication will remain with book at least as long as the first edition is in print. The sentiment behind the dedication ought to be at least as enduring.

Epigraph. The epigraph—a brief quotation—is optional. It may be a verse that contains the words that gave rise to the title of the book. It might be words from a speech or a poem or other inspirational matter. Sometimes it is an imaginary quotation from a character in the book which may or may not be repeated somewhere in the text.

The epigraph goes on a separate page in the manuscript. Sometimes there are several quotations; they all go on the same page. An epigraph requiring more than a few lines is likely to be tedious. In the finished book, the epigraph may appear in an unusual fashion, such as flush right and ragged left. But type it normally, double-spaced. Include the source of the epigraph on the line following.

Be sure to consider whether the epigraph will require permission, as it surely will if it comes from a popular song. Not every work will benefit by having an epigraph, and unless a epigraph is chosen wisely, it may seem an affectation.

Contents. The contents page is mandatory, if it is applicable. Novels no longer invariably bear a contents page; certainly it is silly for them to do so if the chapters are not titled.

Center the word "Contents" on the first text line of this page. Double-space twice and list double-spaced the titles of the stories, chapters, or other parts of the book.

You cannot know the page numbers of the parts in the finished book. Do not type in the page numbers of the manuscript pages. Pencil and circle the manuscript page numbers in the left margin. If you see this page in proof, the spaces for the page numbers will be filled with zeros. If the numbers are filled in, you have page proofs, not galleys.

Preface. A preface is presumptuous in a first work of fiction and is seldom called for in any novel, except those novels in which the preface is part of the fiction. The preface may be replaced with an author's note if there are those who must be thanked. Brevity is essential.

A good story collection ought have a theme, and a publisher may want a few words from the author to strike the keynote. This brief passage may be called a preface.

Center the word "Preface" or the title "Author's Note" on the line you would use to start a chapter. The preface is supposed to be the author's work and does not bear a byline. At the bottom of the text, it is customary for the preface to bear the author's name, the place of composition, and the month or season that the work was completed.

In fiction, an introduction is a work of commentary by someone other than the author of the book. While you are living, your fictional works probably will not have introductions, again excepting the case where the introduction is part of the fiction, in which case it will be written by you and attributed to a fictional character.

Real introductions are not your responsibility, but will be commissioned separately by the publisher, if they are desired.

The first page of text is page one. Leave extra space at the top of this page as you will for the first pages of other chapters or parts. Begin each chapter or part on a fresh page. If you have a fairly slender book to begin with, it is silly and tasteless to divide it into "Book I," "Book II," et cetera, unless you are imitating a classical text.

Chapter titles are very useful in composing a book, but you may or may not choose to title chapters in the finished book. Whether or not titled, chapters are numbered. Use an arabic number followed by a period. Numbering short stories is pointless, unless they form a short-story cycle. Short stories are very likely to be rearranged in the editing process, anyway.

Double-space twice after the line that contains the chapter or story title and begin typing your text.

Fiction almost never has back matter, but usually the last page of the text is the last page of the manuscript.

Mailing the book manuscript.

Book manuscripts should not be sent unless and until they are expected. When they are expected, they are sent as loose pages in a box, like the box that typing paper comes in. Do not bind a book manuscript. The top page in the box should be a cover letter showing, at the very least, the person to whom the manuscript is sent (usually the person who requested it), your name and address, and a prominent statement indicating that the manuscript has been requested.

The return envelope should be a large padded mailer; it is very likely that if the pages come back, they will come back without the box. If possible, fold the return envelope and put it on top of the manuscript in the box. Tape the top and bottom of the box together with as little tape as possible. The box should be placed in a large padded mailer or can be wrapped in kraft paper and sealed with strapping tape.

Sending manuscripts.

Short-story manuscripts should be sent by first-class mail. Although there is a special parcel-post rate for manuscripts, it offers no advantage for story-sized manuscripts.

The weight of the paper is the weight in pounds of 2,000 sheets of $8^{1/2}$" by 11" paper. That is, 2,000 sheets of 20-pound paper weigh 20 pounds; 2,000 sheets of 18-pound paper weigh 18 pounds, and so forth. Therefore, 100 sheets of 20-pound paper weigh 1 pound, or 6 sheets to the ounce. By including an allowance for the envelopes, you can calculate the weight of the manuscript without a scale.

The first-class rate is lower for additional ounces. Keep stamps of two denominations: the one for the first ounces and the one for additional ounces. Do not stick three first-class stamps on a three-ounce manuscript; affix one first-class stamp and two stamps in the denomination for additional ounces.

The large envelope in which the manuscript is mailed should be clearly marked "First Class Mail." Although priority mail is a form of first-class mail, if you mark an envelope "Priority Mail," you must affix priority postage, which is more than the first-class rate for manuscripts of twelve ounces or less.

Some writers, especially those who send photocopies or who can run out another copy of manuscript easily with a word processor, find it cheaper to mark their manuscripts "Disposable" and include a letter-sized SASE for the editor's report. If he does not accept the manuscript, the editor discards the manuscript and returns a rejection slip in the letter-sized SASE. Such savings are slight. To save anything at all, at present postal rates, the writer must be able to make new copies for less than 4¢ per page. But the psychology of this process seems wrong. The writer should consider his manuscript valuable and should want it back. He should avoid creating the impression that it is worthless if this editor does not want it. The last image an editor has of a manuscript should not be of it in the wastebasket, but should be one of a manuscript that he might see again, printed in a competing publication.

Sending a fax across the country is now cheaper and surer than mailing a letter, if you own the fax machine. Contracts, checks, and manuscripts cannot be faxed. But much editorial correspondence is now done via fax, including, sometimes, last-minute corrections to proofs and other emergency queries. No beginner should initiate a correspondence with an editor by fax. But as a writer's career advances, the advantages of having ready access to a fax machine increase.

Book manuscripts should not be mailed until they are requested. When a book manuscript is requested, the savings available by sending it at the special parcel-post rate should be weighed against the delay and risk of loss entailed in parcel post. Consider priority mail if you can afford it. Second-day service from private express companies is considerably cheaper than their overnight services but afford the same security and certainty of delivery.

An author who is returning edited pages or proofs should not hesitate to employ a reliable—that is, a private—express service. Second-day delivery from a private express service is available at a reasonable rate considering the peace of mind the author gains in the bargain. The United States Postal Service will not guarantee delivery within any specified time, which shows that it understands the quality of its service very well. Private services are more expensive, but this is a case of getting what you pay for.

Print.

A good editor saves an author considerable embarrassment. The editor's job includes correcting the author's manuscript without damaging variations in usage which are considered literary style and without altering the voices of the narrator or the characters. Some editors are not so good as others; an author must make the manuscript as consistent and as nearly perfect as he can. If an error in print reproduces an error in manuscript, the author may blame no one but himself.

All large type belongs to the editor. The editor may paraphrase portions of the text to be set in large type (pullouts), write blurbs (or, in the case of a book, solicit blurbs from others and choose among them), and retitle the piece as he sees fit. Especially in titles, a courteous editor may advise the author of a change. That is only a courtesy; the author must consent promptly. The editor determines the size and style of type for the large type and the text. The editor may and should make changes in the copy to conform it to the editorial style of the periodical or the publishing house. Finally, the editor makes changes to fit the work into the space allotted for it.

If the editor cannot print the writer's work, he should decline to buy it. The editor ought not to rewrite whole passages and certainly should not alter the substance of the work. Yet such things happen. An author has a justifiable complaint—though whether voicing it is wise is another matter—when the heart of the work is violated, but the author must not criticize the editor for doing what an editor does. The author should consider the possibility that the editor is correct and that the result is an improvement. Like some authors, some editors are fools, and some are meddling busybodies. But the good that editors have done has accumulated a treasury of merits that we may indulge them a few evils.

The author's manuscript is the copy. What is done with it is copyediting. If the material is a book that is to be published by a large house, the author may be given the chance to review the edited pages, although this is unlikely in gay erotica. The edited copy is sent to the typesetter. In theory, the typesetter sets the copy exactly as it is presented to him, even if he perceives obvious errors. Also in theory, the edited copy never presents the typesetter with ambiguities: the typesetter never has to make a decision. A copy is made of the typeset text. This is called a proof. What is done with it is proofreading.

If an error in material is missed by a reader, that same reader is very likely to miss the error however many times he reviews the material. For this reason, the author should never edit his own copy. By the same token, the person who edited the copy should never attempt to proofread the work. In reality, these rules must be violated when the publisher's staff is small.

The object of proofreading is to correct the typesetter's errors; to indicate on the proof what must be done to make the type agree with the copy. Doing this correctly requires two persons: one to hold the copy and to read it word for word, pronouncing the names of the punctuation marks and indicating capitalization, italics, and the spelling of unusual names, and another to follow the proof and to mark corrections on it as necessary. Where the proof does not match the copy, the typesetter is at fault, and this is called a printer's error (PE). The printer is obliged to correct printer's errors at his own expense.

Invariably, errors in the copy itself are detected in proofreading. The typesetter cannot be blamed for an error in type if it reproduces an error in the copy. A correction of an error that appeared in the copy is called an author's alteration (AA), and the printer will charge for making such changes. The cost of some minor corrections should have been included when the publisher estimated the cost of typesetting. Proofreaders should not hesitate to make occasional minor corrections.

If the author has the chance of reviewing proofs, she will usually have an allowance for author's alterations—often 10 percent of the original cost of the typesetting. Making changes, however, is much more expensive than setting type to begin with. The author's allowance of 10 percent will not allow her to change 10 percent of the text. It should allow her to correct misspelled words, to insert an occasionally omitted "not," or delete a duplicated word. The author will be charged if the cost of her alterations exceed her allowance.

Do not revise in proof!

An excuse for making a substantial change in proof is to remove a libel or to correct an error in a recipe which if followed would produce a lethal bomb instead of chocolate cake. Less serious errors of substance must be lived with once the work is in proof.

Unfortunate turns of phrase must remain in the book. The

author must live with a poorly chosen word if it is spelled correctly and not libelous. If the author husbands her alterations allowance carefully, she can afford to correct such occasional lapses as having called a character by the wrong name in a few places.

Proofreading marks are given in a table that can be found in most dictionaries. Notice that each mark consists of two parts: a mark made in the line of print and a symbol entered in the margin. Both are necessary. A mark in the line of type will certainly be overlooked if there is not a symbol in the margin. When material must be changed, it is not enough to insert the correct material. The deletion of the incorrect material must be indicated as well.

The transposition symbol should not be used unless the parts to be transposed are immediately adjacent. If the error is more complicated, delete and insert. Unlike changes in the copy, insertions in proofs may be written down the margins and often are more legible if so written. Do not attempt to write insertions between the lines of type.

Bad garbles are often the fault of the typesetter. If a garble is extensive, and some may run for many lines, the author should not attempt to correct it, but should circle the offending material and enter the marginal note "folo copy." The author should watch carefully for duplicated matter, a common typesetting error that is easily missed.

When a line in the early part of a paragraph is changed, usually all of the remainder of the paragraph will have to be reset. Transpositions in a single line can be corrected by resetting only that line. Spelling corrections requiring only the substitution of a correct letter for an incorrect one can often be made by resetting only that line. Any substitution is likely to be cheaper when the material to be inserted is the same length—or nearly— as the material to be deleted. Deleting material from the end of a paragraph is usually an inexpensive change, as is deletion of exactly one line as set.

In theory, the author should have the edited pages in order to read proofs properly. Otherwise he has no way of knowing whether a variation from his manuscript is the result of the copyediting or is a printer's error. The author may written "salon," but "saloon" appears on the proof. The author wrote "trapezius" (a large muscle of the neck and back), but the galley reads "trapezium" (a bone of the wrist). Whether the author has edited pages or not, he should recheck such variations. Perhaps there is a good reason the proof reads "callus" where the author wrote "callous."

An author who is fortunate enough to be given proofs should make sure to return the proofs on time.

Corrections are made by the typesetter, and the changes are checked. Then all is well if the text fits the space allotted for it exactly. If it is short by a little, slight adjustments in the white space may resolve the problem. But if it is long, the editor must shorten the text in a way that requires as little new typesetting as possible.

Most books are made up of signatures of sixteen pages. The publisher is unlikely to allow thirteen blank pages in order to accommodate three extra pages of text. Moreover, editors will want to remove widows and orphans: paragraphs which break badly, so that only a few words are carried to a following page, or a very short word that appears alone on the last line. Sometimes the spaces between words will line up on a page or in a column so that a long valley of white seem to flow through the text. Careful editors will make adjustments to eliminate this valley.

The author will not be consulted when these kinds of final adjustments must be made. The editor must make these adjustments quickly. Often no good solution is evident and the editor is compelled to choose the least objectionable of unattractive alternatives. The wonder is not that authors are sometimes displeased, but that editors ever find agreeable solutions at all.

In many respects, literature is a collective art: a performance frozen in ink and paper. The literary work bears the personal imprint of its author to much greater degree than a drama or a motion picture or a ballet. Yet the author of a literary work must rely on people of many crafts to produce his work.

A beautiful book is a work of art. The editor is no less an artist than a director or a conductor; a typesetter no less an artist than a violinist; a bookbinder no less an artist than a set designer. The author must respect his collaborators, acknowledge them, and even at times defer to them. Without them his work is idle scribbling, as all who were born unpublished should remember.

11. *A Writer's Guide to Style*

If all goes well, the author's typescript is not the final form of the work. Once the substance of the work is fixed, the typescript is reviewed by a copy editor. (At many magazines, the copy editor will be the same associate editor who is the person the writer has been dealing with all along and whom I have called an editor elsewhere in this book. For present purposes, whoever edits the copy is the copy editor, whatever his or her job title might be.) The copy editor marks up the manuscript for the typesetters. The copy editor is supposed to resolve every question and ambiguity in the material because typesetters are supposed to set the material exactly as it is presented to them, whether or not they perceive errors in it. In traditional publishing, typesetters were not really the automatons that they were supposed to be, and they did occasionally detect potentially embarrassing errors. But increasingly, typesetting is done by computers, and those human beings still employed in the trade often are not native speakers of English. Proofreading of the typeset work is supposed only to check the work of the typesetters, not to review the form or substance of the work. The task of the copy editor, then, is vital to the final appearance of the work because not many changes can be made in proofs.

Beyond correcting obvious errors, the copy editor seeks to bring some consistency to the finished product. The copy editor resolves the fine points of style and selects among the several ways that expressions can be rendered in print. The sum of the editor's policies regarding these fine points is called "editorial style." Because many questions of editorial style tend to recur, a publisher may adopt a "house style," which may be codified in a few mimeographed pages or printed in a booklet. Staff writers or writers producing a series of works may be provided with a copy of the house style and may be asked to prepare their manuscripts according to the house style.

Freelance writers, however, need not know what the house style is, or even whether there is one. House styles differ from publisher to publisher, and especially from one kind of publication to another. The freelance's work may be offered to several publishers before it is sold, and no one expects the freelance to reedit the work every time he sends it to another publisher.

A freelance is expected to prepare his manuscript in an internally consistent manner. When the manuscript is prepared consistently, the copy editor's job of reconciling it with the house style is much easier and less prone to error. If, in addition to applying points of style consistently, the author has made reasonable choices in rendering a typescript of her thoughts, the copy editor will have few changes to make, and the whole process of bringing the manuscript to print will be simpler and surer.

Most American editors will prefer "gray" to "grey" and will want the word spelled "gray" throughout the material they handle. The question of this spelling variant is largely settled in American English, and the word will be spelled "gray" in virtually all American publications. Other issues of editorial style, however, will depend upon the nature of the publication. Newspaper editors will usually prefer "20-year-old" (using figures), while almost all book editors will insist on "twenty-year-old" (the age spelled out). Magazine editors will differ in their preferences, and some will want "20-year-old" in titles and headings, but "twenty-year-old" in the body of stories. Publishers of academic books and journals are likely to have extensive style policies for footnotes, while newspapers will print footnotes so infrequently that few newspaper editors will bother to establish a footnote style. A poetry editor may have an editorial style that differs in many ways from that of an articles editor. But most styles will agree on most points because there seldom are more than two or three reasonable alternatives at each point. Though one publication may prefer "$25" and another will want "twenty-five dollars," almost all editors will reject "$ twenty-five" and "25 dollars."

The style introduced in the following pages is one that is suitable for writers of erotic fiction and many other kinds of fiction and articles. Certainly some editors will insist that some of these points should be handled differently, and some writers will be certain that they know better. Even those who agree that this style is essentially sound will encounter situations in which they see reasons to depart from it. Nonetheless, the style presented is thoroughly acceptable, and a new writer should adhere to it until he has a good reason to do otherwise. These style policies should be consulted as the writer composes the typescript and encounters the various points treated, but it should also be read through a few times, until the writer has learned what the issues of style are.

1 *Spelling.*

The burden of English spelling is borne by us all. Some writer's books try to be helpful by citing a number of rules of thumb. Unfortunately, the rules of thumb work best on common words which are likely to be learned by rote anyway. Exceptions are too numerous to make the rules worthwhile. A rule which gives the correct answer most of the time might help a student obtain a passing percentage, but the writer must aim to be correct every time.

1.1 *The Dictionary.*

Helpful as electronic spelling checkers may be, none will replace a good, current, standard dictionary. Most writers love words and will acquire a number of dictionaries. But a writer should use only one—a current American college-sized dictionary—as his or her standard of composition.

Look in the dictionary first. Modern dictionaries contain many citations from gay speech and many items of sexual language, both new words and those old words that once were not printed in dictionaries, but have always been part of the language. Do not waste time wondering or risk an error by guessing. Form the habit of consulting the dictionary the moment a question occurs.

A computer program to check spelling can catch many careless errors. Those who have such programs should use them. But electronic spelling checkers are unreliable in many aspects of spelling, and they cannot be regarded as the principal defense against misspellings.

Spelling checkers often will pass every variant spelling of a word, and some spelling checkers sold in America will pass British spellings. In matter prepared for publication, a word must be spelled the same way every time it occurs, and the variants acceptable to the electronic spelling checker are undesirable. Adding words to a spelling checker's lexicon is easy, but because the main lexicons of most spelling checkers are encoded to save disk space, most users will be unable to remove the unwanted entries.

Electronic spelling checkers will pass hyphenated expressions if each part of the expression is recognizable as a word. This is next to useless because the commonest spelling problem with hyphenated expressions is whether they should be hyphenated. The spelling checker does not know the answer to such questions and cannot advise the writer.

And, of course, spelling checkers will pass any recognizable word, including many common typos such as "form" for "from," and careless slips such as "their" for "there." Some spelling checkers will fail utterly when confronted with the special characters required by some English words, such as "naïve," and with common contractions, such as "won't." Many will be unable to learn such items.

When a spelling checker rejects a word, do not attempt to use the spelling checker's lexicon to guess the correct spelling, but look up the word in a real dictionary.

Spelling variants are common in American English. The writer should consult the front matter of her dictionary to learn how preferred spellings are indicated. But when several spellings are equally acceptable, the first one listed should be used as a matter of course. If the writer has a reason to choose the second spelling, she should make a marginal note in the dictionary so that she will use the same spelling when she consults the entry again.

Consistency in spelling has long been admired by editors for its own sake. Electronic word processing has provided a very practical reason for such consistency. When words and expressions are spelled consistently, search and search-and-replace functions of word processors can be used to locate all occurrences of particular words or expressions and to make consistent substitutions when it is desirable to do so.

1.2 *Odd Spellings.*

British spelling by American writers is in very poor taste. *Not:* centre, colour, gaol, grey, kerb, or tyre (but it is "greyhound").

Even when there is a dictionary entry for a foreign spelling, prefer the American version. *Not:* thé dansant, *but:* tea dance. But it is not necessary to accept the most ignorant of Americanisms: it is chaise longue, *not* chaise lounge.

Do not plunge into the morass of simplified spelling. *Not*: alright, e-z, nite, thru—*except* to quote signs or advertising copy.

1.3 *Modern Spellings.*

Though simplified spelling has lost the war, spelling, like other aspects of the language, is changing, albeit slowly. Some changes are purely literary; others reflect changes in speech. A few examples should make the need to consult the dictionary clear, especially to those who learned to spell more than a few years ago.

Modern usage tends to use a single consonant in some places where two were once preferred:

libeling, traveling, reveler, leveled, busing.

(This last may be to avoid confusion with an obsolescent synonym for "kissing." "Court orders bussing of students," might give unwarranted encouragement to pedophiles.)

Final -e is now often dropped when a suffix is added to words ending -dge:

judgment, acknowledgment.

A number of good, stylistically strong verbs had or have alternative spellings in the past and perfect tenses: dream, spell, weep, kneel, spoil, spill, creep, deal, feel, burn, smell, learn, leap. A few of these seem securely settled on the -t endings: wept, dealt, felt. Most of the others take -ed in modern usage although many persons are yet alive who know and use the -t version: spelled, spoiled, burned, smelled, spilled, and (alas) dreamed. Consult the dictionary for normal use, but for the speech of quaint characters, keep notes (called a "style sheet") to ensure that the characters use such words consistently.

1.4 Sex and Scat Words.

Dictionaries, except for public school use, are no longer compiled by prim Victorians. Many sex and scat terms are given, as are camp senses of ordinary words. (But I discover that "scat" itself is not given in my dictionary in precisely the sense I have used it. As I have used it here, it means pertaining to excrement and erotic practices involving the same.)

An unsettled question is whether, in its sexual sense, the word should be "come" or "cum." Those who favor "cum" as a verb should be prepared to say what its simple past tense is.

(The past tense of "cum" is of course "came," which proves that the word really is "come.")

Editors I consulted when I prepared the first edition of this book told me they preferred "come," both as a verb and a noun. But, as the second edition is being prepared, I note a considerable trend back to "cum." Allowances are made, in any event, for writers whose works seem to require "cum." Writers who submit their work on disk may wish to enter "cum" because it is a simple matter to change "cum" to "come" electronically, but the reverse is not practical because "come" has other senses.

The perfect and past senses of "shit" are now "shit" and "shit," unless you intend to be humorous or quaint.

When the dictionary fails, Bruce Rodgers's *Gay Talk* may be helpful, but prefer the dictionary entry if there is one. In some cases it is necessary to apply to principle. For example, should it be "jism" or "gysm"? My college-sized dictionary is silent on the point. *Gay Talk* gives "gism" and "jizzum," with the related verb "to jizz." In America, "gism" cannot be correct since the correct pronunciation, given by Rodgers, is "jiz'-m." We can argue it should be "jism" because Americans prefer *j* to *g* ("jail," not "gaol") and *i* to *y* ("tire," not "tyre"). In fact, this is the right answer. The word is entered as "jism" with "gism" given as an alternative spelling in *Webster's Third New International Dictionary*.

1.5 *Checking Sense*.

When consulting the dictionary, check the sense of the word and be alert for usage notes. A critic referred to an erotic book as "...fulsomely resolved. Meaning you come at the end." Although the critic may have an etymological defense for his use of the word "fulsomely," his dictionary should have warned him that to many people, the word does not mean anything complimentary. The wonder was that the very literate publisher of the book used this critic's remark as a blurb.

The writer might have looked up "fulsome" in his dictionary and found that the first definition *did* seem complimentary.

Some dictionaries are organized on historic principles, which means that the first definition given for the word is also the one most likely to be out of date. A careful writer should read the front matter of the dictionary to understand how the editors of the dictionary have organized the information. Historic organization can be a useful feature in a dictionary, but only if the person consulting the dictionary is aware of the scheme.

A number of words that are often confused occur in pairs (called "doublets"). Not only are the spellings and pronunciations of doublets similar, but also doublets tend to have common elements of sense because they are derived of the same root. Writers who know the difference can easily spell the one word, while meaning the other, but commonly new writers are not aware that there are two different words. A student who has always thought that "principle" and "principal" are the same word may have great difficulty in learning to distinguish the senses of these words.

Unfortunately, grammar school teachers sometimes do more harm than good. Some teach that "principal" is "princiPAL," in order to remember that "principal" refers to a person. And indeed, when a person is meant, "principal" is always the right word. But "principal" has some senses that do not refer a person.

A copy editor at a prestigious publishing house had been taught that "affect" is a verb, while "effect" was a noun. This rule of thumb will work most of the time; the noun "affect" is very rare, and many people who write "effect" as a verb mean "affect." But there is a verb "effect," and it is not rare. The verb "affect" means to influence or to make a pretense, and the verb "effect" means to enact or to bring about. Authors who knew what the verb "effect" meant and who used it correctly were in an unfortunate situation if their copy was handled by this copy editor.

Writers of highfalutin, abstract, or academic prose will think of many more examples, but some of the most frequently confused words, including many doublets, are given below.

Words to Watch Out For:

Allude/elude

Allusion/illusion

Alternate/alternative

Breeches/breaches

Callous: insensitive/callus: thickened skin

Canvas/canvass

Capital/capitol—a good example of a doublet. Both are derived from the Latin root meaning "head." Most people understand that "Capitol" means the building. The confusion is that the city that contains the "capitol" is the "capital" city. All senses except the building are "capital."

Clinch/clench/chinch/cinch

Complement/compliment: The one that complEtes is the complEment; the other is praise

Compose/comprise: Controversy can be avoided if used in accordance with the rule: the parts compose the whole, the whole comprises the parts.

Continual/continuous

Desert/dessert

Discreet/discrete

Enormity: not accepted universally as synonymous with "enormousness"

Farther/further: Most people will be satisfied if "farther" is used only when referring to actual physical distances and "further" is applied in all other cases

Famous/infamous

Flaunt/flout

Flounder/founder

Fulsome: When a compliment is intended, this word is best avoided because many people think first of its negative sense.

Gantlet/gauntlet/gamut

Gibe/jibe

Hardy/hearty

Infer/imply

Lay/lie (place)/lie (tell an untruth)—three verbs, three conjugations

Loan: Some educated people think that "loan" must be used only as a noun and that the correct verb is "lend." This belief is not well-grounded in the history of the language, but the writer may find it wise to please those who hold this prejudice.

Meretricious: does not mean meritorious, but does mean nearly the opposite.

Moisturize: Use "moisten" where possible.

Move: an impotent verb that ought to be replaced by a more precise verb.

Nauseous/nauseated—A surprising number of otherwise-well-educated people are willing to admit they are "nauseous" (which means likely to induce nausea).

Noisome/noisy

Notable/notorious

Ordinance/ordnance

Palate/palette/pallet—Not many people will be certain of all three without looking them up.

Perpetrate/perpetuate

Prescribe/proscribe

Persecution/prosecution

Principle/principal—The correct rule of thumb: principAl is the mAin, and principLE is the ruLE—flour is the principal ingredient in bread, but yeast is the active principle; the principal is the main guy at school, and a principal is one of the main players in a drama.

Poor/pore/pour—"to study" is "to pore (over)."

Rack/wrack

Route/root/rout

Sensuous/sensual—Historically, "sensual" is the word more

nearly synonymous with "voluptuous," and the word erotic writers would most often want, as it had particular reference to the senses of the flesh. "Sensuous" once referred to the intellectual "senses" and senses besides touch and taste. For practical purposes, the distinction between these words is now lost.

Stationery/stationary

Straight/strait—The problem here is compounds, which often take "strait": "straitlaced," "straitjacket." Some gay and lesbian writers now use "strait" to refer to heterosexuals because "straight" has connotations of ethical rectitude which are not the province of heterosexuals alone, but this usage and an understanding of its rationale are not common.

Torturous/tortuous

Utilize: Almost always should be "use."

Wreak/wreck

Wright/write/right—Correct spellings are "playwright," "copywriter," and "copyright."

Common homophones, though much drilled in grammar school, are easily mistaken in writing: their/there, its/it's, whose/who's, and so forth.

In erotic fiction, it no longer matters much whether you write "sensuous" or "sensual," and many readers now think that "sensuous" is the sexier word. A few of the other words to watch out for are debatable: the "loan/lend" pair, for example. But a writer who uses "principal" for "principle" has not had a lapse of taste or judgment. He is wrong. And his spelling checker will not help him avoid this error. A spelling checker cannot help when the writer enters a wrong word. John Preston's favorite example is "brining." "Brining" is a perfectly good word, meaning what is done to cabbage to make it sauerkraut. If your spelling checker has a large lexicon, it will pass "brining," not knowing that there is virtually no chance that you meant "brining," but that you almost certainly were trying to type "bringing."

Electronic grammar and usage checkers exist, and many of them will call the user's attention to "altogether." perhaps with a brief explanation of the distinction between "altogether" and "all together." Most will flag "principal" and "principle," which will be helpful if you tend to type the wrong one, but the help offered may not be sufficient if you really have confused the senses. Some programs will suggest that "one" or some other nonsexist expression be substituted for every occurrence of "he" or "man." Such a suggestion, desirable as it might be in the workplace, will seldom be helpful to the writer of erotica or of any other kind of fiction. A usage checker may detect the passive voice, and this may be helpful to writers who have a severe problem with overuse of this voice. But some sentences *should* be in the passive voice.

Someone who uses a usage checker regularly should try the experiment of running a passage of great writing through the usage checker. Follow the checker's advice and see what becomes of the great writing. Lincoln's Gettysburg Address fed to a popular usage checker did not become gobbledygook, but it certainly did lose its music. Writers may use usage checkers to catch careless errors, but the writer who does not know better than the usage checker or who is unwilling to ignore much of the usage checker's advice might be better off without one.

2 *Possessive case.*

2.1 *Possessive case of singular nouns.*

For singular nouns no better advice can be given than Strunk and White's first rule: form the possessive by adding apostrophe and *s*. The few exceptions are some biblical and classical names and abstract nouns. A few of these ending in s take only the apostrophe to form the possessive.

James's tool, Jess's knife, Bess's home.

This rule, however, is controversial. Some respected editors are very certain that all single nouns ending in *s* take only the apostrophe.

The source of the problem is that in speech we pronounce the extra *s* in some cases, but not in others. "Jess's knife" is not a problem for most people, but "Bruce Rodgers's *Gay Talk*" is difficult. An essayist may hear nothing wrong with "Charles's parents," but "Dickens's family" grates on the ear. A rule of the ear is impractical because the result would look inconsistent in print and, in many cases, the author's subjective judgment would differ from the editor's.

The solution is to duck this problem so far as it is possible to do so. Writers of fiction can avoid giving characters names that end in *s*. When the problem cannot be avoided, the writer should add apostrophe and *s* unless she knows she is preparing material for an editor who has strong objections to this style.

2.2 *Possessive case of plural nouns.*

Plural nouns ending in *s* take only the apostrophe, but those not ending in *s* take apostrophe and *s*.

> girls' hats, men's furnishings, the Joneses' house, the boys'
>   brown torsos,
> a men's bar
> brothers-in-law's deer lease.

This rule is not controversial.

2.3 *Other uses of the possessive.*

Abstract and inanimate nouns take the possessive in some cases:

> a month's back rent, a year's time, for pity's sake, the
>   soap's lather.

Often words ending -ing are modified by words in the possessive:

> Jim's cruising
> his coming was noisy
> imagine our meeting by chance.

In these cases the verb ending in -ing is treated as noun and is known as a gerund. But not every word ending -ing is a gerund.

"I watched Jim's cruising" means I observed his technique. The thing I was watching was the cruising. Used as a noun here, "cruising" is a gerund and requires "Jim's," the possessive case. On the other hand, "I watched Jim cruising" means I watched Jim while he was cruising. In this case, "Jim" is the noun and "cruising" is used like an adjective. Whether "Jim's cruising" or "Jim cruising" is correct depends upon the writer's meaning (in spite of some grammar school teachers who have given up trying to teach the distinction and who teach that the possessive is always required).

2.4 *Possessive case of pronouns.*

The definite pronoun "it" takes only *s* to form the possessive. "It's" is a contraction for "it is" or "it has." "Who," though it does not seem very definite, is a definite pronoun and its possessive is "whose." "Who's" is a contraction for "who is" or "who has."

The possessives of the other definite pronouns seldom are the occasion for error. "My," "your," "his," "her," "their," and "our" are used when they precede the name of the thing possessed. "Mine," "yours," "his," "hers," "theirs," and "ours" are used when the name of the thing possessed is not given. "Its" and "his" are the same in both cases.

"That one is mine."
"He is my trick."
her handbag
that awful handbag of hers

Indefinite pronouns form the possessive with apostrophe and *s*, just as singular nouns do:

one's first love
everybody's buddy.

2.5 *Possessive case of nouns linked by "and."*

When several possessors are linked by "and," determine whether the thing is held in common and whether the possessors can be considered a unit. If both conditions are met, only the last possessor takes the apostrophe and *s*:

Just Marion and Lynn's (name of a bar)
Phil and Mark's apartment (they are as good as married)

Bob's and Bill's houseboy (they do not live together, or
   they are only roommates)
Falwell and Bush's policies (one set of policies)
Falwell's and Bush's policies (perceived distinctions in
   the sets of policies).

2.6 *Possessive case of hyphenated names and phrases.*
   Add the apostrophe and *s* at the end of noun formation
whether it is hyphenated or not:

brother-in-law's gym
poet manqué's book.

It is no shame to avoid doubtful formulations:

the finish of the chest of drawers.

Note: The rule for the formation of plurals differs.

3 *Formation of plurals.*
   For most ordinary words, form plurals as suggested in your
dictionary. Many dictionaries do not give plurals if they are
formed regularly. Consult the front matter of your dictionary.
Note that a very few words, "index" for one, have different
plurals for different meanings.

3.1 *Plurals of proper nouns.*
   Add only -s or -es to proper nouns to form the plural. Do not
change the base spelling of the name:

a bar full of Marys
two Larrys, two Tys, and three Jameses.

3.2 *Plurals in erotic usages.*
   The tendency of foreign words to adopt English plural forms
is greatly accelerated in erotic usages, the dictionary to the contrary notwithstanding:

penis, *plural:* penises (academic: penes)

torso, *plural:* torsos, (academic: torsi)

and similarly when anatomical parts are given their Latin names.

"Biceps" and "triceps" are probably best spelled the same in singular and plural (*academic plurals:* "bicepses," "tricepses"). There is no such thing as "a bicep." The erotic coinages "abs" and "pecs" are generally used in the plural. The singular of "pecs" may well be "pec," but "a pectoral" is something *worn* on the breast. The singulars of "abs," "delts," and "lats" are so seldom seen that they may puzzle the reader. "Delts" usually reverts to "deltoid" for the singular:

rose tattoo on his right deltoid.

3.3 Plurals of hyphenated nouns and phrases.
The plural ending, unlike the possessive ending, goes on the principal noun:

brothers-in-law
romans à clef.

Questionable cases usually involve fixed forms which are treated in the dictionary. The writer must prepared to exercise judgment. One dictionary gives "attorneys general" as the preferred plural. In fiction it might be wiser to choose "attorney generals," and to make a marginal note in the dictionary and your style sheet of having done so.

3.4 *Plurals of formations of capital letters and figures.*
Form the plurals of acronyms and initials that are shown in capital letters without periods by adding lowercase s only:

YMCAs
RBIs
KOs
Js,

but not with single letters that would form unintended words.
Add *s* only to figures when it is desirable to use them:

1970s
at 6s and 7s.

3.5 *Plurals that take the apostrophe.*
Use the apostrophe in forming the plurals of abbreviations which take periods:

Ph.D.'s
M.A.'s,

with capital letters that would otherwise form words:

I's
A's
U's,

and with abbreviations set in lowercase and with single lowercase letters:

aka's
p's and q's.

Take care to avoid inserting apostrophes in the plurals of ordinary words:

not: dildo's (*right:* dildos)
not: tattoo's (*right:* tattoos).

3.6 *Plurals of number plus unit.*
The adjective formula number plus hyphen plus unit does not take the plural of the unit:

nine-inch tool
but: it was more like ten inches;
thousand-dinar note
but: The check was for twenty dollars;
twenty-year-old student
but: He was twenty years old.

4 *Italicized titles and their plurals.*

Indicate italics in the manuscript by underlining. Do not use an italic typeface.

Form plurals and possessives by adding the appropriate ending in roman (non-italic) type. Add only -s or -es to form plurals. Do not change the base spelling of the title:

*Drummer*s
*RFD*s
The Advocate's cartoonist
Natural Histories.

Avoid constructions which offer no good way out:

On Our Backs' editor; *better:* editor of *On Our Backs*
"Have you seen my *Numbers*es?" *better:* "Have you seen my *Numbers* magazines?"

The distinction between major and minor works which in academic writing calls for italics on the one hand and quotation marks on the other may be ignored and italics used in both cases as a courtesy:

Aaron Travis's *Big Shots* and *Flesh Fables.*

However, in your own titles which appear at the beginning of the work, do not use either italics or quotation marks, but use normal body type and capitalize important words.

Initial articles *The*, *A,* and *An* are sometimes omitted from titles in running text:

Rechy's *Sexual Outlaw*
Preston's *Love of a Master,*

but may be included if omission would leave a single word or an expression that might not be recognized to be a title:

John Preston's *The Heir.*

5 *"A" vs. "An."*

Use the indefinite article "a" when followed by a consonant sound however the following word is spelled or represented:

a one-night stand (consonant *w* sound)
a usual occurrence (consonant *y* sound)
a homo
a Ph.D.
a yoga instructor.

Use "an" when the following sound is a vowel sound, however spelled or represented:

an hour
an umlaut
an X ray
an M.A.
an herb
an 18-year-old hustler (although usually this should be
   spelled out).

6 *Numbers*

Set in figures: years, phone numbers, addresses, serial numbers, and large exact numbers which could not be readily understood if spelled out, time when used with A.M. or P.M. or with hours and minutes both given, money when dollars and cents are given:

455–5732
4110 South Sixth Avenue
45,157,327
AO–45551–2057–1
1933,
June 6, 1944
7:00 P.M.
8:53
$9.95.

Spell out: other numbers if small or if round, and ordinal numbers such as first, third, and thirty-third:

ten
fifty million
one hundred
twenty-seventh
ten dollars
eight o'clock.

This is the general rule of many publishers, the only difference among them being the definition of small versus large numbers. Newspapers and magazines often define small as less than eleven, less than twenty-one, or less than one hundred one. Some will have one policy for headlines and captions and another for text. Book editors usually prefer quantities to be spelled out, but often will recognize that figures ought to be used for a quantity like 10,217,506.

A writer who does not know where he might be published might best chose to spell numbers under one hundred one.

Numbers which are meant to be compared should be set in the same way regardless of other rules:

His temperature was 98 at nine o'clock, 99.5 at ten-fifteen, and 101.8 at five after midnight.
not: His temperature was ninety-eight at nine o'clock, 99.5 at 10:15, and 101.8 at 12:05 A.M.

When the money amount is set in figures, use the dollar sign, but spell out "dollars" if the amount is spelled.

In titles and trademarks, follow the style of the original:

Fahrenheit 451
Levi's 501s.

Although such elements are pronounced "the third," "the fifth," and so forth, use roman numerals when persons bearing the same name are distinguished by number. Use capital letters without spaces or periods for roman numerals: III, IV, VIII.

Although its meaning is derived of the shape of the figures, spell out "sixty-nine" (in English, *not:* "soixante-neuf" except in the speeches of queens who talk like that).

Likewise, spell out most code numbers:

eighty-six
ten-four.

7 *Abbreviations.*

The general rule is to use abbreviations only when the abbreviation is what is usually pronounced:

twenty cc's of morphine
but: fifty-five-millimeter shells.
Ph.D.
but: et cetera.

7.1 *Abbreviations without periods.*

Most abbreviations in modern use do not take periods (here "abbreviations" embraces acronyms, initials, and some kinds of contractions):

YMCA
aka
SIDS
AIDS
GQ.

(A good way of treating such abbreviations is to set them in small capitals. Such a determination is made only by the editor. Do not indicate small capitals on the manuscript.)

7.2 *Abbreviations with periods and spelled phonetically.*

A few abbreviations still require periods:

Ph.D.
M.A.

Modern postal abbreviations are two capital letters without periods. Periods may be used to distinguish abbreviations which might otherwise be confused with postal abbreviations:

LA (Louisiana)
L.A. (Los Angeles)
MD (Maryland)
M.D. (doctor of medicine), and so forth.

For the time of day use "A.M." and "P.M." Editorial styles vary widely in the treatment of these items.

Scholarly abbreviations, which mostly still take periods, are best avoided, though some have worked their way into common speech:

e.g. (write: for example)
i.e. (write: that is)
etc. (write: et cetera or and so forth).

Ibid., op. cit., loc. cit. and similar terms have little place in fiction and are now seldom used even in scholarly journals.

A few abbreviations are commonly spelled phonetically:

emcee
deejay
okay.

Note: Many who are interested in the subject of sado-masochism object to the abbreviation S&M on the grounds that it is not two things, but one. Prefer SM or S-M. S/M is objectionable typographically.

7.3 *Abbreviations of courtesy titles and rank.*

Courtesy titles and rank are abbreviated when they immediately precede the name, but not otherwise:

"Doctor, Dr. Smith would like to see you."
The general met Pvt. Cassidy behind the latrine.
"Have you got the time, mister?"

Less common titles (honorable, senator, reverend) and foreign titles (señor, mademoiselle) should probably be spelled out however they occur, except in works where they are very common.

7.4 *Abbreviations of Saint, Fort, Mount.*
Use "Saint" when referring to the person, "Fort" when naming the military installation, and "Mount" for the peak itself. Use the abbreviation in names of cities, towns, or other derived names:

> Saint Louis (Louis IX of France)
> St. Louis (American city)
> St. Elmo's fire (meteorologic phenomenon)
> Fort Hood (army base)
> Ft. Worth (American city)
> Mount Magnolia (a peak)
> Mt. Magnolia (a nearby town).

In surnames, spell according to the preference of the person bearing the name:

> Saint Clair, St. Clair, Sinclair (name as spelled by various holders of it).

8 *Capitalization.*
Modern style favors the use of least capitalization required. This is called *down* style; its opposite is *up* style.

8.1 *Capitalization of proper nouns and titles.*
Proper nouns including tradenames are capitalized.

> "Did you see that, Mary?"
> Dr Pepper (note: no period)
> Lucky Strike
> 7Up
> Jeep
> Velcro
> Hoover.

But personal names that are used generically and eponyms are not capitalized:

"Is that her john?"
cardigan
derby
sandwich
mackintosh (raincoat)
silhouette
but: Mae West (life jacket or drag appliance).

Titles are often capitalized when they stand for the name of the current holder of the title or office, but not when the title or office is referred to in a general way:

the President (of the U.S.), *but:* a president
The Pope (bishop of Rome), *but:* a pope, the papacy.

Kinship terms may be capitalized when used as nouns of address or in place of personal names; pet names are lower cased.

"Are you taking me to dinner, honey?"
"I got this watch from Daddy."

But not when used with other modifiers:

my honey and I
from my daddy.

8.2 *Capitalization of sacred and profane expressions.*

No part of a profane expression is capitalized. Proper nouns referring to deities are capitalized, and so is the English word "god" when it refers to a specific deity. Pronouns referring to deities are no longer commonly capitalized. "Bible" is not capitalized when it refers only to the main reference work of a discipline or trade. Figurative names of deities and personified abstractions may be capitalized:

"Let Gray-Eyed Wisdom guide us now."
"Trusting Providence, we persevered."

8.3 *Capitalization of geographic names.*

So far as possible, nouns following proper adjectives are capitalized:

Missouri River
Atlantic Ocean

In extreme down styles, the nouns are not capitalized. In both down and up styles, some features, especially those without a proper adjective, require both capitals:

Dead Sea
Great Lakes

When the name of the kind of feature comes first, both are capitalized:

Key West
Rio Grande
Sierra Madres.

Beware of redundancy: not: Rio Grande river, not: Key West island, not: Sierra Madres mountains.

Compass directions are capitalized only when they refer to regions:

the South
the Southwest.

Some districts are know by names which may be capitalized:

the South End
the Tenderloin
the Combat Zone,

and a few figurative and fictional names of places are capitalized:

Grub Street
Tin Pan Alley.

8.4 *Capitalization of figurative and special uses.*
Occasionally certain terms are capitalized to indicate a figurative or special use:

Lucky Pierre
Bloody Mary (cocktail).

The usefulness of this device is limited, and in particular, capitalizing a cliché does not make it fresh or amusing:

not: Rolf's Pride and Joy
not: the American's Family Jewels.

(Several other cocktails are capitalized because the name is derived of one or more tradenames: Seven and Seven.)
While personified abstractions may be capitalized, not every occurrence of an abstraction is personification:

What I did for love; he was overcome with hate.

8.5 *Proper adjectives.*
Proper adjectives remain capitalized, even to the point of detaching prefixes:

pre-Stonewall
sub-Saharan.

Generally, adjectives derived from the names of peoples, languages, races, states, religions, and nations are capitalized, but it is now usual to lowercase "gay," "lesbian," "brown," "black," etcetera.

8.6 *Shapes and letters.*
Capitals are used when the meaning of the word derives of the shape of the capital letter:

T-shirt
G-string
O-ring
T-square
V neck
I beam.

Consult the dictionary to determine which uses take the hyphen and which do not.

Letters per se are lowercased:

mind your p's and q's
x number of dollars
the nth degree.

But capitals are used when letters distinguish things as if they were enumerated:

plan A
plan B
the A list.

9 *Foreign words and phrases.*

Passages in a foreign language should be avoided as a matter of taste. Editors (alerted by similar advice in Fowler and in Strunk and White) and readers will regard a passage in a foreign tongue as an affectation.

Speeches by characters who we know to be speaking a foreign tongue can often be given in English without comment. A precious character may affect a few words in French, but nothing important should turn on the meaning of the French words.

If it is necessary to enter a passage in a foreign language, underline the words (indicating they are to be set in italics), punctuate using the marks of English, and capitalize according to the language used (likely to be an issue in German).

Occasional words or phrases from another language are set in italics (underlined in the manuscript), but those common enough to occur among the regular entries of an American dictionary are not italicized, including:

señor
je ne sais quoi
tête-à-tête.

10 *The hyphen.*

No other mark is so full of peril as the hyphen. As in much else, the dictionary is the first recourse. Consulting the dictionary would have save authors the following errors:

re-introductions (*correct:* reintroductions)
faded cut-offs (*correct:* cutoffs)
skin-tight chaps (*correct:* skintight)
co-workers (*correct:* coworkers)
had been stood-up (meaning an appointment was not kept,
   correct: stood up)
teen-age romance (*correct:* teenage)
no knock-out (*correct:* knockout)
nearly K-O'd (*correct:* KO'd)
a pile-driver (*correct:* pile driver).

Most electronic spelling checkers are unable to detect errors such as these, but will pass any hyphenated expression if each of its parts forms a correctly spelled word. "Streetwise" is a relatively new word given in the current *Collegiate*. It means knowledgeable in methods of urban survival. Some spelling checkers will pass "street-wise" (which is wrong) because both parts are spelled correctly, but will reject "streetwise" (which is correct) because it is too new or too obscure to be in the spelling checker's lexicon. That is, the machine may tell the writer he is right when he is wrong and that he is wrong when he is right.

Even the dictionary is not foolproof:

called out-of-town unexpectedly *(wrong)*.

Many dictionaries will list the hyphenated expression "out-of-town," because the adjective is indeed hyphenated in formulations like:

He went to meet an out-of-town client.

That is no excuse to insert the hyphens every time the phrase "out of town" occurs.

10.1 *Breaking words with hyphens.*

Do not use hyphens to break words or expressions at the end of a line in the manuscript. Do not end any line of the manuscript with a hyphen. Carry the whole word or expression to the next line, even if this makes the lines very uneven on the right.

The problem with a hyphen that occurs at the end of the line is whether the hyphen should be retained if the line breaks differently, and the line set in type will often break differently. For this reason, word processors often provide a hard hyphen, which is supposed to be retained however the line breaks, and a soft hyphen, which is supposed to be deleted if the line breaks differently. Unfortunately, both hyphens look precisely the same as they come out of the printer, and the distinction between hard and soft hyphens may be lost if the electronic file is converted from one word processor to another.

For this reason, the only hyphens that should appear in the manuscript are hard hyphens, and all of them should occur within a line, where they will be unambiguous. This means that if your word processor usually breaks words with a hyphen at the end of the line to make the right margin come out more nearly even, you must find the way to turn off this feature.

Nonetheless, commonly extraneous hyphens are introduced into the text when it is typeset, and hyphenation programs break words in the wrong places. If you get proofs of your work, look carefully at each hyphen.

10.2 *Compound words.*

Hyphens are middle stage in the forming of compound words. Generally, when words are first associated, they are set as separate words (set *open*). As the association between the words occurs more frequently, the words are often joined with a hyphen. At last, when it is clear that the words have fused to form a new compound, the words are set together without a space or hyphen (set *closed* or *closed-up*). When the compound word is used very frequently indeed, the changes can occur very rapidly. A careful writer may discover that such a change has occurred in even the few short years since he was in school. No doubt rapid change was the cause of many errors given above and of some of the following:

trouble-makers (*correct:* troublemakers)
felt like a non-person (*correct:* nonperson)
life-long buddy (*correct:* lifelong)
heart-beat (*correct:* heartbeat)
check-book (*correct:* checkbook).

The opposite error, that of inserting a hyphen in an expression that should be set open is less common:

the usual small-talk (*correct:* small talk).

Even so, the dictionary does not solve all problems. For example, the dictionary gives "sweatshirt," and "sweatpants" (both closed), but "sweat suit" (open). There is no entry for the socks. You will have to exercise judgment in deciding whether it should be "sweat socks," "sweat-socks," or "sweatsocks." The latter seems like a reasonable guess, but if you would rather write "sweatsox," think what you would write if you meant only one of them.

Coined erotic compounds should be set solid. The hyphen should be avoided if possible, and gay writers should be the master of gay words. Writing full of erotic compounds is criticized and parodied easily. Spelling the words with hyphens would not eliminate those problems:

bubblebutt
cockmeat
cockshaft
comeshot

fuckpole
fuckshute
mancock
mantits.

10.3 *Prefixes and suffixes.*

By far most prefixes and suffixes used in fiction are attached without hyphens, unless they are attached to proper nouns or proper adjectives. Again, the dictionary is the first resort.

In particular, "re-" is attached without a hyphen except in a very few cases to distinguish different senses as "re-creation" (creating anew, as when an actor plays a role made famous by another) from "recreation" (leisure time activities). "Co-" takes the hyphen with only a very few words beginning with *o*. "Pre" does not take the hyphen with any dictionary word; therefore the word should be "precome" (meaning the seminal fluid emitted before ejaculation), and not "pre-come."

Even fewer suffixes take the hyphen. The rule for "-like" is supposed to be that it takes the hyphen with new coinages, but not with established formations. It seems to me better to omit the hyphen except to avoid impossible spellings (triple *l* does not occur in English) or to attach "-like" to proper nouns or adjectives:

animallike
stonelike hardness
but: shell-like
Wilde-like wit.

10.4 *Prepositional particles.*

Verbs with prepositional particles never take the hyphen. They are always set open (with a space between the parts). Indeed, an object or other matter may come between the verb and the prepositional particle—a common occurrence in Germanic languages, of which English is one:

stood up
stood Jerry up
stood all of us up

jack off
jacked Jim off
jack each other off.

The verb is set open even when it is intransitive and no object could intervene:

come on
come on to Mark
come out
came out at the age of nineteen.

Nouns and adjectives, on the other hand, take the hyphen or are closed up:

pickup (a truck or a trick)
a beat-off video
gave him the come-on
a jack-off club.

10.5 *Electric blue eyes.*

Perhaps the most difficult hyphenation problem, because the dictionary is only occasionally helpful, is that of adjective formation.

What is meant by "electric blue eyes"? It could mean that the eyes were the particular color called electric blue. Or it might as easily mean that the eyes were blue and sparkling or lively or in some other metaphoric sense "electric." Or again, what is a "tan lined ass"? Perhaps it is an attractive ass with a tan line. Or perhaps, it is a tan ass that is lined with wrinkles.

When the adjectives are meant to be taken together the hyphen is used to join them. When each adjective is supposed to apply to the noun separately, they are separated by commas. Thus, if we are pretty sure the writer meant a compliment, it should be "tan-lined ass." But both "electric-blue eyes" and "electric, blue eyes" might have been intended as compliments.

In most cases, the hyphen is dropped when the formation follows the noun:

His eyes were electric blue.

The meaning is clear, for in this position the "and" would appear if it were meant:

His eyes were electric and blue.

Adjectives with past participles take the hyphen when they occur before the noun:

long-limbed lumberjack
lumberjack was long limbed
black-haired youth
youth was black haired.

But some formations (found in the dictionary) have fused into single words:

redheaded surfer
surfer was redheaded.

When one of the elements is an adverb ending in -ly, the hyphen is not used:

highly developed biceps
tightly packed jeans.

Most combinations including well-, half-, all-, self-, and cross- take the hyphen, but consult the dictionary because some of the most commonly occurring ones are set solid.

Of formations that take the hyphen, some drop it when another modifier is added, and some retain the hyphen even when the noun comes first. On these points, the dictionary is not always helpful:

a well-hung athlete
a very well hung athlete
athlete was well hung

half-hard teamster
teamster was half-hard
all-powerful thighs
thighs were all-powerful
cross-country runner.

When terms of equal value are fitted for use as adjectives, the hyphen is used:

man-monkey stance
blue-green eyes
blue-black bruise,

but not when one modifies the other:

pinkish brown cock.

Phrases used as adjectives take the hyphens; otherwise the hyphens must be removed:

turn-of-the-century style
parsonage was turn-of-the-century,
but: Drag courts were documented by the turn of the century.

A very large book of principles and examples could be written about hyphenation, yet cases not covered would occur. Particularly in the matter of compounds, the writer may differ with authority on occasion. For example, the dictionary says it is "long johns." The writer may insist on "longjohns." You ought not to ignore your dictionary and call your careless errors "style," but it is the writer's use of words upon which dictionary makers base their entries.

11 *Punctuation.*
The modern trend in punctuation is to use the least punctuation required for clarity. This is called *open* style. The older

style, called *close,* was to use all the punctuation the syntax would bear. Many writers working today learned *close* punctuation in school. In some ways, *close* punctuation is suitable for schools because it requires no judgment, but only the learning of a large set of rules.

Punctuation is near the boundary between editorial style and literary style. To their credit, many editors will not trespass on the author's punctuation, except in cases of obvious error. Authors then must take care to punctuate consistently and accurately.

Open punctuation avoids interrupting the flow of words when the only purpose served is the satisfaction of a rule. Naturally, where sense requires it, punctuation must not be omitted. The principal effect of open style is on the use of the comma.

11.1 *The comma.*

The trend toward omitting the comma dates at least to Gertrude Stein, who was really nasty about the comma.

The comma is used before conjunctions that join clauses. When the clauses are short, and especially when they are parallel, either the comma or the conjunction is often omitted:

> I came, I saw, I conquered.
> Jerry went to the bar and Mark went home.
> Time slowed and space contracted.

Although the semicolon is often pressed into service in such cases, it is best reserved for situations in which the second clause is a consequence of the first:

> He ordered; I obeyed.

When the comma is used with the conjunction, it suffices as the first comma of a parenthetical pair:

> *not:* heavily, and, in an instant, he
> *but:* heavily, and in an instant, he

The comma is used to set off introductory words or phrases. When that material is a brief expression of time or place, or is a phrase modifying the following subject, the comma is best omitted:

Recently David agreed to appear...
Finally he stretched his legs out...
In the summer we went to Padre Island...
In the last week of January the hyacinths...
In fact it was not even necessary to...
Without opening the door I knew what was going on...

"However" and "so" may need to be set off because their other senses could mislead the reader:

However late in the day we got home Jim would...
However, late in the evening he returned...
So far from the crowd that our nakedness couldn't be seen...
So, far from the crowd we unbuttoned...

Some trailing and embedded elements do not have to be set off with commas:

Close: I wanted to go, too, because I had heard...
Open: I wanted to go too because I had heard...
Close: ...and don't you forget it, either.
Open: ...and don't you forget it either.
Close: I didn't mind, though, for I knew...
Open: I didn't mind though for I knew...

The comma is still required when a modifying phrase is displaced from the element it modifies:

We lay still for several minutes, catching our breaths.

Even so, the comma cannot overcome some disasters of word order:

not: I met a man with seven wives, coming from St. Ives.
but: Coming from St. Ives I met a man with...

When a phrase is truly dangling, when it cannot possibly modify anything in the sentence, a comma is of no use:

not: My emotional response was equally intense, appreciating the shared intimacy with Jim.
but: My emotional response was equally intense. I appreciated...
or: I responded with equal intensity, appreciating...
or: My emotional response was equally intense: appreciation of...

Commas are used for items in a series when only one conjunction or no conjunction is used:

At first he did not want to do this, that, or the other thing.
or: ...this or that or the other thing.

The serial comma is the one that comes before the conjunction. Do not omit it.

Phil, Howard, Ty, and George

is a very different social group from

Phil, Howard, and Ty and George.

Because it unclear which of the two groups is meant, avoid:

Phil, Howard, Ty and George.

The comma is used to end a statement in a quotation when the sentence containing the quotation is not finished. Do not use a period.

not: "I'll be back." he promised.

but: "I'll be back," he promised.
not: "It is that." I said. "And more."
but: "It is that," I said, "and more."

Pairs of commas are used to set off nonrestrictive phrases and slightly parenthetical matter within a sentence. When such material is brief and not too far removed, the commas are now often omitted. If one of a pair of commas is removed, however, the other must be removed as well, unless it is serving some other purpose.

A restrictive phrase is supposed to bear directly on the meaning of the sentence. A nonrestrictive phrase merely adds some less-pertinent detail:

Nonrestrictive: Jim Martin my physician attended Philip's vernissage.
Restrictive: The two paintings he most admired were male nudes.

If the italicized part of the first sentence is removed, little damage is done. But if the italicized part of the second sentence were removed, it would become "The two paintings were male nudes," which clearly lacks an essential aspect of the meaning of the sentence. Commas should never be used to set off the restrictive—or essential—parts of a sentence. Non-restrictive—or nonessential—parts of a sentence may be set off by commas.

Nonrestrictive phrases are always set off by commas in close style. In open style, short and simple nonrestrictive phrases are not set off:

Commas in general are too widely used.
He was introduced as Larry the director.

Sometimes commas can be eliminated by casting a sentence in a better order:

Jim, already stroking his cock, stepped out of the...
Already stroking his cock Jim stepped out of the...
He was getting near, I thought, and I...

I thought he was getting near, and I...

Beware of commas which have no reason to exist in either open or close style:

not: He was red-bearded and short, with a perfectly
   muscled body, and he...,
but: He was red-bearded and short with a perfectly muscled
   body, and he...

The comma is necessary and is retained in elliptical constructions:

Gene slept with me; Joe, with Tim.

Do not allow an unpaired comma to intervene between the subject and verb of a sentence:

not: I, after all was said and done wanted Kyle still.
but: After all was said and done I still wanted Kyle.
or: I, after all was said and done, wanted Kyle still.
not: How could anyone with such a beautiful body and so
   many friends, do his laundry on a Saturday night?

11.2 *The dash.*

The dash is widely overused, perhaps by those who know no better way to punctuate. The proper use of the dash is limited.

The dash is used to indicate a sharp break, as when one speaker is interrupted by another. The dash does not indicate a pause; use the ellipsis for pauses:

not: "I want—you—to come back—Jess."
but: "I want...you...to come back...Jess."
not: "It's just that—" he began, wondering what would
   come next.
but: "It's just that..." he began, wondering what would
   come next.

or handled properly as a true interruption:

"It's just that—"
"Just what? Don't bother thinking of an excuse."
"—that I did not know what Phil expected."

Pairs of dashes are used to set off parenthetical material:

He poured himself another drink—his fourth? his fifth?—
   and saw that...
Jack dropped by one day—he had just returned from
   Europe—to tell me that...

Paired dashes indicate material that is more remote than that set off by commas. In this example it is not clear that dashes, or even commas, are called for:

"This hunk—who was in the bar—suddenly..."

When the parenthetical material occurs at the end of a sentence, the period that concludes the sentence takes the place of the second dash. Logic suggests that the comma, the period, the colon, or the semicolon ought not to appear adjacent to the dash; although, as in one of the examples above, the question mark or exclamation point may occur within the dashes.

The surest test of whether parenthetical dashes have been used correctly is to see if the sentence can be read without the material within the dashes. When dashes are used too often, even if they are used correctly, readers will lose the distinction between the main and the parenthetical matter.

Unfortunately, some new writers think of a dash as a sort of conjunction that can be used to join any two vaguely related phrases or clauses and feel entitled to use three, four, or five dashes per sentence. Readers will not mistake the result for art, but will call it nonsense.

Very rarely a leading dash is used to indicate special types of dialogue: dream speeches, the movie dialogue when two characters (whose own speeches are set in quotes) watch a movie, bits of speeches overheard in a crowd. Such speeches cannot be attributed; there is no place for the "Mary said." The writer should not affect this device without good reason. Normal speeches should be set in quotes. (Mass-market writer Joel Rosenberg recommends setting telepathic communications in asterisks.)

Dashes in print come in a variety of sizes from the n dash, which is so nearly the size of a hyphen that some publications use it in place of the hyphen (because the n dash is less likely than the hyphen to get lost in the typesetting process), to the 2-em dash which is frequently seen in print, to a line that extends across the page. Specifying the size of the dashes is the editor's prerogative; do not trespass.

11.3 *Parentheses and brackets.*

Parentheses and brackets are not especially useful in fiction. Brackets should be reserved for editorial emendations in quoted documents. A few works of fiction have used documents as a device: *The Frog Who Dared to Croak; Dracula*. Consult an appropriate authority such as Kate Turabin's *Manual for Writers* (Chicago) if you mean to proceed in this manner.

Parentheses have the character of an aside to the reader which belongs to the nineteenth century. The writer has available three other levels of parenthetical expression; no mark for brief, slightly parenthetical material, pairs of commas for longer, more complicated material; pairs of dashes for more remote matter.

If parentheses must be used, use them correctly. Parentheses must occur in pairs. A comma does not precede the parenthetical matter, but may follow it if the comma would have occurred in the absence of the parentheses. If the parenthetical material itself forms a question, the question mark goes within the parentheses, and any following period is omitted. That is, terminal mark, close parenthesis, terminal mark should not occur.

11.4 *The period.*

The period is used at the end of ordinary sentences and fragments that are allowed to stand as sentences. Although in modern use a question mark or an exclamation point may occur in a sentence without terminating it, the period may not.

The dot which ends some abbreviations is not considered to be punctuation unless it falls at the end of a sentence, in which case it stands for the period which ends the sentence as well as the abbreviating dot. That is, the dot that ends an abbreviation may be followed by a comma, a colon, a question mark—anything except a period.

When a close quotation mark and a period occur together, the period goes before the close quotation mark, even if the period does not belong to the quoted material. When parenthetical material occurs at the end of a sentence, the period follows the close parenthesis. When a whole sentence, outside of any other sentence, is enclosed in parentheses, the period goes before the close parenthesis. The period and the dash should not occur together: the period should not occur in material set off by dashes, and the period takes the place of the second dash when such material falls at the end of a sentence.

11.5 *The ellipsis.*

The ellipsis is formed by three periods, separated with spaces, not by asterisks or dashes. Although in academic work ellipses are used to indicate omissions from quoted material, in fiction ellipses are used to indicate pauses in speech:

> "She...he...certainly is unusual," Timmy said. "How does...it make a living?"

Normal speech is full of pauses. In fiction the ellipsis is reserved for a pause of special significance. In the example, the ellipses indicate, or perhaps overindicate, Timmy's inability to deal with the concept of transpersons. Besides pauses caused by the speaker's inability to find the words to speak, ellipses can also be used to indicate a passage of time, as when only one side of a telephone conversation is heard.

Ellipses may precede or follow commas or periods in certain cases, making four marks in all. Do not attempt to indicate greater or lesser pauses with two, four, five, or six periods.

Ellipsis has little place in narration. Most narrators should be sufficiently well spoken to avoid finding themselves at a loss for words and sufficiently frank not to use ellipsis in a coy attempt at making the reader supply missing words.

11.6 *Exclamation point and question mark.*

Reach for an exclamation point as you would for a rattlesnake.

The exclamation point (in printer's slang: "bang") should reserved for emphatic interjections and imperatives. A look at the Sunday comics, where most cartoons follow the convention of ending each sentence with an exclamation point (presumably because a hand-lettered period would be too easily lost) shows what happens when the exclamation point is debased: nothing except more and more exclamation points can show true exclamation. That is where writing full of exclamation points belongs: in the funny papers.

Never set an exclamation point or a question mark by itself in parentheses. That does not show irony, but only auctorial impotence. Never place exclamation points in a series, and do not mix exclamation points and question marks in a series. If you know what an interrobang is, forget it.

The question mark should be used with true questions, whether or not in the grammatical form of a question. The question mark is not required with rhetorical questions or demands which are in the form of a question for courtesy's sake.

In speeches, the question mark or exclamation point goes before the close quotation mark. If attribution accompanies the speech, it continues as if the mark were a comma (the next word is not capitalized unless it is a proper noun). In narration the mark is placed on either side of a closing quotation mark or close parenthesis, as sense dictates. But if the mark is placed inside, another terminal mark is not used on the outside.

> *not:* He had asked me "Have you got the time?"
> *but:* He had asked me, "have you got the time?"
> *okay:* Was it Shakespeare who wrote: "All that glisters is not gold"?

11.7 *Colon and semicolon.*

The colon is used for definition: what follows the colon

defines or restates what went before. The commonest special case of this use is that of stating a property on one side of the colon and listing items which share that property on the other side.

> Bedroll, lanterns, tents, axes: camping gear piled up in the living room.
> He took everything off: boots, belt, socks, tie, shirt, athletic undershirt, slacks, jock, even his wrist watch.

The common property in the first example is "gear"; in the second, "everything."

The colon may introduce certain quotations:

> A handsomely lettered sign hung on the door: "Temporarily out of order."

This is another case of definition: the sign is defined by the words on it. Do not write speeches as if you were a playwright, but reserve the colon for special kinds of quotations, such as that in the example.

The colon is used to join independent clauses. This is best done when the clauses are so closely related that one is immediately inherent in the other, or in other cases that preserve the definitive function of the colon:

> At last I knew the truth: Les was not coming home.

Here the second clause is a definition of "the truth."

> You'll never know when he'll rise to the bait: always be ready.

The imperative "always be ready" is presented as if it is immediately implied by the first clause. It is restated in the second clause to be blunt. This summary power of the colon is employed so often that some readers expect the second clause to seem very much more important than the first.

The semicolon can also join independent clauses. The semicolon is best used to represent a causal connection between the clauses:

> I left the brake off; the car rolled down the slope.
> Let's go to the steak house instead; I had Chinese for lunch.

The semicolon is sometimes used as a supercomma to separate items in a series when the comma will not serve this function because it is being put to another use:

This town has three bars: boots, flannel shirts, and jeans; Izods, cords, and boat shoes; and chiffon, pumps, and tasteful handbags.

Jill, whose sister Jean was watching the kids; Jim, whose lover Bob was taking an extended vacation in Key West; and George, who would have had nothing better to do anyway, completed our hiking party.

11.8 *Quotation marks.*

Quotation marks set off speeches. In America, the double mark is used for ordinary quotations, and the single mark is used for quotations within quotations. Exactly the opposite system is used in the United Kingdom.

Do not use the quotation mark to set off parts of a speech that is presented indirectly:

> *not:* Jack said that he "will be at least an hour late."

Only one closing quotation mark is used per speech. If a speech goes on for several paragraphs without interruption, each of the paragraphs begins with an open quotation mark, but the close quotation mark goes only at the end of the speech.

Do not use quotation marks for inner thoughts. Treat inner thoughts indirectly (Al thought that...) or are attributed (Well, Al thought, this certainly...) or use italics.

The comma or period always precedes the close quotation mark whether it belongs to the quoted material or not. The question mark or exclamation point may go inside or outside the close quotation mark, whichever sense dictates. In ordinary dialogue all such marks will fall within the quotation marks.

Words per se are enclosed in quotation marks, but do not use quotation marks to indicate a special or slang use:

okay: "Blue" can mean many things.
wrong: The party was dull until Amos decided to "get down."

11.9 *Foreign punctuation marks.*

Do not use foreign punctuation marks even if you insist on writing a passage in a foreign language. American editors, type-setters, and proofreaders are unprepared for guillemets, inverted exclamation points, and dashes used with guillemets to set off attribution. Do enter diacritical marks that may be necessary in the language—tildes, umlauts, and so forth—but do not be surprised if something unfortunate happens to these characters.

11.10 *The solidus.*

Use the solidus, if for some reason, it is necessary to enter a common fraction in figures. Do not use the solidus between words to indicate alternative readings:

right if not spelled out for some reason: My hat size is 7–7/8.
wrong: It was Jerry and/or Carl.

12 *Italics and other typefaces.*

Italics are required for titles, except that of the work in progress, and for foreign words and phrases that cannot be found in the main entries of a standard dictionary. These uses of italics are above reproach.

Italics are also used for special material such as real or fictional editorial comments, inner thoughts, and flashbacks, but they are by no means required for these special kinds of material. When an author chooses to use italics for such a purpose, very long passages—even whole chapters—may be entered in italics. Then the relation between italics and the ordinary body type is reversed: titles, foreign words, and words with special emphasis are set in roman (non-italic) type. The dangers in these special uses are that some editors will not like the appearance of a large block of italic type, that readers will become confused if italics mean a flashback in one chapter but inner thoughts in the next, and that the expedient of italics may obscure a more effective way of handling the material. Italics are also harder to read.

The use of italics that is always problematic is to show some special emphasis on occasional words or phrases. As a good dramatist avoids giving elaborate instruction on the delivery of each speech, so the good writer should avoid instructing the reader on the interpretation of the material. When a particular reading is important, the writer should cast and recast the sentence until it cannot be misread.

In gay writing the temptation is to scatter italics through speeches in the attempt to represent a particular twist on some words in camp dialect:

> "How could I help but be aroused—even by *your* pathetic charms."
> "Let me tell you, *my* mouth started to water."
> "I'm sure *I* don't know what you mean."

Notice that in such uses the italics do not really help the reader understand what is meant. Someone familiar with camp speech knows where the twists go. One who does not know camp speech is hardly helped by the italics. Especially an*noy*ing is the more-or-less random em*pha*sis scattered by the syllable through*out* a passage.

Italics should not be used in the attempt to represent the manner in which each speech is delivered or to indicate speech mannerism. Italics for emphasis should be strictly limited in narration.

Authors do not have a right to call upon boldface, small capitals, or entirely different typefaces. Editors often have special uses in mind for variations in type. Sometimes an initial letter of a paragraph is set in a large or ornate typeface, or the first few words of a passage are set in small capitals. Such occurrences are determined by the editor, often with the object of breaking up what would otherwise be whole pages of gray type. Such indications are not made by the author.

12. *A Selected Glossary of Publishing and Literary Terms*

ADVANCE: A payment to an author against anticipated royalties. If the advance is for a promised manuscript, the author may have to return it if he cannot deliver an acceptable manuscript. But once a manuscript has been accepted, the author's advance is his to keep even if royalties are less than the advance. If royalties exceed the advance, the book is said to have earned back its advance, and the author receives the excess.

AGON: The chief conflict that is the basis of the plot.

AGONIST: A party of the agon. Agonists are usually available in two flavors: protAGONIST and antAGONIST. One of each is recommended. However, the chief conflict of the story is not necessarily between the good guy and the bad guy. The conflict may pit your protagonist against nature or adverse circumstances or between conflicting impulses or values within him- or herself.

AGONY: Not suffering for its own sake, but the stuff of the agon. More is better.

ALLEGORY: A story meant to express observations or truths about human existence. Individuals usually stand for humanity as a whole or for whole classes of people. Personified ideals may appear as characters, and particulars often symbolize more general concepts.

ALLITERATION: The repetition of initial consonant sounds for effect. *Compare:* ASSONANCE, CONSONANCE.

ANACHRONISM: A thing out of its time. A problem in historical fiction in that a writer may make reference to an invention or custom that was not known in the period in which his or her story is set. The classic example is the chiming of a clock in Shakespeare's *Julius Caesar*.

ANACOLUTHON: Grammatical discontinuity in a sentence, as when one thought is interrupted by another or a tentative beginning is rejected for another thought entirely. Anacoluthon is often better represented with a dash than with ellipsis. Example: Well, I suppose we could—no, no, we must proceed as we planned.

ANADIPLOSIS: Repetition of part of a preceding expression at the beginning of the following expression. Example: After we buried the old man, we went to town. We went to town as if it were a holiday. As if it were a holiday, but no holiday in particular.

ANAPHORA: Repetition of words or phrases at the beginnings of successive utterances.

ANASTROPHE: Reversal of the usual grammatical order for effect. Example: He hated the opera. He could hardly think of anything he hated more. But he had no choice. To the opera he went.

ANTHROPOMORPHISM: The ascribing of human characteristics to nonhuman and possibly nonexistent beings. The most common form of anthropomorphism is supposing that animals, such as pets, feel and think as human beings do.

ANTIPHRASIS: Use of an expression where its exact opposite would be appropriate. Antiphrasis is usually intended to produce an ironic or humorous effect. Examples: a bald man called "Curly" or a tall fat man called "Tiny."

APHORISM: A pithy statement or observation, not necessarily prescriptive.

APOSTROPHE: (1) A mark used to indicate absent letters in contractions, dialect, and the possessive case. On many typewriters and word processors, the apostrophe is the same as the single quotation mark.

(2) A speech to an absent person or to a personification. When a soap opera character in an empty room says, "Greg,

when will you come back to me?" this is apostrophe, and so are all speeches addressed to love, death, war, lust, or hate.

ASSOCIATE EDITOR: At many magazines, the person who selects stories for publication (subject to the editor's approval), who corresponds with writers to arrange terms, and edits copy.

ASSONANCE: The repetition of similar vowel sounds for effect.

BACK MATTER: Appendices, notes, indexes or other material which may appear in a book after the conclusion of the text.

BAD BREAK: When typesetting has resulted in a poor appearance of the work or introduced the possibly of a loss of meaning simply because of where the divisions between lines or pages fall, the result is called a bad break. Editors differ in their definitions of bad breaks. A WIDOW is a bad break. Other bad breaks may occur when part of a hyphenated word is carried to the next page, when a hyphen inserted in a word to make a line come out even results in a possible misreading of the word (as when one cannot tell whether "re-creation" or "recreation" is meant), or when a blank line supposed to represent a change of scene falls at the bottom or the top of a page. An editor may have to alter the text to avoid the bad break and, if so, the author will not be consulted.

BARBARISM: An error in the formation of a word, such as the combination of Greek and Latin roots in the same word, or a wrongly formed inflection. Examples: "homosexual" (combines a Greek root and a Latin root), "teached" (past tense formed by the wrong rule).

BILDUNGSROMAN: A coming-of-age novel, *Tom Jones,* for example. In gay literature, the form is known as a coming-out novel.

BLURB: Coined by American poet Gelett Burgess, the enthusiastic recommendation from a critic or other promotional passage printed on the jacket of a book, in advertisements, or on the beginning pages. Sometimes a critic's remarks are edited carefully to produce a blurb. "You are in trouble when you begin to believe your blurbs."—Quentin Crisp

BYLINE: The line that contains the word "by" followed by a name. In the manuscript, this is the line that contains a pen name if the author uses one. In correspondence with the editor or publisher, the author should use his legal name, and the author's legal name should appear in the heading of the manuscript.

CAMERA-READY: An adjective applied to the typeset work when it is ready to be photographed in order to produce the plates used in the offset process. When camera-ready, the work appears exactly as it will in the finished book or magazine. Manuscripts the author submits should not be camera-ready, but should look like a double-spaced typescript.

CATACHRESIS: An inappropriate word or a perplexing figure of speech.

CATASTROPHE: The climactic event of the plot, especially of a tragedy.

CHIASMUS: An expression of two parts in which the elements of the second are reversed. So called because the similar elements *cross* between the two parts. Example: Jason said little and knew much; Phil knew nothing and spoke at length.

CLICHÉ: A threadbare or trite expression. Examples: hard as steel, hot as a poker, burning with desire.

COLOPHON: A publisher's logo, especially as embossed on the spine of a book or as printed on the title page; also the information concerning the production of a book sometimes included on the last page.

CONCEIT: An elaborated or extended, perhaps overextended, figure. Archaic sense: jokes, humorous speeches, et cetera, as in "The historye of Henry iiiith with the battell at Shrewsburie, betweene the King and Lord Henry Percie, surnamed Henrie Hotspur of the North. With the humorous conceits of Sir Iohn Falstaffe" [title of the First Quarto].

CONSONANCE: The repetition of similar consonant sounds for effect. *Compare:* ALLITERATION.

COPY: Material the typesetter is supposed to copy into type; loosely, the manuscript at any stage of production, or the material composed of words, as opposed to photographs and illustrations. Dead copy is copy that has already been set in type.

CRITICASTER: A bad critic.

DINGBAT: Special character which is not a letter, such as the pointing hand. Authors of fiction should not feel entitled to call upon these characters as a matter of course.

DOWN STYLE: Editorial style that favors less capitalization. Down style is increasingly popular. The opposite of down style is up style. An example of down style is that the type of geographical feature named is not capitalized when it follows a proper adjective. For example, down style is "french fries," whereas in up style it would be "French fries."

ELLIPSIS: (1) (grammatical) Omission of words that are implied by the context. Example: Penny went to the mall and Julie to the shoe store.

In the second clause the verb "went" is implied. In many cases, a comma clarifies the situation.

(2) (punctuation) A mark that indicates the omission of one or more words. In the past asterisks or long dashes have been used for ellipsis. At present, three periods separated by spaces (...) are the universally acceptable mark. Ellipses have little place in fiction, so the same mark is used to indicate hesitation or pauses in dialogue.

Neither hesitancy nor omission are wanted in narration.

ENTHYMENE: A syllogism, one leg of which is implicit. Example: Of course he was Irish. He was red-haired. (The tacit premise: Red-haired men are Irish.)

EPENTHESIS: Insertion of a spurious sound or syllable in a word. Example: "Nuclear" when pronounced "nuculer."

EPIGRAPH: An introductory quotation.

EPISTOLARY: Written in the form of letters. This form of fiction is seldom seen anymore, but *Dracula* by Bram Stoker is an example and so is the erotic short story "A Roman Scandal" by Aaron Travis.

EPISTROPHE: Repetition of words or phrases at the ends of successive utterances.

EPITAPH: A brief commemorative statement, not to be confused with an epithet. A eulogy is a speech of praise. Now eulogies are pronounced over the dead, but in the past a eulogy might be offered to a living person.

EPITHET: a descriptive phrase used in addition to or in place of a name for a person or thing. "City of Light" is an epithet for

Paris and "Bard of Avon" is an epithet for Shakespeare. Poets, notably Homer, have used epithets to make their meter come out right. Beware of using epithets too freely in prose. Do not call your protagonist "the red-haired genius" simply because you are tired of calling him Mike. Confusion will result if you refer to characters only by epithets and vary the epithets at every reference.

EPONYM: A word derived from a person's name. Examples: sideburns (from Ambrose E. Burnside), cardigan (from the seventh earl of Cardigan), sandwich (from the seventh earl of Sandwich).

ERASABLE BOND: An unacceptable kind of typing paper available under several trade names that is coated with a substance that makes typewriting easily erasable and easily lost.

ERRATA: A list of corrections to a work, more properly called corrigenda.

EXPOSITION: Information about the circumstances of a story or the background of characters which readers need to know to understand what is happening. Unfortunately, exposition is difficult to digest, and is often offered in an "expository lump" which puts readers off. Skillful writers keep exposition to a minimum and feed the necessary exposition to the reader a bit at a time.

FABLE: A story meant to illustrate a moral point, usually involving anthropomorphized animals representing particular kinds of people or various aspects of human character. The moral of a fable is usually stated explicitly.

FOLO: An abbreviation for "follow," often in the notation "folo copy," used in copyediting and proofreading to indicate that the typesetter should set the copy as it is. An author might use this notation if words in the manuscript are misspelled intentionally.

FREELANCE: A self-employed writer, in contrast to a staff writer who works for a publisher. A freelance sells work to a publisher, but is not employed by the publisher.

FRONT MATTER: The pages of a book before the one on which the text of the book begins.

HOMOGRAPHS: Words spelled the same, although perhaps pronounced differently; example: the present and past tenses of "read"— one pronounced "reed" and the other pronounced "red."

HOMONYMS: Words spelled and pronounced the same, but having different meanings; example: "set" (which has more meanings than any other spelling in the language).

HOMOPHONES: Words which sound the same; example: "night" and "knight" which are pronounced the same in most modern dialects.

HYPERBOLE and MEIOSIS: Respectively, overstatement and understatement. Advertising and, perhaps, erotic writers who pander to size queens have saturated us with hyperbole. For this reason, hyperbole may best be reserved for satire or sarcasm: "Oh, yes, it's huge, it's bigger than a horse's, it's tremendous, it might put the Chrysler Building to shame, I'm impressed, who knows, it might grow to reach to the moon."

Judicious use of meiosis, however, can be devastating as when, in a classic example, the British refer to the Second World War as "that spot of unpleasantness involving the gentleman with the mustache."

HYSTERON PROTERON: A figure of speech in which things are named in the reverse of their normal order. Examples: So he came, cart and horse. Night and day—Cole Porter. We never wondered how he garnered his butter and bread.

GALLEYS: Images drawn from long trays of type, used to check the typesetter's work. In modern printing, galleys are no longer common, but the word is sometimes applied to modern proofs. Bound copies of page proofs that are circulated to elicit blurbs are often called bound galleys.

KILL FEE: A prearranged amount a magazine publisher promises to pay if a proposed and delivered article cannot be used by the magazine. Since fiction writers usually submit whole stories to magazines, a kill fee has little application to fiction. If a magazine has accepted a piece of fiction, it should pay the whole price agreed upon, even if it decides not to print the story.

KÜNSTLERROMAN: A novel tracing the development of an artist; for example, *Portrait of the Artist as a Young Man*.

L.C.: Abbreviation for "lowercase."

LITTLE MAGAZINE: A periodical, usually not published for profit, that prints reviews, essays, fiction, or poetry, or more usually some combination of them, supposed devoted to high literary standards. Little magazines often run innovative or experimental works. A few little magazines pay for contributions, many do not. Some are widely influential, but others are virtually unknown except to the editors and contributors. Little magazines may be very helpful to a new writer who is selective in sending submissions.

MALAPROPISM: (from the name of a character by Sheridan) A similar-sounding but incorrect word that renders an utterance ridiculous. Usually the mistake occurs when the speaker affects a vocabulary much beyond his or her learning. Example: "A man his age is very likely to experience difficulty with his prostitute gland."

MANUSCRIPT: This term dates to a time when type was set from the author's handwritten copy. This time is long past. Now the term is best understood to mean the author's typescript.

MASS-MARKET PAPERBACK: A paperback book printed on paper like newsprint, usually selling for under $10, and available in grocery stores or adult arcades or newsstands. *Compare:* TRADE PAPERBACK.

MEIOSIS: *see* HYPERBOLE

MS: A common abbreviation for "manuscript."

NOVEL OF MANNERS: A novel concerning the intrigues (usually romantic) of upper-class people. The novels of Anthony Trollope are examples.

OPEN STYLE: An editorial style that favors less punctuation. The trend toward open style has been evident for quite a few years. The opposite of open style is close style, which requires all the punctuation the syntax will bear. In open style, brief introductory phrases, especially those pertaining to the subject of the sentence, are not set off by commas. Neither are brief references to time and place. Brief, parallel clauses are sometimes joined with "and," and the usual comma is omitted. Open style does not require omission of punctuation when doing so confuses the sense.

ONOMATOPOEIA: A figure of speech in which the words when pronounced are supposed to sound like what they mean—e.g., "hiss."

OXYMORON: A contradiction in terms, sometimes an error and sometimes a figure of speech. Some fun is had by finding accidental oxymorons or by alleging that certain terms, such as "military intelligence," are oxymorons. But some oxymorons, such as "deafening silence," are intended figures of speech: "The searing cold of the frozen pipe seized my tongue." "Searing" is an effect of great heat, not of cold. But in the extreme the sensations of heat and cold may be almost indistinguishable, and that is the point of the figure. Similarly, one may be just as blind in a great light as in total darkness, and this might be the basis of an oxymoron.

PARABLE: A story involving plausible characters and situations meant to illustrate a moral point.

PARADOX: A contradiction, beyond the contradiction in terms that is an oxymoron. "We fucked until we were virgins." While this seems quite paradoxical, the reader may figure out that what is meant is that the parties exhausted their sexual desire and then related to each other as innocents would.

PARALLELISM: (1.) Repetition of a grammatical structure for effect. (2.) Expression of similar ideas in similar structures.

PERIPHRASIS: Use of a longer expression in place of a shorter one.

PERSONIFICATION: The ascribing of personal qualities to things or ideas. "Demon rum" is two figures. First, "rum" is synecdoche because "rum" stands for the whole class of alcoholic beverages of which it is really only a part. Then it is personification, for it ascribes to a thing the personal qualities of a minor evil deity.

PROLEPSIS: A figure in which a future situation is referred to as if it had already occurred. Example: "The first time he looked at me, I was fucked." Not yet, really, but very soon.

PROOF: An image of the type as set used to check for errors in the typesetting. Page proofs are proofs that are set up like pages in the final book; as opposed to galleys, in which the text lines follow one after another without page breaks.

PROSOPOEIA: A figure of speech in which a nonexistent or absent person or personification is supposed to speak or to act.

PULLOUT: A quotation or paraphrase from a story that is set in large type to attract the reader's attention.

PULPS and SLICKS: Slicks are magazines printed on slick paper, usually with four-color illustrations and pictures on the inside pages. Usually, but not invariably, magazines that can afford to be slicks pay better and afford better treatment to writers. The opposite of slicks is pulps. Pulps are printed on newsprint and contain black-and-white illustrations, if any. Some pulps, as in the mystery and science-fiction genres, are good markets, if not because they pay especially well, then because they buy many stories.

RECTO AND VERSO: Books are usually composed of signatures, being sections of eight leaves (=16 pages). Each leaf is two pages. Recto is the front of the page—it will be on the right in the printed book. Verso is the back of the leaf. It will appear on the left in the open book. Where pages are numbered, recto pages bear odd numbers and verso pages bear even numbers. Recto and verso refer to the leaf. The verso of one leaf faces the recto of another.

ROMAN (type): The usual body type—i.e., type that is not italicized.

ROMAN À CLEF: Novel about real persons whose identities are thinly veiled. Example: *Valley of the Dolls*.

ROYALTIES: Payments due a copyright owner for the use of copyrighted material. In common use, royalties refer to payments due an author as a percentage of the price of his books. Payments for the use of a writer's material in magazines and books by others are usually not called royalties, but permission fees, or even merely "payments."

SERIAL: A periodical such as a newspaper or magazine. Serial rights are the rights to publish a work in a periodical and have nothing to do with whether the work might appear in installments.

SOLECISM: A substandard usage, usually an inadvertent slip.

SPOONERISM: A slip of the tongue involving the transposition of two or more sounds in an utterance (after English cleric William A. Spooner). Example: The Lord is a shoving leopard.—Spooner.

SPRACHGEFÜHL: A feeling for language; the ability of using apt language.

STET: An abbreviation in copyediting or proofreading meaning "let it stand," usually an indication that deleted material is to be restored. Dots are placed under the material to be restored.

SUBSIDIARY RIGHTS: The variety of rights contained in a literary work which the publisher of a book is not exercising, but often administers for the author. These include motion-picture and television rights, paperback and book-club rights, rights to make various kinds of adaptations and sequels, sound-recording rights, foreign publications rights, et cetera.

SYNECDOCHE: A figure of speech in which the whole is allowed to stand for the part, the part for the whole; the individual for the group, the group for the individual; the specific for the general, or the general for the specific. Example: "Back in the ozone again," means returning to the upper atmosphere, where ozone is only one of the several gases. The expression as a whole is a metaphor for being under the influence of drugs.

Pachyderm (for elephant), since pachyderm is a class of which elephant is but one member.

TABOO: The editorial or publishing policy which excludes publication of works dealing with certain subject matter without regard to the merit of the work.

TRADE PAPERBACK: A paperback intended to be sold in bookstores. Trade paperbacks are printed on high-quality paper and are bound by a method similar to one used for hardcover books. Trade paperbacks usually sell for more than $10. *Compare:* MASS-MARKET PAPERBACK.

VOGUE WORDS: Occasionally a word may become especially popular and may be so bandied about as to become nearly meaningless. Sometimes such a word was perfectly respectable to begin with. Other times the word was born a bastard. In either event, careful writers should avoid words that have become too trendy. Examples: charisma, codependent, epiphany, paradigm.

WIDOW: A small part of a paragraph that has been carried to the top of a new page. Widows are avoided for the sake of the appearance of a page. Exactly how much of a paragraph must appear on a page to avoid a widow is a matter of opinion. A widow is one kind of BAD BREAK.

ZEUGMA: Usage in which a single modifier seems to apply in differing senses to several words or cannot apply in any sense to some of the words it would appear to govern. Example: "The tea and the sympathy were no better than lukewarm."

Zeugma here is intended and is perhaps mildly witty.

"She wore bargain-basement clothes and diamonds."

This is probably meant to contrast her cheap clothes with her expensive jewels; but, as written, the sentence seems to suggest the existence of bargain-basement diamonds.

Afterword: Why I Write Gay Erotica

I write gay erotica because gay erotica is fun. I write gay erotica because it is the one form of gay literature that cannot be co-opted. That may seem like two reasons, but they are one and the same. Although the fantasy sex described in a work of gay erotica may be scary or tragic or considerably rougher than anyone would care to experience in reality, the message still comes through. In reality, gay sex is fun. And whether the work is produced well in a slick magazine or printed with the worst typography on the cheapest pulp paper, the second message is equally clear. Gay people are numerous. Gay readers are numerous enough that the publisher had some hope of making a profit.

The second message is perhaps not now as controversial as it was when I first read *Clint Wins His Letter* (by Lance Lester, a great author of the pre-Stonewall era who worked under a variety of names including Clay Caldwell; some of his titles are being revived by Badboy Books), a generic-looking dirty book. Books of the same physical appearance, if not so well written, are still available in adult bookstores or by mail from companies that take out tiny ads in the back pages of magazines. My first impression was that *Clint* had been written just for me. I knew that this impression could not be entirely correct, and I pondered at length the existence of this book which I held so often in one hand. The truth seemed so fantastic that I resisted it for some time. *Clint Wins His Letter* was not published only for me, but for *many, many people like me.*

That gay men are numerous has not been altogether a secret since Kinsey published his work in 1948. But it was news to me when I discovered *Clint* many years later. In spite of all the gay-pride marches and mass gatherings, this is still news to new gay people.

In many respects, "guys who are likely to enjoy reading *Clint Wins His Letter*" is a much better definition of "gay men" than the one likely to be induced from the majority culture's many sexless, unattractive, and stereotypical images of gay men. For this reason, gay erotica will remain an essential tool in the formation of gay identity and gay community for a long time.

The gay movement can be—and has been—co-opted in many ways. While the early movement aimed for revolution, or even reform, more recently gay spokespeople seem to be willing to settle for assimilation. But the assimilation the majority culture offers to gay culture is not the melting pot of pluralism, but the kind of assimilation the frog's stomach offers the fly.

Gay sex can be co-opted. When gay sex is painted as joyless and obsessive, the majority culture can tolerate it. Where gay sex has been decriminalized, the majority has conceded only that the attempt to suppress gay sex is troublesome and counter-productive. The majority culture never accepts that gay sex is a matter of right, that gay is good, or that gay sexuality is something in which to take pride.

Similarly, the majority culture can accept and even celebrate literature that seems to have gay elements. For example, the majority culture can award a literary prize to a novel that depicts a lesbian relationship—but only if all the male characters in the book are abusive monsters. And even so, the relationship between the women must not be primarily sexual.

Does any work that is not explicitly erotic deserve to be called "gay literature"? I sometimes wonder.

A novel about a gay detective may contain the message that gay men can be detectives as well as they can be hairdressers. But the majority culture can easily accept this as a story about an exceptional individual who overcame what is perceived to be a handicap. Gay novels without explicit sex can show that gay people do not think about sex all the time. But gay people who are not thinking about sex are the majority culture's third-favorite kind of gay people (after dead gay people and dying gay people). If gay erotica is not the whole of gay literature, it certainly is the most essential part.

That the majority culture can never accept gay erotica is no surprise. Naturally, the assimilationists and sycophants among gay critics will favor eviscerated volumes which are gay in name only; and co-opted gay writers, publishers, and bookstores will pander to them.

Yet even among gay people who do not consciously subscribe to the values of the dominant culture, gay erotica is not regarded highly. Perhaps some people who buy gay erotica and then hide it away have unresolved internal conflicts about their sexualities. The standard of literature held up for admiration in the public schools is not even that of the present majority culture, but rather is the one the majority culture professed a century ago. For that reason, perhaps, some gay readers think that any book with a sexual theme, whether gay or not, is trash. Other readers may think that the position of gay erotica in gay literature is analogous to the position of heterosexual erotica in the majority culture's literature. (It is not).

No doubt there are several of reasons why gay readers do not think highly of gay erotica. But is there not some way in which gay erotica has been at fault in this matter?

Certainly gay erotica could have given a better account of itself. Unfortunately, not much of it is very good.

George Orwell distinguished two senses in which a work of letters may be good or bad. He thought highly of good bad books, by which he meant books of little or no substance that are highly entertaining. An example of a good bad author whom Orwell cites is P. G. Wodehouse. The opposite of good bad books is bad good books. These are undoubted works of Literature that are unreadable. Most required reading in American secondary schools consists of bad good books—*Silas Marner,* to name but one. On this scale, the typical work of gay erotica is mediocre minimally good.

Gay erotica has a minimal amount of substance because it contains the two messages I have mentioned that are fatal to the premises supporting the majority culture's dominance. This minimal good is hardly a credit to the author, for it is inherent in the genre. Few authors aspire to anything more, although some works incidentally include circumstances of historic or cultural significance.

Most readers, I suspect, do not expect gay erotica to have any substance. If they think it is possible for gay erotica to have any value, its value must be as entertainment. Unfortunately, little gay erotica is very entertaining. "Mediocre" is the word for it.

For a number of years, Boyd McDonald has solicited and edited the sexual histories of gay men. This work appears in several magazines and in a number of books, usually with the words: "The truth is more pornographic than pornography." To the writer of gay erotic fiction, this is a hard saying. I admire McDonald's work greatly, and I do not doubt that in general his slogan is true. I can only hope it is not necessarily true.

Everything is wrong with the way McDonald's correspondents write. Many of them are barely literate. They are clueless as to how to set up a narrative. They tell their stories out of order and often step on their punch lines. Everything is wrong with the stories—except that most of them are doubtlessly authentic, and they are stories the authors believe to be worth telling.

Against them, what chance has fiction?

Fiction cannot be authentic. Fiction can aim for verisimilitude; and if it is very good fiction, it can achieve a kind of truth that transcends fact—but never authenticity. The erotic excitement in McDonald's work derives largely from its authenticity, which cannot be matched by any quality that fiction can muster.

But in the author's belief in the worth of the work, surely fiction need not take a backseat.

Unfortunately, I think it is in this last that the overall mediocre quality of gay erotica can best be explained. The gay community provides many messages that it does not expect much of gay erotica, and that it will not value even the best work highly. To one degree or another, writers cannot help absorbing these messages. They become discouraged. They discover that shoddy work will be accepted because the community expects no better. In a variety of ways, the quality of the work is depressed. This, of course, justifies the community's opinion of gay erotica. It is a vicious circle. In the end, even those who believe in the principle of gay erotica cannot be happy in endorsing its practice.

This is the situation.

Perhaps a dozen, more or less small publishers who issue high-quality paperback books are supposed to be gay publishers. Most large publishers in the majority culture have lines of books that are supposed to be of interest to gay people. Yet, aside from the manufacturers of generic-looking dirty books that are sold in adult bookstores, only one or two publishers regularly issue books of frank gay erotica. Many books with lurid covers are issued, but nothing so erotic can be found between the covers.

The generic-looking pulp books are no longer like *Clint Wins His Letter*. Now the pages are fewer, the type is larger, and there are many lines of only one or two words. These books are commissioned as piecework. Writers are encouraged to fill as much space with as few words as possible and are discouraged from doing anything so literary as developing characters or a plot.

Writers of gay erotica are paid poorly. While this does not in itself excuse poor work, it is yet another message that gay erotica is not considered valuable. Unfortunately, many of these messages are amplified by gay people who hope to be assimilated.

People who aspire to change their status in society often adopt an exaggerated version of the attitudes that they suppose are held by people who have already achieved that status. Thus, assimilationist gay people often are in the forefront of efforts to belittle or suppress gay erotica, even when nongay people of a similar class may tolerate, accept, or celebrate nongay erotica. For this reason, it is sometimes easier to place a work of gay erotica with a nongay publisher or to find it in general-interest bookstores than to place such a book with gay-identified publishers or to find it in some gay-interest bookstores.

Magazines editor are something of a bright spot in this otherwise-dismal picture. They usually struggle mightily to find the best stories they can and to produce the stories well. But when they go to their mail, they find dozens and dozens of letters praising the obvious attributes of the photographic models. Did anyone get off on the fiction? Not so far as the mail reveals. The editor will have to take the reader response into account in budgeting space as well as money. For this reason, or some other, a gay magazine's standard rates tend to be truly standard, and an excellent story will bring its author no more than a merely acceptable one would have.

The wonder is that any writer ever overcomes the voice of internal homophobia that says erotic writing is wicked and the voices of the co-opted leaders of the gay community who say that gay erotica is trivial at best.

This is a sad situation, and I have not yet devised a program certain to reverse it.

While I cannot defend gay erotica with reason from the attacks of people who believe without reason that gay sex is wrong and gay people are wicked, some people of otherwise evident good-will have raised some questions about gay erotica. I do not think these questions really account for much of the low repute of gay erotica among those who ought to esteem it. But insofar as these questions are put in good faith, they deserve to be answered in like manner.

Almost all the questions come down to this: Can readers tell fantasy from reality? Or, to put it differently, will a work of fiction be likely to cause its readers to do something bad when they would not otherwise do anything as bad?

Implicit in such questions is the assertion that characters in gay erotica often do bad things. I think, to the contrary, that characters in gay erotica most often behave better than real people. Some people, however, want characters to be perfect and want fictional worlds to be paradises. I admit that gay erotica neither often attains this standard nor commonly aspires to it.

Miguel de Cervantes gave us Don Quixote, who was overly influenced by good bad novels of chivalry. Clarence Darrow, in a brilliant defense that saved his clients from execution, claimed that Nathan Leopold and Richard Loeb had been overly influenced by cheap crime novels. Can we say no one will be overly influenced by gay erotica?

Well, Don Quixote was himself a fiction. Darrow was desperate in his attempt to mitigate one of the most senseless crimes of all time. Leopold and Loeb had read Friedrich Nietzsche, too—or, rather, had misread him. Shall Nietzsche go into the fire with the sleazy sleuths?

I have seen, more than once, paranoid lunatics discover conspiracies in telephone directories and sinister imperatives in laundry lists. Some imbecile or lunatic can find a twisted plan in even the most innocuous writing. Even the majority culture now admits that literature cannot be judged by its effects on exceptional individuals; for, in that case, there could be no literature at all.

Or so the reasoning goes. In fact, it is not well established that the coincidence of harmful acts by exceptional individuals and their possession of literature that portrays similar acts means that the literature is to blame. Plausibly, persons of murderous frames of mind are likely to acquire murderous literature. The telephone directory cannot be blamed for the plot a paranoid lunatic discovers in it, for the lunatic will also discover a plot without a telephone directory.

In truth, almost all people know the difference between fantasy and reality. Even children know perfectly well that they cannot do as Nancy Drew does, although they may skulk around in play.

Yet people do learn things from fiction. Certainly, that is what I claimed when I wrote that gay erotica contains two messages the majority culture cannot stand. How can we be sure people will learn only the good things in fiction?

I think we cannot be sure. We cannot be sure that people will learn only the good in fiction any more than we can be sure they will follow only the good examples they encounter in life. Putting only good examples in literature, if that were possible, would most likely produce a bad good literature—stacks of uplifting books that no one would read.

The reason reformers always want to start by reforming literature is that it is much easier to attack ideas and their expression in print than it is to change material reality. Even some who claim to be bedrock materialists fall into this trap. Similarly, reformers who claim to be gay, attack gay erotica first because gay publishers and writers, already besieged by the forces of the majority culture, seem likely to wither under criticism be it well- or ill-founded. If the reformers succeed in destroying gay literature, that will be the end of it. The time will never be quite ripe for a campaign against similar flaws in the literature of the majority culture.

As to particulars: I am sometimes asked why gay erotica does not show partners in loving, committed relationships. Of course it does sometimes do just that, but I won't quibble. I suspect this question means: Why doesn't gay erotica portray gay people as living the way heterosexuals claim to live? If that is the question, the answer is: for the same reason that fiction seldom portrays trees that pretend to be rocks.

In truth, an average sexual act between partners in an average, loving, committed relationship is not good erotica because the situation is not good fiction. On the other hand, how the couple met—or how they overcame some crisis in the relationship—is good fiction and quite a number of erotic stories are of this kind, ending either explicitly or implicitly, "And so they lived happily ever after." Living happily ever after is not fiction— because nothing ever happens. What would *Ulysses* be if the Blooms had the sort of relationship some critics advocate? There is no fairy tale about Mr. and Mrs. Prince Charming at home.

There remain quite a number of promiscuous stories. I see nothing wrong with gay promiscuity. I think it is one of the most positive aspects of gay life that people of very different circumstances can achieve intimacy very quickly. Those who think promiscuity is blameworthy have quite a task ahead of them if they mean to show that gay promiscuity arises from gay erotica.

Of late there have been many questions about safe sex in gay erotica. In particular, I have heard stories criticized because the characters therein do unsafe things. This is very curious.

I seriously doubt it is a very safe thing for stout and aged Englishwomen who live in small villages to go about sticking their noses into unsolved murders. I have not yet heard Agatha Christie criticized on the grounds that Miss Marple is an unfortunate influence.

Fiction is just the place to experience what would be unsafe or unwise to attempt in reality.

Gay erotica can emphasize the erotic aspects of acts that are inherently safe. It can provide a model of how one partner raises the issue of safety in a firm and tactful way. It can even provide an instructive and erotic description of the proper use of a condom.

But that gay erotica can and should do these things does not mean that every story ought to do so. Indeed, when magazines were insisting on safe sex in every story, the mention of the condom became so perfunctory that it was meaningless. The stories were not safe-sex stories, but were only fuck stories into which a couple of lines about a condom had been inserted. If anything, the message of these stories was that the use of a condom involves an unwelcome and intrusive interruption. Surely one story celebrating the eroticism of mutual masturbation is worth any number of stories in which the mention of the condom seems an afterthought. It is not, of course, that condoms are antierotic—before AIDS there were occasional gay stories into which condoms were introduced as toys. What is antierotic is the requirement of explicit mention of condoms in stories as a rule. It is the rule that makes stories into propaganda.

Propaganda seldom is good literature. And, after a while, propaganda is not even good propaganda. That a reader can learn safe sex from one story does not mean he will forget it if the next story does not contain safe sex. Critics worry about some hypothetical nitwit who will decide to practice unsafe sex if most of the stories he reads contain unsafe sex. Such critics always think that they themselves will practice safe sex no matter what they read. Censors are always concerned about the possible effects on someone other than themselves.

The principal use of gay erotica is as an enhancement to masturbation. Masturbation is the safest form of sex. So long as some gay erotica does provide safe-sex information incidentally, it seems to me gay erotica has done its duty.

I wonder, really, whether anyone learns—aside from masturbation—any sexual technique, safe or otherwise, from gay erotica. And this brings me to questions about SM and related activities.

Bondage, psychic and physical domination, and sadomasochism appear in some stories of gay erotica. This bothers some people. I think good writing reveals very quickly what a story is about. Then it should be a simple matter for a reader to avoid a story which he finds distasteful. But, of course, it is not for themselves that people are bothered by such stories; it is out of concern for the hypothetical nitwit.

When this concern is genuine, it seems to stem from a lack of understanding of what SM is when it is practiced in reality. People who practice SM and related activities in reality have a very clear understanding of the difference between fantasy and reality, and in many communities they organize educational and outreach programs to ensure that the distinction is clear to newcomers.

Curiously, the more fantastic a story, the more the critic fears it will be mistaken for reality. What shall we do? Put a disclaimer on every story: "Do not play with people who are untrustworthy"?

Most often, I think, the real concern about these stories is that some gay people find the SM scene embarrassing, and they wish it would go away. They think that suppressing SM stories will make the SM scene go away. That will not work. If the concern were really for the safety of neophytes, the best way to encourage safety is to keep the SM scene above ground, visible, and accessible. Stumbling around in the dark, the neophyte might very well encounter a homicidal lunatic.

Finally, there is a group of interrelated questions. Why are there not more older people in gay erotica? More blacks? I have read a reader's complaint that redheads are underrepresented. Why always the same stock characters, doing the same old things, in the same old places?

At last, some questions that are more literary than political!

All genre fiction has its stock characters and its set-piece scenes. Gothics have grim old houses. Romances have tall, dark strangers. Mysteries have drawing-room denouements. Gay erotica has motorcycle cops, drill instructors, jocks, frats, locker rooms, hitchhikers, public restrooms, backseats, front seats, and a great deal more. Once these were powerful images—nothing lives long enough to become trite that is not vigorous in its youth.

Women seldom appear in men's stories for the same reason that dolphins seldom appear in Westerns. Modern length requirements do not allow for much development of secondary characters, and so it is probably just as well to have no women in these stories as to have cardboard-cutout women making cameo appearances.

Men of color are not really so rare in gay men's stories. Unfortunately, they often appear in roles that bear a disquieting resemblance to the racial stereotypes of the hypersexual black stud and the fiery, macho, Latin lover. Racism is not the whole explanation. Queens and androgynous types of all races are rarely given principal parts. Partly this is a reaction to the many less-than-studly gay men who appear in the majority culture's literature.

Many stories are of the first-time or coming-out kind, with few places for older men. A very few May-and-September stories are written. but it is true that almost no September-and-September stories exist.

In short, sexism, racism, and ageism exist in gay erotica. But as a literature available only to adults, gay erotica can hardly be blamed for shaping the attitudes of its readers. The scourge of Political Correctness could be applied to other targets with greater effect. Editors and writers of gay erotica are especially eager to produce innovative stories. But most of us have been burned more than once when we have failed to take proper account of our readers' rather rigid expectations.

Occasionally one of us finds a new idea that works, and there is rejoicing all around. But day in and day out no one can write gay erotica for long without having to reuse one of the stock elements, and eventually all of them. Good writers, willing to work hard, can still bring some life to the stock characters and can move them around the stage while avoiding the well-worn ruts. But this brings us back to the problem: Is it worth the writer's while to exert the extra effort? Why should he take a chance on something new? If the community will value the good erotic story no more than it values the poor one, and the payment is the same, why bother?

I bother.

I would like to save myself some excuse in case my stories are not found to be good. Perhaps that I only write for the money. Perhaps that I think my work is only a little amusement, and thus I have not brought my full powers to bear on the writing of gay erotica. Perhaps that I have had a hard life, full of the kinds of distractions that prevent my doing my best. Alas, I have no excuse.

My stories of gay erotica are written as well as I know how to write. If I have perceived something I could do to make a story better, I have done it.

And, so far as I can judge, my stories are pretty good. My stories are welcome at virtually every gay magazine that accepts typewritten submissions. I cannot recall when I last wrote a story I could not place. That is another reason I write gay erotica: for the same reason that anyone does what he has reason to believe he is good at doing.

But there is yet another reason.

If, as I suppose, my stories are better than average, perhaps they will just a bit—as a stone tossed into a lake—raise people's expectations of gay erotica. Perhaps other writers, writers of inherent talents greater than mine, will then take a little more care with their stories of gay erotica.

And then, after a time, perhaps some very talented writers indeed will feel it worth their while to write a story or two of gay erotica. And perhaps, by that time, gay people will have noticed that gay erotica has gotten very much better and will encourage the very talented writers to produce more gay erotica.

Then there will start to be a very fine and powerful literature, all of which contains two messages deadly poisonous to the culture that oppresses gay people.

I write gay erotica so that one day there will be much gay erotica, all of it better than my best.